A timeline chart of mathematical history.

Top entries (above timeline):

- Chu Shih-Chieh — binomial coefficients (1303)
- Ockham — formal logic (1320)
- Oresme — fractional exponents (1360)
- Hindu-Arabic numerals take present form (1479)
- Chuquet — notation for +, − of fractions (1484)
- Calandri — long division process (1491)
- Rudoff — square root symbol ($\sqrt{\ }$) (1525)
- Diez Feile — writes 1st math book in Mexico (1556)
- Recorde — symbol for the equal sign (=) (1557)
- Clavius — the dot (•) for multiplication (1583)
- Napier — logarithms (1614)
- Kepler and Briggs — tables of logarithms (1624)
- Descartes — analytic geometry (1637)
- Fermat — probability, analytic geometry, number theory, calculus (1629–1654)
- Pascal — projective geometry, calculating machine, probability, binomial coefficients (1642–1654)
- Seki Kōwa — determinants, magic squares (1685)
- Newton — calculus (1687)
- Jakob Bernoulli — theory of probability (1713)
- DeMoivre — actuary math, complex numbers (1720)
- Maria Agnesi — popular math text book (1748)
- Euler — uses the symbols i, e, and Σ (1750)
- First Bank of the U.S. (1791)
- Babbage — steam powered calculator (1823)
- Lobachevsky — non-Euclidean geometry (1829)
- Georg Riemann — non-Euclidean geometry, calculus (1850–1854)
- Weierstrass — absolute value symbol ($|\ |$), foundations of calculus (1841–1874)
- Hollerith — electrical tabulating device (1880)
- Markov — probability theory, Markov Chains (1907)
- Federal Reserve Act — U.S. banking system (1913)
- Ronald Fisher — statistics sampling techniques (1920)
- Thomas Watson forms IBM (1924)
- Mauchley and Eckert — ENIAC computer (1945)
- Gertrude Cox — statistical design (1950)
- Mandelbrot — fractal geometry (1967)
- Hewlett Packard — programmable calculator (1974)
- Seymour Cray — CRAY super computer (1976)
- Amdahl Corp. Computer — 65,087 digit prime (1989)

Timeline bars:

- OF TRANSMISSION (1000–1500)
- EARLY MODERN PERIOD (1450 TO 1800)
- MODERN PERIOD (1800 TO PRESENT)

Bottom entries (below timeline):

- Florence, Italy outlaws Hindu-Arabic numerals (1299)
- Burley — formal logic (1325)
- Regiomontanus — trigonometry (1464)
- Widmann — addition (+), subtraction (−) signs (1489)
- Apianus — notation for ×, ÷ of fractions (1527)
- Cardano — cubic equations (1545)
- Rheticus — right triangle trigonometry (1551)
- Bombelli — imaginary numbers (1572)
- Stevin — decimal fractions (1585)
- Oughtred — multiplication sign (×), slide rule (1621)
- Cavalieri — indivisibles in calculus (1635)
- Desargues — projective geometry (1640)
- Wallis — negative exponents, infinity symbol (∞) (1655)
- Rahn — division sign (÷) (1659)
- Isomura — magic circles (1660)
- Barrow — calculus, differentiation (1663)
- Leibniz — symbolic logic, calculating machine, calculus (1666–1684)
- William Jones — symbol for pi (π) (1706)
- First math book printed in America (1719)
- Greenwood — writes 1st American math book (1729)
- Achenwall — the word *statistik* (1749)
- Gabriel Cramer — systems of equations (1750)
- Bayes — statistics, origin of polls (1763)
- LaPlace — probability theory (1814)
- Gauss — statistics, normal curve, the term *complex number* (1809–1832)
- Carl Jacobi — theory of determinants (1841)
- Ada Byron — computer programming (1843)
- George Boole — logic, Boolean algebra (1847)
- Möbius — topology (1865)
- John Venn — logic, Venn diagrams (1880)
- Burroughs — practical adding machine (1894)
- Whitehead, Russell — Principia Mathematica (1910)
- Lukasiewicz, Post, Wittgenstein — truth tables (1920)
- Kilby, Texas Instruments — integrated circuit (1958)
- Gilbert Hyatt — computer microprocessor chip (1968)
- Edward Roberts — first personal computer (1971)
- Chudnovsky — 480 million digits of π (1989)

THE
MATHEMATICAL PALETTE

Ronald Staszkow

Robert Bradshaw

Ohlone College
Fremont, CA

SAUNDERS COLLEGE PUBLISHING

Philadelphia   Fort Worth   Chicago
San Francisco   Montreal   Toronto
London   Sydney   Tokyo

Text Typeface: Times Roman
Compositor: Waldman Graphics
Acquisitions Editor: Robert Stern
Developmental Editor: Lloyd W. Black
Managing Editor: Carol Field
Project Editor: Mary Patton and Becca Gruliow
Copy Editor: Tom Whipple
Manager of Art and Design: Carol Bleistine
Art Director: Christine Schueler
Art and Design Coordinator: Doris Bruey
Text Designer: York Production Services
Cover Designer: Lawrence R. Didona
Text Artwork: Grafacon
Director of EDP: Tim Frelick
Production Manager: Charlene Squibb
Marketing Manager: Denise Watrobsky

Cover Credit: Detail of *The Dream Garden,* a 15′ × 49′ glass mosaic in The Curtis Center, Philadelphia. Commissioned by publishers Cyrus Curtis and Edward Bok, the mosaic was designed and constructed by the famed Tiffany Studios and is based on an oil painting by Maxfield Parrish. (Courtesy of John Merriam and The Curtis Center) (Cover photographed by Susan Robins)

Printed in the United States of America

THE MATHEMATICAL PALETTE

ISBN 0-03-033274-5

Library of Congress Catalog Card Number: 90-053332

1234   039   987654321

THE DREAM GARDEN

The cover of *The Mathematical Palette* shows a close-up of the spectacular 15′ × 49′ glass mosaic "The Dream Garden." This mosaic—essentially an intricate tessellation based on a complex interplay of colors and shapes—is an inspiring example of creative collaboration and artistic innovation on a grand scale. One of only three such works of its kind ever undertaken by the famed Tiffany Studios, it was the last created (under the direction of Louis Comfort Tiffany) and is generally considered the most beautiful.

"The Dream Garden" originated as an oil painting commissioned of Philadelphia-born artist Maxfield Parrish. Saturday Evening Post publisher Cyrus Curtis and Ladies Home Journal publisher Edward Bok believed that art belonged in public buildings where many people could enjoy it and chose a sweeping wall space in the Curtis Publishing Company's headquarters in Philadelphia. In June 1914, Tiffany began the work of translating Parrish's vision into this glass mosaic.

The mosaic's images are rendered with more than 100,000 pieces of "favrile" glass in 260 color tones, produced by a complex hand-firing process that was developed by Tiffany. Most of the glass was set in 24 panels in Tiffany's New York studios. Installing the panels in the Curtis building took six months, and the finished work was put on display in 1916. During the extensive renovation of 1985–1986 that transformed the historic building into The Curtis Center, "The Dream Garden" was cleaned and protected.

The "Dream Garden" was chosen for the cover of *The Mathematical Palette* because it displays a visual image reminiscent of a rich palette of colors, its mosaic construction links it to discussions of tilings and patterns in Chapter 3 of the text, and it is found in the lobby of The Curtis Center, the current home of Saunders College Publishing.

PREFACE

The Mathematical Palette is written for the liberal arts college student who has a good background in high school algebra or who has successfully completed intermediate algebra in college. The text is designed not only to meet college general education requirements but to help generate a positive attitude toward and an interest in mathematics. The text stresses *learning* mathematics rather than just learning *about* mathematical ideas. This approach is directly tied to an emphasis on solving problems and the development of problem-solving skills. Greater appreciation of the beauty and power of mathematics is gained when students become active participants.

The Mathematical Palette attempts to make mathematics enjoyable, practical, understandable, and informative, stimulating the creativity of the liberal arts student. Just as an artist mixes paints upon a palette, so *The Mathematical Palette* mixes the history of mathematics, its mathematicians, and its problems with a variety of real-life applications. The text presents this sampling of mathematics in a straightforward, interesting manner and is designed expressly for the liberal arts student, not an advanced mathematician.

The Mathematical Palette provides additional material not ordinarily available to mathematics students. The history sections, Check Your Reading questions, research questions, and many open-ended problems provide students the opportunity to write about mathematics and mathematicians. The bibliography of sources used in preparing this text is included at the end of the book and gives students guidance in investigating further historical aspects of mathematics.

We hope that this survey approach will encourage students to take more mathematics courses and stimulate them to enjoy and appreciate the story of the many areas of mathematics rather than be overwhelmed with myriad details. Students will appreciate the simplicity of language and numerous examples and solved problems.

The Mathematical Palette has been written with a prerequisite of a course in intermediate algebra in mind. However, because of the ample review material at the start of each chapter and the step-by-step explanations, even those students who are not completely confident about their algebra skills can master the material contained in the text.

FEATURES

Instructors will find that *The Mathematical Palette* is a very teachable text. Its organization, style, and format have been developed with both the student and the instructor in mind. Each chapter is a self-contained unit and may be taught in any order according to the instructor's or student's interests. The history sections at the beginnings of the chapters present material and questions that are ideal for classroom discussions, research papers, projects, speeches, and reports. The text's readable style, clear explanations, numerous solved examples, well-thought-out problem sets, chapter summaries, and accurate answer section are valuable resources for the instructor. In particular, instructors should find that the following features of each chapter are real assets in teaching mathematics to liberal arts students:

- Each chapter's short history of the development of the mathematics introduces students to important dates, mathematicians, and events.
- Questions at the end of each history section review the content of the section and relate mathematical events to other historical milestones; over 100 total questions are presented.
- Research questions at the end of each history section go beyond the material presented and serve as an ideal source for projects or written papers; nearly 100 total research questions are presented.
- Readable explanations present a total of over 250 worked examples and numerous illustrations.
- Sectional problem-sets include a variety of skill-building exercises along with some thought-provoking problems.
- End-of-chapter problems serve as a comprehensive review of problems presented in the chapter.
- Over 1,000 problems are presented in the text.
- Review sections present the algebraic formulas and techniques used in the chapter.
- The full-color format highlights important concepts and formulas and provides students with visual guideposts.
- The artwork and photographs provide arresting images of the mathematics being discussed.
- The consistent use of calculators eliminates the drudgery of paper-and-pencil computation.

ORGANIZATION

Except for Section 4.5, which uses the material in Sections 3.1 and 3.2, each chapter is self-contained and can be treated as a separate unit. The nine chapters contain ample material for a one-semester three-credit course.

Chapter 1 introduces the student to the basic building blocks of mathematics—numbers. It begins with ancient systems of numeration, progresses through the Hindu-Arabic system and the number systems of computers, and ends with some creative investigation of numbers including curiosities such as magic squares and circles.

Chapter 2 examines the use of algebraic functions as a model in various situations. Linear, quadratic, exponential, and logarithmic functions are used in a variety of real-life applications.

Chapter 3 begins with a review of some of the postulates, definitions, and theorems of Euclidean geometry and an introduction to non-Euclidean geometry. With this as a base one is introduced to an investigation of the Golden Ratio, polygons, stars, tessallations, and fractals.

Chapter 4 investigates logic and methods of proof. It begins with basic statements and types of reasoning and proceeds to using Venn diagrams and truth tables as methods of proof. The chapter concludes by proving some of the Euclidean and non-Euclidean theorems presented in Sections 3.1 and 3.2.

Chapter 5 focuses on some of the practical applications found in the study of trigonometry. The trigonometry of right triangles and acute triangles are applied to a variety of situations.

Chapter 6 continues to look at mathematics as the practical tool that began in Chapter 5. It examines the world of finance through a realistic study of simple and compound interest, loans and annuities.

Chapter 7 examines another very practical topic, probability. It investigates methods of counting, probability, odds, and expected values by looking at various games of chance and other events.

Chapter 8 looks at basic statistics as a means of arranging and reporting data. It begins with simple statistical graphs, examines measures of central tendency, and investigates the normal distribution.

Chapter 9 completes the mathematical palette presented in the text by developing an understanding of the derivative and the integral and some of the applications of those two important concepts of mathematics.

ANCILLARY MATERIALS

The following ancillary materials are available to all adopters of *The Mathematical Palette*:

Instructor's Manual with Solutions and Transparency Masters contains answers and worked-out solutions to all problems, 100 transparency masters created from text illustrations, and a mini-manual (composed of a chart, summaries, and question sets) correlating sectional content with the Annenberg/CPB video series "For All Practical Purposes."

Prepared Tests contain over 1,600 questions that can be used for testing or as a source of additional problems.

ExaMaster™ computerized testing system for IBM and Macintosh computers presents the same questions contained in the Prepared Tests in a powerful, easy-to-use format.

Student Activity Book and Study Guide with Selected Solutions is available for purchase by students and includes solutions to selected problems and crossword puzzles that will challenge students as well as assist them in reviewing the concepts discussed in each chapter.

▼

ACKNOWLEDGMENTS We would like to thank those who were instrumental in developing this text:

Our wives, Dianne and Theresa, for putting up with us.

David McLaughlin, Ohlone College, for his art work and art research.

Kurt Viegelmann, Ohlone College, for his many photographs.

John O'Connor, Geoffrey Hirsch, Anitra Dark, and our Ohlone College students for their proofreading and suggestions.

The staff of the Ohlone College Word Processing Center for accepting our constant presence.

Bob Stern, Lloyd Black, Alicia Jackson, Mary Patton, Becca Gruliow, Christine Schueler, Bob Butler, Denise Watrobsky, and the staff at Saunders College Publishing for their concern for every detail in producing our book.

We wish to thank the following instructors for their insightful reviews of our manuscript:

Joane W. Anderson, West Valley Joint Community College District

Gary Brown, College of St. Benedict

Warren J. Burch, Brevard Community College

John W. Emert, Ball State University

Mark Greenhalgh, Fullerton College

Suzanne Larson, Loyola Marymount University

Thomas J. Miles, Central Michigan University

Steven L. Thomassin, Ventura College

We especially want to thank John W. Emert of Ball State University for his work in creating the set of Prepared Tests and Kay Meeks of Ball State University for her work in preparing the correlation between the Annenberg video series and our text. We also thank Richard A. Quint of Ventura College for his work in reviewing the accuracy of all examples and problems.

R. Staszkow
R. Bradshaw
February 1991

CONTENTS

CHAPTER 5   TRIGONOMETRY   250

CHAPTER 6   MATH OF FINANCE   305

CHAPTER 7   PROBABILITY   340

CHAPTER 8   STATISTICS   389

THE
MATHEMATICAL PALETTE

1

NUMBERS AND NUMERALS

I Saw the Figure 5 in Gold by Charles Henry Demuth (The Metropolitan Museum of Art) and *Figure 7* by Jasper Johns (National Gallery of Art): modern artists' visual interpretations of the Hindu-Arabic digits five and seven.

TALLIES, NUMBERS, NUMERALS, AND WORDS

It seems appropriate to embark on our journey through mathematics by studying math's basic building blocks, numbers. Ever since prehistoric times, human beings have concerned themselves with numbers. During the Paleolithic period (1,000,000 B.C.–10,000 B.C.) men and women were almost totally consumed with survival. However, it is believed that they possessed a basic sense of numbers and had the ability to distinguish between more, less, and equal. Their language may have been lacking in the words to represent numbers, but anthropologists agree that, at the very least, they possessed a visual number sense and an awareness of form.

As humans progressed through the Neolithic period (8000 B.C.), they became civilized. They grew crops, domesticated animals, wove cloth, made pottery, and lived in villages. Their number sense also grew. Though we have no written records, archaeological findings and opinions of anthropologists suggest that by the beginning of recorded history (3000 B.C.), human beings had developed the ability to tally and count.

A **tally** is a mark that represents the object being counted. This process of tallying took the form of scratches on the ground or on cave walls, as knots on ropes or vines, as piles of pebbles or sticks, and as notches on pieces of bone or wood. For example, to count the number of days between full moons, you could make a mark each evening on the wall of your bedroom until the next full moon appeared. Such a tally might look like this:

$$///// \quad ///// \quad ///// \quad ///// \quad ///// \quad ///$$

However, if the number of objects to be counted is very large, the tally method becomes very cumbersome. For example, if you wanted to record the population of the United States (246.9 million in 1989) using the tally system shown above, and the tallies were typed on both sides of standard $8\frac{1}{2}$-by-11-inch paper, you would end up with a pile of more than 155,000 pieces of paper.

As society became more involved in measurement, commerce, and taxes, more efficient means of representing numbers were needed, so different systems of numeration were developed. In this chapter we will study systems of numeration.

What Is a System of Numeration?

A **number** is a quantity that answers the questions, ''How much?'' or ''How many?'' Numbers are given a name in words or are represented by symbols. The symbols that are used to represent numbers are called **numerals.** In common usage number and numeral are used interchangeably, but the number is really the abstract concept, the amount or value, and the numeral is a symbolic representation of that amount or value. For example, the quantity of trees shown below can be represented by the numeral 10 in our Hindu-Arabic system, $=$ in the Mayan system, $\cap$ in the Egyptian system, X in Roman numerals, $\triangle$ in the Attic system, 1010 in the binary system, $+$ in the traditional Chinese system, and so on. The word used for that amount of trees is *ten* in English, *zehn* in German, *diez* in Spanish, *i'wes* in Ohlone Indian of California, *decem* in Latin, *'umi* in Hawaiian, *dix* in French, *shyr* in Chinese, *tiz* in Hungarian, *daca* in Sanskrit, *desiat* in Russian, and so on.

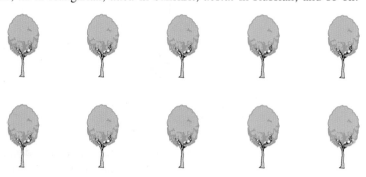

No matter what symbols or words are used, it is understood that there are ten trees.

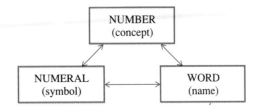

A system of numeration gives us a means of finding the numeral that is associated with a given number. A system of numeration consists of a set of symbols and a method for combining those symbols to represent numbers. As we study different systems of numeration, our goal is to develop a richer understanding of the system of numeration that we presently use, the Hindu-Arabic system.

Some of the important dates, people, and events associated with the development of that system and basic arithmetic are as follows:

c. 150 B.C.	Brahmi numerals appeared in the Nana Ghat inscriptions. These numerals are the origins of the Hindu-Arabic numerals.
A.D. 825	Base 10 place-value numeration system (with a symbol for zero) was well established in India, as seen in the work of Persian mathematician Al-Khowârizmî.
1202	Leonardo Fibonacci encouraged the use of Hindu-Arabic numerals in his work *Liber Abaci*.
1299	City-state of Florence outlawed the Hindu-Arabic system of numeration.
1479	Hindu-Arabic digits first appeared in their present form.
1484	Nicolas Chuquet introduced notation for adding and subtracting fractions.
1489	Johann Widmann used the + and − signs to denote addition and subtraction.
1491	Filippo Calandri introduced the long-division process that is still used today.
c. 1500	The Hindu-Arabic system of numeration replaced Roman numerals in Europe.
1527	Petrino Apianus introduced notation for multiplying and dividing fractions.
1556	Spaniard Juan Diez Feile wrote the first math book in Mexico, *Sumario Compendioso*.
1585	Simon Stevin gave the first systematic account of decimal fractions and their use.
1617	John Napier introduced present-day notation by using the decimal point when writing numerals.
1631	William Oughtred used the × sign for multiplication.

1659	J. H. Rahn introduced the $\div$ sign for division.
1719	The first math book was printed in America: James Hoddler's *Arithmetick,* printed in Boston.
1729	Isaac Greenwood was the first American to write a mathematics book, *Arithmetick, Vulgar and Decimal.*

CHECK YOUR READING

1. Compare the terms ''tally,'' ''numeral,'' and ''number.'' How are they different? How are they the same? Use examples in your explanation.
2. Suppose a fisherman has caught twenty fish. Use our Hindu-Arabic numeration system to:
   (a) Explain how tallies are used in conjunction with the idea of ''twenty fish.''
   (b) Explain how numerals are used in conjunction with the idea of ''twenty fish.''
   (c) Explain how numbers are used in conjunction with the idea of ''twenty fish.''
   (d) Explain how ''twenty'' is used in conjunction with the idea of ''twenty fish.''
3. In the opinion of anthropologists, by what time in history did people learn to count?
4. By 146 B.C., when the Roman Empire was established, which numerals had made an appearance in India?
5. In the year 1484, the Portuguese navigator Diego Cam discovered the mouth of the Congo River. What discoveries were made in arithmetic during that year?
6. When did the present form of our numerals appear?
7. The Roman symbol representing the number 10 is X. Is X a numeral or a number?
8. When the first court jesters appeared in European courts in 1202, what was Leonardo Fibonacci doing?
9. The year 1490 marked the births of King Henry VIII of England and Ignatius Loyola, founder of the Jesuit order. What was Filippo Calandri introducing to the world at about this time?
10. When Columbus landed in North America in 1492, what arithmetic process had just been introduced in Europe?
11. When the Vikings were discovering Greenland in A.D. 985, were the modern forms of fractions and decimals in use? About what time did they come into use?
12. When the new settlement was started in Jamestown (Virginia) in 1607, were our modern symbols for multiplication and division in common use?
13. In the year 1617, the Native American princess Pocahontas died. What was John Napier introducing in Scotland during the same year?

14. Write the numeral for the number of days between consecutive full moons.
15. Match each of the following names with the correct mathematical discovery or event.

(a) Al Khowârizmi	Adding and subtracting fractions
(b) Calandri	Early user of base 10 place-value system
(c) Chuquet	Decimal fractions
(d) Fibonacci	Long-division process
(e) Oughtred	Wrote *Liber Abaci*
(f) Rahn	+ for addition and − for subtraction
(g) Stevin	× for multiplication
(h) Widmann	÷ for division

RESEARCH QUESTIONS

In order to answer the following questions, you will need to refer to material not contained in the text. Possible sources of information are listed in the bibliography at the end of the book.

1. In *The World of Mathematics,* edited by James Newman, and *Number: The Language of Science,* by Tobias Dantzig, studies are cited that indicate that certain birds and insects also have a sense of numbers. Explain these studies and their results.
2. The Hindu-Arabic digits that we use today are 0, 1, 2, 3, 4, 5, 6, 7, 8, 9. Trace the development of these digits.
3. Do some research on two of the people mentioned in this section. What other interests did they have? What else are they famous for?
4. The word used to represent a certain number varies from language to language. What are some ways in which the numerals from 0 to 9 are written in different languages?
5. The ratio of the circumference of a circle to its diameter is known as π ($\pi \approx 3.14159$). The Greek letter ϕ is used to represent a number called the Golden Ratio. What is this number and how is it used?
6. Trace the history of negative numbers and zero.
7. What are Fibonacci numbers? What applications in the real world have been found for these numbers?
8. Trace the development of some of the basic symbols used in arithmetic for addition, subtraction, multiplication, and division.
9. What is a ''googol''? What is a ''googolplex''?
10. What are picoseconds and nanoseconds? In what discipline are they used?
11. What are magic squares? What cultures have studied them?
12. What is cryptography? What is the RSA method invented by Rivest, Shamir, and Adelman?

A copy of a wall painting from the tomb of Menna, Thebes, XVIII Dynasty (c. 1420 B.C.), shows ancient Egyptians using tallying to record the amount of wheat harvested. (The Metropolitan Museum of Art)

SECTION 1.1

▼
ANCIENT SYSTEMS OF NUMERATION

In this section we examine the four basic types of ancient systems of numeration. Each system uses symbols to represent numbers or a set of tallies. We examine how different systems of numeration use symbols to represent numbers. We do not expect you to be an expert in ancient systems of numeration. We merely want to expose you to a very important area of mathematics. Furthermore, we do not expect you to memorize all the symbols in this section. As you read this section and solve the problems at the end, you will need to refer frequently to the lists of symbols for a given system of numeration.

Systems Using Addition

Egyptian Hieroglyphic System

The oldest type of numeration system using addition is the Egyptian hieroglyphic system (c. 3400 B.C.). The numerals used in this system are shown in the table below. The value of the number is simply obtained by finding the sum of the value of each numeral.

1	|	Staff	10,000		Pointing finger
10	∩	Heel bone	100,000		Tadpole
100	ᓯ	Spiral	1,000,000		Astonished man
1000	⚘	Lotus blossom	10,000,000	○	Sun

Example 1:

Find the number represented by 

Solution: Using the table above, add the value of each of the numerals:

$$1{,}000{,}000 + 10{,}000 + 10{,}000 + 10 + 10 + 10 + 1 + 1 = 1{,}020{,}032$$

Example 2:

Write the number 1753 as a numeral in the Egyptian hieroglyphic system.

Solution: $1753 = 1000 + 700 + 50 + 3$, which in Egyptian hieroglyphics is 

In such an additive system the symbols can be placed in any order.

123 =  and so on

Attic System

Another example of a system of numeration that uses an additive grouping scheme was found in records in Athens, Greece, around 300 B.C. The Attic system uses the numerals

1 5 10 50 100 500 1000 5000 10,000 50,000

Example 3:

Find the number represented by the Attic numeral

Solution: Using the chart above, add the value of each numeral.

$$10{,}000 + 10{,}000 + 500 + 100 + 100 + 100 + 10 + 5 + 1 + 1 + 1 + 1 = 20{,}819$$

Example 4:

Write 6376 in the Attic system of numeration.

Solution: Using the chart above, we get

$$6376 = 5000 + 1000 + 100 + 100 + 100 + 50 + 10 + 10 + 5 + 1$$

= 

Systems Using Addition and Subtraction

Roman System

Around 200 B.C., the Romans also developed a system of numeration that used grouping symbols in conjunction with addition. This system also utilized an abacus to perform computation. In the following table you will find the standardized numerals used in the Roman system.

1	5	10	50	100	500	1,000
I	V	X	L	C	D	M
5000	10,000	50,000	100,000	500,000	1,000,000
$\overline{\text{V}}$	$\overline{\text{X}}$	$\overline{\text{L}}$	$\overline{\text{C}}$	$\overline{\text{D}}$	$\overline{\text{M}}$

In this system the value of a numeral was originally obtained by adding the value of each symbol. Later, Roman numerals also included subtraction. Subtraction was used when the numerals were written with "4's" and "9's"—that is, 4 (IV), 9 (IX), 40 (XL), 90 (XC), 400 (CD), 900 (CM), and so on. With these numbers, the numeral representing a smaller number is placed before the numeral that represents a larger number. This indicates that the smaller numeral is to be subtracted from the larger one.

Example 5:

What number is represented by $\overline{\text{DMV}}\text{CCLIV}$ in Roman numerals?

Solution: Using the table above, we get

$$\overline{\text{D}} = 500,000$$
$$\text{M}\overline{\text{V}} = 5000 - 1000 = 4000$$
$$\text{CC} = 100 + 100 = 200$$
$$\text{L} = 50$$
$$\text{IV} = 5 - 1 = 4$$

Thus,

$$\overline{\text{DMV}}\text{CCLIV} = 500,000 + 4000 + 200 + 50 + 4 = 504,254$$

Example 6:

Write 1989 in the Roman numeration system.

Solution:

$$1989 = 1000 + 900 + 80 + 9$$

$$1000 = M$$

$$900 = CM$$

$$80 = LXXX$$

$$9 = IX$$

This gives 1989 = MCMLXXXIX.

Systems Using Addition and Multiplication

Traditional Chinese System

The traditional Chinese system of numeration appearing in the Han dynasty around 200 B.C. also used grouping symbols and addition of numerals to represent numbers. However, instead of repeating a symbol when many of the same symbols are needed, multiplication factors are placed above the numeral. Numerals are written vertically with the symbols

1	2	3	4	5	6	7	8	9
一	二	三	四	五	六	七	八	九

10	100	1000	10,000
十	百	千	万

Example 7:

Find the number represented by

三
十

六
百

一
十

八

Solution:

$3 \times 1000 = 3000$

$6 \times 100 = 600$

$1 \times 10 = 10$

8

This gives a total of 3618.

Notice that each digit of the numeral 3618, except for the units digit, is represented by two characters in the Chinese system.

Example 8:

Write 453 in the traditional Chinese system.

Solution:

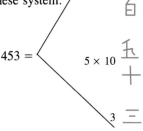

$$453 = \begin{cases} 4 \times 100 \\ 5 \times 10 \\ 3 \end{cases}$$

Ionic Greek System

The Greeks (c. 450 B.C.) used the 24 letters of their alphabet along with 3 ancient Phoenician letters for 6, 90, and 900, to represent numbers. Originally the capital Greek letters were used, but they gave way to the lowercase letters. The symbols used to represent numbers in the Ionic Greek system are shown in the chart below.

1	α	10	ι	100	ρ
2	β	20	κ	200	σ
3	γ	30	λ	300	τ
4	δ	40	μ	400	υ
5	ϵ	50	ν	500	ϕ
6	ς	60	ξ	600	χ
7	ζ	70	o	700	ψ
8	η	80	π	800	ω
9	θ	90	Q	900	T

To represent a number from 1 to 999, write the appropriate symbols next to each other; for example, $\pi\delta = 84$ and $\omega\kappa\gamma = 823$. To obtain numerals for the multiples of 1000, place a prime to the left of the symbols for 1 to 9 to signify that it is multiplied by 1000; for example,

$$'\alpha = 1000 \qquad '\zeta = 7000 \qquad '\theta = 9000$$

One way to obtain the numerals that represent the multiples of 10,000 is to place the symbols for 1 to 9 above the letter M; for example,

$$\overset{\alpha}{M} = 10,000 \qquad \overset{\beta}{M} = 20,000 \qquad \overset{\theta}{M} = 90,000$$

A system in which many different symbols are used to represent the digits is called a ciphered system. This type of a system allows numbers to be written in a simple compact form but requires memorization of many different symbols.

Example 9:

What number is represented by $\overset{\eta}{M}\,'\theta\phi\xi\epsilon$?

Solution:

$$\overset{\eta}{M} = 80,000$$
$$'\theta = 9,000$$
$$\phi = 500$$
$$\xi = 60$$
$$\epsilon = 5$$

This gives $80,000 + 9000 + 500 + 60 + 5 = 89,565.$

Example 10:

Write 2734 in the Ionic Greek system.

Solution:
$$2734 = 2000 + 700 + 30 + 4 = '\beta\psi\lambda\delta$$

Systems Using Place Values

Babylonian System

The most advanced numeration systems are those that not only use symbols, addition, and multiplication, but also give a certain value to the position a numeral occupies. The Babylonian system (c. 2300 B.C.) is an example of this type of system. The sexagesimal system, based on 60, uses only two symbols, which were formed by making marks on wet clay with a stick.

$$\overset{1}{\vee} \quad \overset{10}{\blacktriangleleft}$$

Groups of numerals separated from each other by a space signify that each group is associated with a different place value. Groups of symbols are given the place values from right to left. The place values are

$$60^0 = 1, \quad 60^1 = 60, \quad 60^2 = 3600, \quad 60^3 = 216,000, \ldots$$

For example, $\blacktriangleleft \vee \vee \quad \blacktriangleleft \blacktriangleleft \blacktriangleleft \vee \quad \blacktriangleleft \blacktriangleleft \vee \vee \vee$ means

$$12 \times 60^2 \quad + \quad 31 \times 60^1 \quad + \quad 23 \times 60^0$$

$$12 \times 3600 \quad + \quad 31 \times 60 \quad + \quad 23 \times 1$$

$$43,200 \quad + \quad 1860 \quad + \quad 23 \quad = \quad 45,083$$

The Babylonian system, however, did not contain a symbol for zero to indicate the absence of a particular place value. Some Babylonian tablets have a larger gap between numerals or the insertion of the symbol $\blacktriangleleft$, which indicates a missing place value.

Example 11:

Find the number represented by

$$\vee \vee \quad \blacktriangleleft \vee \quad \blacktriangleleft \quad \overset{\blacktriangleleft \blacktriangleleft \vee \vee}{\blacktriangleleft \ \vee \vee}$$

Solution: The groupings represent 2, 11, 0, and 34, which gives

$$2 \times 60^3 \quad + \quad 11 \times 60^2 \quad + \quad 0 \times 60^1 \quad + \quad 34 \times 60^0$$

$$2 \times 216,000 \quad + \quad 11 \times 3600 \quad + \quad 0 \times 60 \quad + \quad 34 \times 1$$

$$432,000 \quad + \quad 39,600 \quad + \quad 0 \quad + \quad 34 \quad = \quad 471,634$$

Example 12:

Represent 4507 in the Babylonian numeration system.

Solution: The place values of the Babylonian system that are less than 4507 are 3600, 60, and 1. To determine how many groups of each place value are contained in 4507, we can use the division scheme shown below.

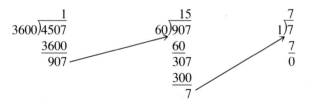

$$(1 \text{ group of } 3600) \qquad (15 \text{ groups of } 60) \qquad (7 \text{ ones})$$
$$4507 = \quad 1 \times 3600 \quad + \quad 15 \times 60 \quad + \quad 7 \times 1$$

$$4507 =$$

Mayan System

In about 300 B.C., the Mayan priests of Central America also developed a place-value numeration system. Their system was an improvement on the Babylonian system because it was the first to have a symbol for zero. The Mayan system is based on 20 and 18. It uses the numerals shown below.

The numerals are written vertically, with the place value assigned from the bottom of the numeral to the top of the numeral. The positional values are

$$20^0 = 1, 20^1 = 20, 18 \times 20^1 = 360, 18 \times 20^2 = 7200, 18 \times 20^3 = 144,000, \ldots$$

Instead of the third position having a place value of 20^2, the Mayans gave it a value of 18×20^1. This was probably done so that the approximate number of days in a year, 360 days, would be a basic part of the numeration system.

For example, in the Mayan system, 168,599 is written as

$$\rightarrow \quad 1 \times (18 \times 20^3) \quad = \quad 1 \times 144,000 \quad = \quad 144,000$$
$$\rightarrow \quad 3 \times (18 \times 20^2) \quad = \quad 3 \times 7200 \quad = \quad 21,600$$
$$\rightarrow \quad 8 \times (18 \times 20^1) \quad = \quad 8 \times 360 \quad = \quad 2,880$$
$$\rightarrow \quad 5 \times 20^1 \quad = \quad 5 \times 20 \quad = \quad 100$$
$$\rightarrow \quad 19 \times 20^0 \quad = \quad 19 \times 1 \quad = \quad \underline{\quad 19}$$
$$168,599$$

The Mayan system does have a zero, but, because of the use of 18 in the third position, its place-value feature is irregular.

Example 13:

Find the number represented by

Solution:

$$\cdots\cdots = 4 \times 7200 = 28{,}800$$

$$\text{\textcircled{\textbf{—}}} = 0 \times 360 = \phantom{28{,}80}0$$

$$\text{\underline{$\cdots$}} = 7 \times 20 = \phantom{28{,}8}140$$

$$\text{\underline{\underline{$\cdots$}}} = 12 \times 1 = \phantom{28{,}80}12$$

This gives a total of 28,952.

Example 14:

Write 17,525 in the Mayan numeration system.

Solution: The place values less than 17,525 in the Mayan system are 7200, 360, 20, and 1. To determine how many groups of each place value are contained in 17,525, we use the division scheme below.

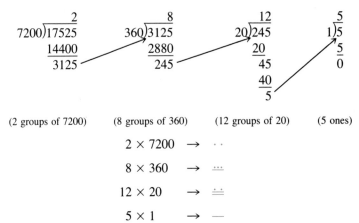

$$
\begin{array}{c}
2 \\
7200\overline{)17525} \\
\underline{14400} \\
3125
\end{array}
\qquad
\begin{array}{c}
8 \\
360\overline{)3125} \\
\underline{2880} \\
245
\end{array}
\qquad
\begin{array}{c}
12 \\
20\overline{)245} \\
\underline{20} \\
45 \\
\underline{40} \\
5
\end{array}
\qquad
\begin{array}{c}
5 \\
1\overline{)5} \\
\underline{5} \\
0
\end{array}
$$

(2 groups of 7200)   (8 groups of 360)   (12 groups of 20)   (5 ones)

$$2 \times 7200 \;\rightarrow\; \cdots$$

$$8 \times 360 \;\rightarrow\; \cdots\cdots$$

$$12 \times 20 \;\rightarrow\; \text{\underline{\underline{$\cdots$}}}$$

$$5 \times 1 \;\rightarrow\; —$$

Our system of numeration originated with the Hindus in India in about 150 B.C., with its base 10 place-value feature and zero placeholder being introduced before 628. By 900, this Hindu-Arabic numeration system had reached Spain, and by 1210 it was spread to the rest of Europe by traders on the Mediterranean Sea and scholars who attended universities in Spain. By 1479, the digits appeared in the form that is used today.

The Hindu-Arabic system of numeration made computation a reasonable task. However, those that used Roman numerals and calculated with their counting board abacus, the "abacists," were opposed to the "algorists," who used and computed with the Hindu-Arabic numerals. In fact, in 1299, the city-state of Florence in Italy outlawed the use of the Hindu-Arabic system. Many banks in Europe also forbade the use of these numerals because they were easily forged and/or altered on bank drafts. However, by 1500 the Hindu-Arabic system had won the battle and became the prevalent numeration system. In the next section, we look more closely at the Hindu-Arabic system of numeration.

SECTION 1.1
PROBLEMS

What number is represented by each Egyptian hieroglyphic numeral?

1. 𓏤𓏤 ⌐⌐

2. ⌐ 𓎆𓎆𓎆

3. 𓏲 ⌐ 𓎆|

What number is represented by each Attic numeral?

4. Μ Γ Γ

5. Χ Η Γ Ι

6. Γ ΓΜΗΗ

What number is represented by each Roman numeral?

7. DCCXXXIV

8. $\overline{\text{CMCM}}$

9. $\overline{\overline{\text{XL}}}$MMCDLVII

What number is represented by each traditional Chinese numeral?

10. 四
    百
    二
    十

11. 七
    千
    五
    百
    二

12. 九
    万
    五
    千
    三
    百
    六
    十

What number is represented by each Ionic Greek numeral?

13. $\lambda\zeta$

14. $\phi\mu\delta$

15. $\overset{\beta}{\text{M}}{}'\epsilon\xi\beta$

What number is represented by each Babylonian numeral?

16. ⟨   ⋁

17. ⟨ ⋁

18. ⟨ ⟨ ⋁ ⋁ ⋁   ⟨ ⋁ ⋁ ⋁ ⋁   ⟨ ⟨ ⋁

What number is represented by each Mayan numeral?

19. ·

  ⊕

  ···

20. ⁚

  ···

  ══

  ···

  ══
  ⁚

21. ⁝

  ≡

  ⁚

  ····

  ⊕

  ⊕

22. Represent the speed of sound (750 mph) in each of the following numeration systems:

(a) Egyptian hieroglyphic
(b) Attic
(c) Roman
(d) Traditional Chinese
(e) Ionic Greek
(f) Babylonian
(g) Mayan

23. Represent the number of minutes in a day (1440 min) in each of the following numeration systems:

(a) Egyptian hieroglyphic
(b) Attic
(c) Roman
(d) Traditional Chinese
(e) Ionic Greek
(f) Babylonian
(g) Mayan

24. (a) Represent the number of chairs shown below in each of the systems of numeration of Problem 23.
  (b) Represent the number of legs on the chairs shown below in each of the systems of numeration of Problem 23.

25. Which of the systems of numeration described in this section would you prefer to use? Give reasons for your choice.

26. After studying seven ancient systems of numeration, you can better understand the advantages of the Hindu-Arabic system we presently use. What are some of these advantages?

27. What are the four kinds of systems of numeration described in this section? How are they the same? How are they different?

*28. Do some research on another ancient system of numeration. Describe the numerals and scheme for representing numbers in this system. Determine which of the four kinds of numeration systems it is.

*29. Suppose that the Egyptian numeral  were converted by people from different cultures into a numeral in their own systems of numeration. How would the Egyptian numeral be represented in the following systems of numeration?

(a) Roman system
(b) Ancient Chinese system
(c) Ionic Greek system
(d) Babylonian system
(e) Mayan system

SECTION 1.2

▼

HINDU-ARABIC SYSTEM AND FRACTIONS

The Hindu-Arabic system is the numeration system used in the United States and many other parts of the world. It is also called the decimal system, from the Latin *deci*, meaning tenth. (Note that the Chinese system of numeration could also be called a decimal system.) The base of the Hindu-Arabic system is 10, and the symbols used in the system are the digits 0, 1, 2, 3, 4, 5, 6, 7, 8, and 9. The position a digit holds in a numeral gives it a certain value. The numeral 1,389,260,547 has place values as follows:

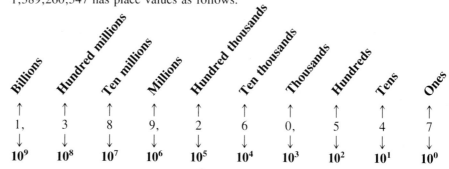

In expanded form,

$$1,389,260,547 = 1 \times 10^9 + 3 \times 10^8 + 8 \times 10^7 + 9 \times 10^6 +$$
$$2 \times 10^5 + 6 \times 10^4 + 0 \times 10^3 + 5 \times 10^2 + 4 \times 10^1 + 7 \times 10^0$$

The position of a digit tells us what it really represents. The 9 represents 9 millions (9,000,000), the 6 represents 6 ten thousands (60,000), the 4 represents 4 tens (40), and so on.

Example 1:

Write 4,175,280 in expanded form.

Solution:

$$4,175,280 = 4,000,000 + 100,000 + 70,000 + 5000 + 200 + 80$$
$$= 4 \times 10^6 + 1 \times 10^5 + 7 \times 10^4 + 5 \times 10^3 + 2 \times 10^2 + 8 \times 10^1$$

Example 2:

In the numeral 576,239, what do the 5, 6, and 2 represent?

Solution: 5 represents 5 hundred thousands (500,000).
6 represents 6 thousands (6000).
2 represents 2 hundreds (200).

Decimal Fractions

The decimal system also gives an efficient means of representing numbers that are less than a whole, numbers that fall between 0 and 1. Such numbers can be represented in two different forms, as a fraction or as a decimal (decimal fraction). For example, the shaded portion of the block shown below can be represented by the fraction 1/2 or the decimal 0.5.

The decimal numbers simply extend the place-value system by using negative powers of 10. For example, 0.943271 means

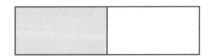

	Tenths	Hundredths	Thousandths	Ten-thousandths	Hundred-thousandths	Millionths
	↑	↑	↑	↑	↑	↑
0.	9	4	3	2	7	1
	↓	↓	↓	↓	↓	↓
	10^{-1}	10^{-2}	10^{-3}	10^{-4}	10^{-5}	10^{-6}

In expanded form,

$$0.943271 = 9 \times 10^{-1} + 4 \times 10^{-2} + 3 \times 10^{-3} + 2 \times 10^{-4} + 7 \times 10^{-5} + 1 \times 10^{-6}$$

$$= \frac{9}{10} + \frac{4}{100} + \frac{3}{1000} + \frac{2}{10,000} + \frac{7}{100,000} + \frac{1}{1,000,000}$$

The position a digit holds to the right of the decimal point tells us what value it represents. The 9 represents 9 tenths (9/10), the 3 represents 3 thousandths (3/1000), the 1 represents 1 millionth (1/1,000,000), and so on.

Example 3:

In the numeral 1.7312, what do the digits 7, 3, and 2 represent?

Solution: The 7 represents 7 tenths (7/10).
The 3 represents 3 hundredths (3/100).
The 2 represents 2 ten-thousandths (2/10,000).

Example 4:

Write 75.324 in expanded form.

Solution:

$$75.324 = 70 + 5 + 3/10 + 2/100 + 4/1000$$

$$= 7 \times 10^1 + 5 \times 10^0 + 3 \times 10^{-1} + 2 \times 10^{-2} + 4 \times 10^{-3}$$

Some of the ancient systems of numeration discussed in the previous section also had methods of representing fractions. Although these systems were not as advanced as the decimal system, a look at them should prove interesting. You will have to refer to the numeration systems in the previous section to obtain the symbols used in ancient fractions.

Egyptian Hieroglyphic Fractions

In this system the sign for a mouth, ◎ , which in this context meant a part, was placed above a numeral to allow the Egyptians to represent fractions with a numerator of 1.

$$\frac{◎}{|||} = \frac{1}{3} \qquad \frac{◎}{∩||} = \frac{1}{12} \qquad \frac{◎}{99∩} = \frac{1}{210}$$

Any fraction whose numerator was not equal to 1 was represented as the sum of distinct fractions whose numerators were equal to 1.

$$\frac{◎}{∩} \ \frac{◎}{||} = \frac{1}{10} + \frac{1}{2} = \frac{3}{5} \qquad \frac{◎}{|||} \ \frac{◎}{|||||} \ \frac{◎}{∩} = \frac{1}{3} + \frac{1}{5} + \frac{1}{10} = \frac{19}{30}$$

Babylonian Fractions

The use of the symbols ⟨⟨ in the initial position of a numeral indicated that the number being represented was a fraction. A group of symbols following the ⟨⟨ became the numerator of a fraction, and successive powers of 60 (60, 3600, 216,000, etc.) were understood to be the denominator for each group of symbols. The Babylonian fraction being represented was the sum of each individual fraction.

$$\text{ᛏᛏ V} = \tfrac{1}{60} \qquad \text{ᛏᛏ < V V V} \quad \text{< V} = \tfrac{13}{60} + \tfrac{11}{3600} = \tfrac{791}{3600}$$

Roman Fractions

Fractions for the Romans were mainly used in connection with their system of weights, 1 *as* (pound) = 12 *unciae* (ounces). Hence, their fractions were limited to parts of 12 (12ths). The table below gives the fractions of the Romans.

.	or	–	→	1/12	S .	or	S –	→	7/12
. .	or	=	→	2/12 or 1/6	S . .	or	S =	→	8/12 or 2/3
. . .	or	= –	→	3/12 or 1/4	S . . .	or	S = –	→	9/12 or 3/4
. . . .	or	= =	→	4/12 or 1/3	S	or	S = =	→	10/12 or 5/6
. . . . .	or	= = –	→	5/12	S	or	S = = –	→	11/12
		S	→	6/12 or 1/2			I	→	12/12 or 1

Ionic Greek Fractions

The Greek scheme for representing fractions involved using the prime on the right side of a numeral. Fractions with a numerator of 1 were written with a single prime to the right of the numeral.

$$\theta' = \frac{1}{9} \qquad \pi\epsilon' = \frac{1}{85} \qquad \rho' = \frac{1}{100}$$

Fractions with numerators greater than 1 were represented with the numerator written as a normal numeral and the denominator written twice with a prime to the right of each.

$$\epsilon\eta'\eta' = \frac{5}{8} \qquad \iota\alpha\,\lambda\epsilon'\,\lambda\epsilon' = \frac{11}{35}$$

Example 5:

For each fraction below, write its equivalent fraction in the Hundi-Arabic system.

(a) Egyptian: ⊚ III   ⊚ ∩I
(b) Babylonian: ᛏᛏV V   <<<
(c) Roman: S . .
(d) Greek: $\theta\ \pi\epsilon'\ \pi\epsilon'$

Solution:

(a) 1/3 + 1/11 = 11/33 + 3/33 = 14/33
(b) 2/60 + 30/3600 = 4/120 + 1/120 = 5/120 = 1/24
(c) 8/12 = 2/3
(d) θ = 9, $\pi\epsilon$ = 85, so the fraction is 9/85

SECTION 1.2

PROBLEMS

Write each in expanded form.

1. 139

2. 0.53

3. 437.15

4. 1,032,742

5. 0.314

6. 5.23

7. 543,867

8. 0.03874

9. 53.171

10. 5083

11. 0.62193

12. 1.043

13. In Problems 1–12, what does the digit 3 represent?

Write the equivalent Hindu-Arabic fraction for each Egyptian fraction in Problems 14–17.

14.

15.

16.

17.

Write the equivalent Hindu-Arabic fraction for each Babylonian fraction in Problems 18–21.

18.

19.

20.

21.

Write the equivalent Hindu-Arabic fraction for each Roman fraction in Problems 22–25 on page 22.

22. . .

23. = =

24. S .

25. S = −

Write the equivalent Hindu-Arabic fraction for each Greek fraction in Problems 26–29.

26. $\kappa\delta'$

27. $\xi\gamma'$

28. $\iota\ \lambda\beta'\ \lambda\beta'$

29. $\mu\theta\ \phi\alpha'\ \phi\alpha'$

The sum of a whole number and a fraction is called a mixed number. In the Hindu-Arabic system 5 + 2/3 is written as 5 2/3. Find the mixed numbers represented by each ancient numeral.

30. Egyptian:

31. Babylonian:

32. Roman: X X I V S =

33. Greek: $\rho\alpha\ \lambda\delta'$

Changing a Hindu-Arabic fraction into the corresponding Egyptian fraction requires that you represent the Hindu-Arabic fraction as the sum of distinct fractions that have a numerator of 1. Find the Egyptian fractions in Problems 34–38.

34. 3/4

35. 5/12

36. 7/10

37. 8/15

38. 31/100

*39. The Chinese rod-numeral system using scientific Chinese numerals is an example of a place-value system that allowed for the representation of decimal fractions. Do some research and explain how this system works.

SECTION 1.3

▼

NUMERATION SYSTEMS WITH OTHER BASES

The decimal system uses the powers of 10 to determine the place value of each digit used in a numeral. The base of 10 is the result of human beings' having ten fingers. However, as we saw in Section 1.1, other place-value systems did not use a base of 10. The Babylonians had a system based on 60, whereas the Mayan system was based on 20. Primitive tribes have been discovered that had a system of numeration based on 5, the number of fingers on one hand. The Duodecimal

Society of America in the 1960s advocated the change to a base of 12. Computers, on the other hand, use a base of 2 since an electric pulse is in one of two states—on or off. If animals could develop a system of numeration, a horse might use a base 4 system, an octopus a base 8, an ant a base 6, and so on. In this section, we investigate how to write numbers in different bases and how to convert a numeral written in one base to the corresponding numeral in another base.

The Place-Value System for Any Base

The first component of any place-value system is its base. The base of a numeration system is a whole number that is larger than 1. The integer powers of the base give each position in a numeral its place value. If we let a dot separate the whole number part and the fractional part of a number, for any base (b) to the left of the dot the place values are the nonnegative integer powers of the base and to the right of the dot the place values are the negative powers of the base.

Whole-number part					**Fractional part**		
#	#	#	# ·	#	#	#	#
↓	↓	↓	↓	↓	↓	↓	↓
$\ldots b^3$	b^2	b^1	b^0	b^{-1}	b^{-2}	b^{-3}	$b^{-4}\ldots$

The second component of a place-value system is the set of digits. The digits are symbols that represent the quantities from 0 to 1 less than the base. The base determines the number of symbols that are in the system. In the decimal system the base is 10, and it has 10 digits (0, 1, 2, 3, 4, 5, 6, 7, 8, and 9). The following is a summary of some numeration systems with various bases. It includes the base, the digits, and the place value for whole numbers from the right to the left of the numeral. Notice that base 12 and base 16 require the use of letters to represent some numbers greater than 9. For example, the letter A represents the number 10.

System	Base	Digits	Place Values
Binary	2	0, 1	1, 2, 4, 8, 16, . . .
Quintary	5	0, 1, 2, 3, 4	1, 5, 25, 125, 625, . . .
Octal	8	0, 1, 2, 3, 4, 5, 6, 7	1, 8, 64, 512, 4096, 32,768, 262,144, . . .
Duodecimal	12	0, 1, 2, 3, 4, 5, 6, 7, 8, 9, A(10), B(11)	1, 12, 144, 1728, 20,736, 248,832, . . .
Hexadecimal	16	0, 1, 2, 3, 4, 5, 6, 7, 8, 9, A(10), B(11), C(12), D(13), E(14), F(15)	1, 16, 256, 4096, 65,536, 1,048,576, . . .

When you read a numeral in a base other than 10, read each digit separately. For example, the numeral 123_5 is read "one two three, base five" and not "one hundred twenty-three, base five.'' The reason is that the concept of ''hundreds'' is part of the base 10 system and therefore should not be used in other bases.

Converting to a Decimal Numeral

In order to understand what number or amount is being represented by a numeral in a base other than 10, we need to convert it to the system we are familiar with, the decimal system. For example, the numeral 23014 in base 5, written 23014_5, represents an amount. In order to understand what amount that is, we will convert it to a decimal numeral.

Example 1:

Write 23014_5 as a base 10 decimal numeral.

Solution: Use the powers of 5 for the place value for each digit in the numeral.

$$
\begin{array}{rcl}
2\ 3\ 0\ 1\ 4_5 & & \\
4 \times 5^0 = 4 \times 1 & = & 4 \\
+\ 1 \times 5^1 = 1 \times 5 & = & 5 \\
+\ 0 \times 5^2 = 0 \times 25 & = & 0 \\
+\ 3 \times 5^3 = 3 \times 125 & = & 375 \\
+\ 2 \times 5^4 = 2 \times 625 & = & \underline{1250} \\
& & 1634
\end{array}
$$

Thus, $23014_5 = 1634_{10}$.

Example 2:

Write $17A6_{12}$ as a decimal numeral.

Solution: Use the powers of 12 for the place value of each digit in the numeral.

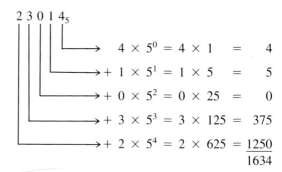

$$
\begin{array}{rcll}
1\ 7\ A\ 6_{12} & & & \\
6 \times 12^0 & = & 6 \times 1 & = & 6 \\
+\ A \times 12^1 & = & 10 \times 12 & = & 120 \\
+\ 7 \times 12^2 & = & 7 \times 144 & = & 1008 \\
+\ 1 \times 12^3 & = & 1 \times 1728 & = & \underline{1728} \\
& & & & 2862
\end{array}
$$

Thus, $17A6_{12} = 2862_{10}$.

Example 3:

Write $101\ 101_2$ in base 10.

Solution: Use the powers of 2 for the place values of each digit in the numeral.

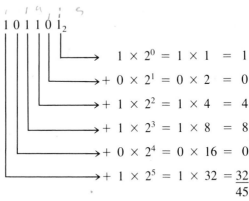

$$1\ 0\ 1\ 1\ 0\ 1_2$$

$$1 \times 2^0 = 1 \times 1\ = 1$$
$$+\ 0 \times 2^1 = 0 \times 2\ = 0$$
$$+\ 1 \times 2^2 = 1 \times 4\ = 4$$
$$+\ 1 \times 2^3 = 1 \times 8\ = 8$$
$$+\ 0 \times 2^4 = 0 \times 16 = 0$$
$$+\ 1 \times 2^5 = 1 \times 32 = \underline{32}$$
$$45$$

Thus, $101\ 101_2 = 45_{10}$.

Example 4:

Write $86,DC0_{16}$ as a numeral in base 10.

Solution: Use the powers of 16 for the place values of each digit in the number.

$$8\ 6\ D\ C\ 0_{16}$$

$$0 \times 16^0 = \ 0 \times 1\ = \ 0$$
$$+\ C \times 16^1 = 12 \times 16\ = \ 192$$
$$+\ D \times 16^2 = 13 \times 256\ = \ 3,328$$
$$+\ 6 \times 16^3 = \ 6 \times 4096\ = \ 24,576$$
$$+\ 8 \times 16^4 = \ 8 \times 65,536 = \underline{524,288}$$
$$552,384$$

Thus, $86,DC0_{16} = 552,384_{10}$.

Converting Decimal Numerals to Other Bases

To convert a decimal number to another base, we need to find how many groups of each appropriate place value are contained in the decimal number. The division scheme shown in the examples that follow will allow you to convert a base 10 numeral into another base.

Example 5:

Write the decimal number 89 as a number in base 5.

Solution: The powers of 5 that are less than 89 are 25, 5, 1. We need to find how many groups of each of those place values are contained in 89. We can do that by using the division scheme shown below.

$$
\begin{array}{ccc}
\dfrac{3}{25\overline{)89}} & \dfrac{2}{5\overline{)14}} & \dfrac{4}{1\overline{)4}} \\
\dfrac{75}{14} & \dfrac{10}{4} & \dfrac{4}{0}
\end{array}
$$

The number 89 contains 3 groups of 25, 2 groups of 5, and 4 groups of 1.

$$
\begin{aligned}
89_{10} &= 3 \times 25 + 2 \times 5 + 4 \times 1 \\
&= 3 \times 5^2 + 2 \times 5^1 + 4 \times 5^0 \\
&= 324_5
\end{aligned}
$$

Example 6:

Write the decimal number 204 as a binary number.

Solution: The powers of 2 that are less than 204 are 128, 64, 32, 16, 8, 4, 2, and 1. Use the division scheme of Example 5.

$$
\begin{array}{cccccccc}
\dfrac{1}{128\overline{)204}} & \dfrac{1}{64\overline{)76}} & \dfrac{0}{32\overline{)12}} & \dfrac{0}{16\overline{)12}} & \dfrac{1}{8\overline{)12}} & \dfrac{1}{4\overline{)4}} & \dfrac{0}{2\overline{)0}} & \dfrac{0}{1\overline{)0}} \\
\dfrac{128}{76} & \dfrac{64}{12} & \dfrac{0}{12} & \dfrac{0}{12} & \dfrac{8}{4} & \dfrac{4}{0} & \dfrac{0}{0} & \dfrac{0}{0}
\end{array}
$$

$$
\begin{aligned}
204_{10} &= 1 \times 128 + 1 \times 64 + 0 \times 32 + 0 \times 16 + 1 \times 8 + 1 \times 4 + 0 \times 2 + 0 \times 1 \\
&= 1 \times 2^7 + 1 \times 2^6 + 0 \times 2^5 + 0 \times 2^4 + 1 \times 2^3 + 1 \times 2^2 + 0 \times 2^1 + 0 \times 2^0 \\
&= 11\,001\,100_2
\end{aligned}
$$

Example 7:

Write the decimal number 10,000 in base 8.

Solution: The powers of 8 that are less than 10,000 are 4096, 512, 64, 8, and 1. Use the division scheme of previous examples.

$$\begin{array}{llll}
\overline{2} & \overline{3} & \overline{4} & \overline{2} & \overline{0} \\
4096\overline{)10000} & 512\overline{)1808} & 64\overline{)272} & 8\overline{)16} & 1\overline{)0} \\
\quad\underline{8192} & \quad\underline{1536} & \quad\underline{256} & \quad\underline{16} & \quad\underline{0} \\
\quad1808 & \quad\;272 & \quad\;16 & \quad\;0 & \quad0
\end{array}$$

$$10{,}000 = 2 \times 4096 + 3 \times 512 + 4 \times 64 + 2 \times 8 + 0 \times 1$$
$$= 2 \times 8^4 + 3 \times 8^3 + 4 \times 8^2 + 2 \times 8^1 + 0 \times 8^0$$
$$= 23{,}420_8 \quad \blacksquare$$

Example 8:

Write the decimal number 40,600 as a hexadecimal number (base 16).

Solution: The powers of 16 that are less than 40,600 are 4096, 256, 16, and 1. Use the division scheme again.

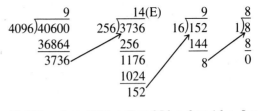

$$\begin{array}{llll}
\overline{9} & \overline{14(E)} & \overline{9} & \overline{8} \\
4096\overline{)40600} & 256\overline{)3736} & 16\overline{)152} & 1\overline{)8} \\
\quad\underline{36864} & \quad\underline{256} & \quad\underline{144} & \quad\underline{8} \\
\quad\;3736 & \quad1176 & \quad\;\;8 & \quad0 \\
 & \quad\underline{1024} & & \\
 & \quad\;152 & &
\end{array}$$

$$40{,}600 = 9 \times 4096 + E \times 256 + 9 \times 16 + 8 \times 1$$
$$= 9 \times 16^3 + E \times 16^2 + 9 \times 16^1 + 8 \times 16^0$$
$$= 9E98_{16} \quad \blacksquare$$

The Link Among the Binary, Octal, and Hexadecimal Systems

Since binary numbers tend to be a very long string of 1's and 0's they are difficult to write and remember. The octal and hexadecimal systems are used along with the binary system in computer applications because they can give a shortened numeral for a binary one. Any octal digit can be represented by a three-digit binary number, and any hexadecimal digit can be represented by a four-digit binary number. Hence, digits of binary numbers are written in groups of three or four, starting from the right side. This allows binary numbers to be easily converted into an octal numeral or a hexadecimal numeral.

Binary (place values)	→	Octal	Binary (place values)	→	Hexadecimal
4 2 1			*16* 8 4 2 1		
0 0 1	→	1	0 0 0 1	→	1
0 1 0	→	2	0 0 1 0	→	2
0 1 1	→	3	0 0 1 1	→	3
1 0 0	→	4	0 1 0 0	→	4
1 0 1	→	5	0 1 0 1	→	5
1 1 0	→	6	0 1 1 0	→	6
1 1 1	→	7	0 1 1 1	→	7
			1 0 0 0	→	8
			1 0 0 1	→	9
			1 0 1 0	→	10 (A)
			1 0 1 1	→	11 (B)
			1 1 0 0	→	12 (C)
			1 1 0 1	→	13 (D)
			1 1 1 0	→	14 (E)
			1 1 1 1	→	15 (F)

(handwritten) 1 0 0 0 0 → 16₅

Example 9:

Write $10\ 110\ 111_2$ as (a) an octal number and (b) a hexadecimal number.

Solution:

(a) Octal: Separate the binary numeral into groups of three digits starting from the right of the numeral and find the octal digit for each group of three digits.

$$1\ 0\ 1\ \ 1\ 0\ 1\ \ 1\ 1 = 267_8$$

$$2\ \ \ \ \ \ 6\ \ \ \ \ \ 7$$

(b) Hexadecimal: Separate the binary numeral into groups of four digits and find the hexadecimal digit for each group of four digits.

$$1\ 0\ 1\ 1\ \ 0\ 1\ 1\ 1 = B7_{16}$$

$$11\ \ \ \ \ \ \ \ \ \ 7$$

$$(B)$$

American Standard Code for Information Exchange

The American Standard Code for Information Interchange (ASCII) is a binary code used by computers to represent information. The characters of the alphabet, the digits 0–9, as well as various special characters such as periods, commas, hyphens, and so on, are represented as a distinct binary pattern of 1's and 0's. The hexadecimal code for the letter A is 41; for the letter Z, it is 5A; and for the greater-than sign, it is 3E.

ASCII (American Standard Code for Information Interchange)

CHR	HEX	CHR	HEX	CHR	HEX	CHR	HEX	CHR	HEX
!	21	-	2D	9	39	E	45	Q	51
"	22	.	2E	:	3A	F	46	R	52
#	23	/	2F	;	3B	G	47	S	53
$	24	0	30	<	3C	H	48	T	54
%	25	1	31	=	3D	I	49	U	55
&	26	2	32	>	3E	J	4A	V	56
'	27	3	33	?	3F	K	4B	W	57
(	28	4	34	@	40	L	4C	X	58
)	29	5	35	A	41	M	4D	Y	59
*	2A	6	36	B	42	N	4E	Z	5A
+	2B	7	37	C	43	O	4F		
,	2C	8	38	D	44	P	50		

Example 10:

Find the actual binary code for A, Z, and >.

Solution: Since every hexadecimal digit is composed of four binary digits, we need to find the four-digit binary numeral for each digit in the hexidecimal representation of A, Z, and >.

$$A = 4 \quad 1 \qquad\qquad Z = 5 \quad A$$

$$0100 \ 0001 = 1 \ 000 \ 001_2 \qquad\qquad 0101 \ 1010 = 1 \ 011 \ 010_2$$

$$> = 3 \quad E$$

$$0011 \ 1110 = 111 \ 110_2$$

Fractions in Other Bases

A base 10 number less than 1 can be represented using a decimal point or negative integer powers of 10. For example,

$$0.2358 = 2 \times 10^{-1} + 3 \times 10^{-2} + 5 \times 10^{-3} + 8 \times 10^{-4}$$

$$= 2 \times \frac{1}{10} + 3 \times \frac{1}{100} + 5 \times \frac{1}{1000} + 8 \times \frac{1}{10,000}$$

In other bases, the dot used to separate the whole number part of a number and the fractional part has different names. It is called the quintary point in base 5, the binary point in base 2, the octal point in base 8, and so on. However, the generic term used for the dot in any base is the **basimal** point. Fractional numbers can be represented in any base by using methods similar to those used with decimal numbers.

Example 11:

Write 0.2314_5 as a base 10 numeral.

Solution:

$0.\ 2\ 3\ 1\ 4_5$

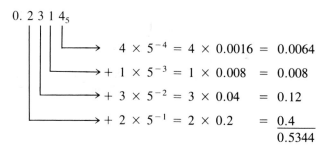

$$4 \times 5^{-4} = 4 \times 0.0016 = 0.0064$$
$$+\ 1 \times 5^{-3} = 1 \times 0.008\ \ = 0.008$$
$$+\ 3 \times 5^{-2} = 3 \times 0.04\ \ \ = 0.12$$
$$+\ 2 \times 5^{-1} = 2 \times 0.2\ \ \ \ = \underline{0.4}$$
$$0.5344$$

Thus, $0.2314_5 = 0.5344_{10}$.

Example 12:

Write 53.72_8 as a base 10 numeral.

Solution:

$5\ 3.7\ 2_8$

$$2 \times 8^{-2} = 2 \times 0.015625 = 0.03125$$
$$+\ 7 \times 8^{-1} = 7 \times 0.125\ \ \ \ \ = 0.875$$
$$+\ 3 \times 8^{0}\ \ = 3 \times 1\ \ \ \ \ \ \ \ \ \ = 3.$$
$$+\ 5 \times 8^{1}\ \ = 5 \times 8\ \ \ \ \ \ \ \ \ \ = \underline{40.}$$
$$43.90625$$

Thus, $53.72_5 = 43.90625_{10}$

Looking back at the survey of the different systems of numeration, the reader can appreciate the advantages of the Hindu-Arabic system. First, the Hindu-Arabic system uses a small number of uncomplicated symbols. After memorizing these ten digits, a person can write any numeral. This is an improvement over the large number of symbols used by the Ionic Greeks and the elaborate characters of the Egyptian system.

Using too few characters also has drawbacks. While the Babylonian system and base 2 use only two characters, both methods require using the symbols many times to express a relatively small number. For example,

$$59 = \text{<<<<<} \text{VVVVV} = 111\ 011_2$$
$$\text{VVV}$$

Our system strikes a balance between using a large number of symbols and requiring a large number of digits to write a relatively small number.

A second advantage of the Hindu-Arabic system is its use of a place value system. While initially more difficult to learn, a place value system is advantageous for writing most large numbers. The advantages of a place value system become clear when writing 888 in a system such as the Roman system:

$$888 = \text{DCCCLXXXVIII}$$

Finally, we leave it to your imagination to envision a long division problem such as $10{,}488 \div 23$ in any system other than our own.

SECTION 1.3

PROBLEMS

Write each of the following as a decimal numeral.

1. 302_5

2. 140.32_5

3. 101.101_2

4. $100\ 111\ 001_2$

5. 5610_8

6. $70{,}037.2_8$

7. $7A4.3_{12}$

8. $B8AA01_{12}$

9. $9F20_{16}$

10. $123ABC.D_{16}$

11. 253_7

12. 1068_9

Write the following decimal numerals in the specified base.

13. Write 401 as a numeral in base 5.

14. Write 990 as a numeral in base 8.

15. Write 5280 as a numeral in base 16.

16. Write 186,000 as a numeral in base 9.

Represent (a) the number of days in a leap year (366) and (b) the number of pounds in a ton (2000) in each of the following systems of numeration.

17. Quintary

18. Binary

19. Octal

20. Duodecimal

21. Hexadecimal

22. Base 6

Convert the following binary numerals to both octal and hexadecimal numerals.

23. $11\ 001\ 011_2$

24. $1\ 010\ 101\ 010_2$

25. $111\ 011\ 101\ 011_2$

26. $100\ 101\ 101\ 111_2$

In Problems 27–32, (a) use the ASCII table of Example 10 to find the hex (hexadecimal) representation for each symbol, and (b) find the binary and decimal representations of each hexadecimal numeral.

27. The letter R

28. The dollar sign $

29. The plus sign +

30. The letter N

31. The numeral 9

32. The numeral 7

In each pair of numerals, determine which one has a larger value.

33. 254_9 or 12202_3

34. $6C_{16}$ or 253_6

35. $101\ 101_2$ or 3033_4

36. 13.421_5 or 1.421_8

0, e, and *i* by David McLaughlin (courtesy of the artist) and π by Tom Marioni (courtesy of Crown Point Press): artists' representations of four historically significant numerical constants.

SECTION 1.4

▼

TYPES OF NUMBERS

Numbers are a basic part of our daily lives. They are all around us. As seen in this chapter, they have been of interest to human beings from earliest times. Just as humans classified the animals, insects, plants, and objects around them, they also classified their numbers. So as we continue our study of mathematics, it would be appropriate to study the many types of numbers that have been classified.

Real Numbers

The **natural numbers,** also called counting numbers, consist of the numbers {1, 2, 3, 4, . . .}. The **whole numbers** consist of the natural numbers and zero {0, 1, 2, 3, 4, . . .}. The **integers** consist of the whole numbers and the negatives of the whole numbers, {. . . −4, −3, −2, −1, 0, 1, 2, 3, 4, . . .}.

The **rational numbers** are numbers that can be represented by the quotient a/b, where a and b are integers and $b \neq 0$. It can be shown that when these quotients are converted into decimals, they are either terminating or repeating decimals. For example, the rational number 3/5 is the terminating decimal 0.6, −7/4 is −1.75, 53 is 53.0, and 156 17/25 is 156.68, and 2/3 is the repeating decimal 0.666 . . . , −36/11 is −3.2727 . . . , and 43 1/7 is 43.142857142857 . . . .

The **irrational numbers** are decimal numbers that do not terminate and do not repeat (as the rational numbers do). It can be shown that an irrational number cannot be written as a ratio of two integers. Included in this group of numbers are radical numbers, such as $\sqrt{2}$, $\sqrt{19}$, $\sqrt[4]{101}$, $\sqrt[3]{34}$, and mathematical constants, such as π and e. The root spiral in Section 5.0 gives a visual representation of the square roots of the natural numbers.

The **real numbers** consist of all the rational and irrational numbers. They can be visualized by using a horizontal number line where a zero point (the origin) and a unit length are marked off. Each real number corresponds to exactly one point on the line, and each point on the line corresponds to exactly one real number. Numbers that are larger than zero, the positive numbers, are placed to the right of zero, and numbers that are less than zero, the negative numbers, are placed to the left of zero.

The Real Number Line

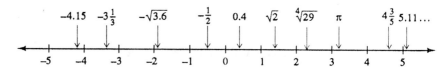

The following chart shows the classification of the real numbers.

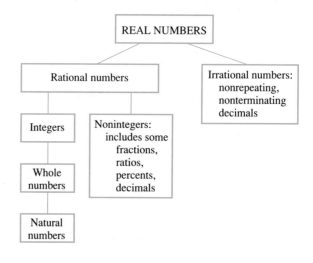

Example 1:

$$-10, -4.67, -\sqrt{17}, -3\tfrac{5}{8}, -\sqrt[5]{2.9}, -1, -\tfrac{2}{3}, 0, 0.333\ldots,$$
$$\sqrt[3]{8.41}, \tfrac{5}{2}, \sqrt{25}, \sqrt{27}, 7.87, 27$$

From the list above, determine which of the numbers are (a) integers, (b) irrational numbers, (c) natural numbers, (d) rational numbers, (e) real numbers, and (f) whole numbers.

Solution:

(a) Integers: $-10, -1, 0, \sqrt{25}, 27$
(b) Irrational numbers: $-\sqrt{17}, -\sqrt[5]{2.9}, \sqrt[3]{8.41}, \sqrt{27}$
(c) Natural numbers: $\sqrt{25}, 27$
(d) Rational numbers: all except those in part (b)
(e) Real numbers: all numbers in the list
(f) Whole numbers: $0, \sqrt{25}, 27$

Example 2:

Explain why $\sqrt{36}$ can be classified as a rational number, a natural number, a whole number, and an integer but not an irrational number.

Solution: Since $\sqrt{36} = 6$, it is a rational number ($6/1$), a natural number ($1, 2, 3, 4, \ldots$), a whole number ($0, 1, 2, 3, 4, \ldots$), and an integer ($\ldots -3, -2, -1, 0, 1, 2, 3, \ldots$). It is not an irrational number because it can be expressed as a quotient of integers ($6/1$) and because, as a decimal, it terminates (6.0).

Zero and Negative Numbers

Before we continue our investigation of other types of numbers, we will look at the origins of zero and negative numbers. Though sometimes taken for granted, zero frequently finds its way into our daily activities. The symbol for zero, 0, is used quite often when we write numerals and perform computations. Negative numbers have also gained acceptance today. We use a negative number for an amount less than zero, such as the temperature at the North Pole or a checking account balance after writing a check for more money than is in the account. Surprisingly, this modern use and acceptance of zero and negative numbers did not occur overnight; it took many centuries for these mathematical concepts to be accepted by the scientific community.

Let's examine some facts about zero. The concept of zero, which indicates the absence of a quantity, has most likely been understood since prehistoric times. Each time a hunter came home without any game, the number zero was experienced. Though the early Egyptian, Greek, and Roman civilizations understood the concept of zero, they had no symbol for zero. Their systems of numerations did not need a symbol for zero. Zero was, however, represented on ancient Babylonian tablets and Chinese counting boards as a blank space used for a missing place value in a numeral. In the fourth century B.C., the symbol ◖ was used by the Babylonians, and the symbol ⊕ was used by the Mayans of South America in place of the blank space. The symbol 0 is believed to have originated in India some 20 years after forms of the other nine numerals appeared. This symbol for zero developed before A.D. 870, since it was contained on an A.D. 870 inscription in Gwalior, India. However, some experts believe that this symbol may have come to India by way of Indochina, since inscriptions in Cambodia and Sumatra (A.D. 683) used this same symbol for zero.

In Western culture, the use of the symbol 0 is a fairly recent development. It became well established in Europe during the late 1400s when the Hindu-Arabic system replaced Roman numerals. Finally, the word ''zero'' comes from the Latin word *ziphrum*. *Ziphrum* is a translation from the Arabic word *sifr*, which came from the Hindu word *sunya*, meaning void or empty.

As with the number zero, negative numbers have an interesting history. There is no trace of negative numbers in ancient Egyptian, Babylonian, or Greek writings. In A.D. 270, when negative numbers occurred as solutions to equations, the Greek mathematician Diophantus dismissed them as being absurd. This had such an effect that it was not until the Renaissance (14th and 15th centuries) that mathematicians began to be more receptive to negative numbers.

Negative numbers gained acceptance in Europe in the 16th century through the work *Ars Magna* by Girolamo Cardano (1545), who used negative numbers as solutions to equations, and the work of Michael Stifel (1544), who described negative numbers as those numbers that are less than zero. The terms ''positive'' and ''affirmative'' were used to indicate positive numbers, and the terms ''privative,'' ''negative,'' and ''minus'' were used for negative numbers.

In non-Western cultures, such as China, India, and Arabia, however, negative numbers were readily accepted. In the second century B.C., Chinese counting boards used red or triangular rods to represent positive numbers and black or square rods to represent negative numbers. In India, c. A.D. 628, Brahmagupta mentioned negative numbers, and the Hindu and Arabian mathematicians that followed continued to use negative numbers in their arithmetic and algebra.

Complex Numbers

Besides the real numbers described previously, there is another set of numbers based on $\sqrt{-1}$. These numbers are called **imaginary numbers** and use the letter i, where $i = \sqrt{-1}$. For example, $\sqrt{-16} = 4\sqrt{-1} = 4i$, $\sqrt{-27} = 3\sqrt{3}\sqrt{-1} = 3\sqrt{3}i$, or $\sqrt{-93} = \sqrt{93}i$. If a real number and an imaginary number are added together, the sum is called a **complex number** and is written in the form $a + bi$, where a and b are real numbers. Thus,

$$5 + \sqrt{-9} = 5 + 3i \qquad \text{and} \qquad -7.2 - \sqrt{-20} = -7.2 - 2\sqrt{5}i$$

Imaginary numbers are a recent mathematical development. Until the 1500s, square roots of negative numbers were considered an impossibility. The work of Girolamo Cardano (1545) and Rafael Bombelli (1572) introduced imaginary numbers as roots of equations. René Descartes (1637) called them ''imaginary,'' and

Leonhard Euler (1748) used i to represent $\sqrt{-1}$. Though imaginary numbers are not used in everyday transactions, they are used to solve problems in mathematics, electronic circuit design, vibration analysis, and other branches of science and engineering.

Numbers Based on Geometric Shapes

Polygonal numbers are numbers that were devised to conform to basic geometric shapes. These geometric-based numbers were of interest especially to the Greeks because of their simplistic geometric beauty and the many different mathematical patterns found between the terms of each number and between different polygonal numbers.

Triangular numbers take the shape of triangles, as pictured below.

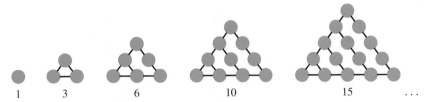

Square numbers take the shape of squares, as pictured below.

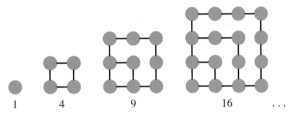

Pentagonal numbers take the shape of pentagons, as pictured below.

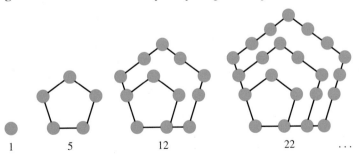

Other polygonal numbers can be formed by using other regular geometric shapes such as hexagons, octagons, decagons, and so on.

Example 3:

Find the next two triangular numbers and describe the pattern that exists in going from one triangular number to the next.

Solution: The next two triangular numbers are 21 and 28. If you list the triangular numbers and find the difference between successive terms, the differences are the whole numbers 2, 3, 4, 5, 6, ... Thus, to get from one triangular number to the next, just continue adding consecutive integers.

1		3		6		10		15		21		28
	+2		+3		+4		+5		+6		+7	

Magic Squares and Cubes

Humankind's fascination with numbers also led to the creation of magic squares and cubes. The ancients believed that square arrays of numbers that had the same sum horizontally, vertically, and diagonally contained mystical powers while exhibiting the harmony of numbers, mathematical regularity, and symmetry. Probably the most ancient of these squares, the Lo Shu square, dates back to the Chinese emperor Yu the Great, who reigned from 2205 to 2198 B.C. In the square array of numbers represented by knots on strings, the black knots represent even numbers and the white knots represent odd numbers. In the square, all rows, columns, and diagonals have a sum of 15.

The Lo Shu
Magic Square

8	3	4
1	5	9
6	7	2

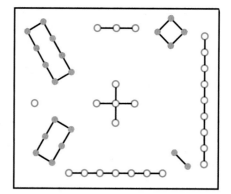

Any one of eight possible arrangements of those nine numbers can be used to give 3 × 3 magic squares. Magic squares have also been found of larger sizes in various cultures throughout history. Japanese mathematicians of the 1600s were especially attracted to magic squares. Muramatsu (1663) determined magic squares up to 19 rows by 19 columns, and Seki Kōwa (1666) developed rules for creating magic squares of various large dimensions. Figure 1.4.1 (page 39) displays 4 × 4 and 5 × 5 magic squares.

In a San Francisco Bay Area science fair project in 1982, Kevin Staszkow, a son of one of the authors, used an Apple II computer to generate magic cubes. In these cubes the whole numbers from 1 to 27 were arranged in three layers with nine numbers in each layer. Forty-two was the identical sum of the three numbers

FIGURE 1.4.1

14	7	11	2
1	12	8	13
4	9	5	16
15	6	10	3

17	24	1	8	15
23	5	7	14	16
4	6	13	20	22
10	12	19	21	3
11	18	25	2	9

in a horizontal row, a vertical column, or one of the cube's four diagonals. Kevin did not know that magic cubes were studied in the past without the use of computers, especially by Japanese mathematicians Tanaka Kisshin (1662) and Kurushima Gita (1757). Kurushima Gita determined a $4 \times 4 \times 4$ magic cube that uses the whole numbers from 1 to 64 and has a magic sum of 130. Kevin's experience does, however, show that mathematics can be rediscovered. It can cause as much excitement and sense of accomplishment in the new discoverer as it did for the original discoverer. The three layers of one of Kevin Staszkow's Apple II–generated magic cubes are shown in Figure 1.4.2.

Example 4:

Verify that the diagonals of the magic cube shown in Figure 1.4.2 do have a sum of 42.

Solution: The diagonals of a cube go from one corner of the cube through the center of the cube to the opposite corner. In the cube shown the diagonals are:

(a) $1 + 14 + 27 = 42$
(b) $18 + 14 + 10 = 42$
(c) $2 + 14 + 26 = 42$
(d) $24 + 14 + 4 = 42$

FIGURE 1.4.2

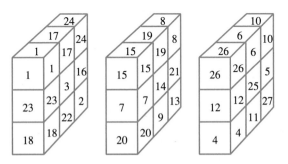

Numbers Based on Factors

A **proper factor** of a natural number is a natural number less than the number that divides evenly into the number. For example, the proper factors of 8 are 1, 2, and

FIGURE 1.4.3

2	3	4	5	6	7	8	9	10	11
12	13	14	15	16	17	18	19	20	21
22	23	24	25	26	27	28	29	30	31
32	33	34	35	36	37	38	39	40	41
42	43	44	45	46	47	48	49	50	51
52	53	54	55	56	57	58	59	60	61
62	63	64	65	66	67	68	69	70	71
72	73	74	75	76	77	78	79	80	81
82	83	84	85	86	87	88	89	90	91
92	93	94	95	96	97	98	99	100	101

4. A **prime number** is a whole number whose only proper factor is 1, and a **composite number** is a whole number that has proper factors greater than 1. According to these definitions, the number 1 is not a prime number. The first ten prime numbers are 2, 3, 5, 7, 11, 13, 17, 19, 23, and 29. It has been proved that there are an infinite number of primes and that every composite number can be represented as a product of prime numbers. The Greek scholar Eratosthenes (274–194 B.C.) invented an arithmetical sieve for finding prime numbers. For example, to find all the prime numbers less than 102, write down all the natural numbers from 2 to 101 (Fig. 1.4.3). The first number, 2, is a prime. Draw a box around it and cross out all other multiples of 2 (every second number: 4, 6, 8, 10, . . .). The next number that is not crossed, 3, is a prime. Draw a box around it and cross out all other multiples of 3 (every third number: 6, 9, 12, 15, 18, . . .). Continuing in this manner, you can see that there are 26 prime numbers less than 102.

To find more prime numbers, one would have to write down more whole numbers and continue in a similar fashion, as above. With the use of computers, very large prime numbers have been found. In 1989, six researchers at Amdahl Corporation in Sunnyvale, CA, calculated the largest known prime number (as of November 1989), $391,581 \times 2^{216,193} - 1$, which consists of 65,087 digits.

Since every composite number has proper factors, the properties of these factors have also been studied. The following types of numbers are a result of these investigations.

A **perfect number** is a whole number with the property that the sum of its proper factors equals the number. Six is the first perfect number because its proper factors, 1, 2, and 3, have a sum of 6 (1 + 2 + 3 = 6). Another perfect number is 496 because the sum of its proper factors, 1, 2, 4, 8, 16, 31, 62, 124, and 248 equals 496. In 1952, there were only 12 known perfect numbers. Since then, with the aid of computers, 30 perfect numbers have been found. The largest of these has over 130,000 digits.

An **abundant number** is a whole number with the property that the sum of its proper factors is greater than the number. Twelve is an abundant number because its proper factors 1, 2, 3, 4, and 6 have a sum of 16. One hundred is an abundant number because its proper factors 1, 2, 4, 5, 10, 20, 25, and 50 have a sum of 117.

A **deficient number** is a whole number with the property that the sum of its proper factors is less than the number. Twenty-seven is a deficient number because the sum of its proper factors 1, 3, and 9 equals 13. Forty-three is a deficient number because its only proper factor is 1.

Amicable numbers are a pair of whole numbers such that the sum of the proper factors of one number equals the other number, and vice versa. The numbers 220 and 284 are amicable because the sum of the proper factors of 220 (1, 2, 4, 5, 10, 11, 20, 22, 44, 55, 110) is 284 and the sum of the proper factors of 284 (1, 2, 4, 71, 142) is 220. This pair of numbers has been ascribed to the Greek mathematician Pythagoras (c. 540 B.C.). The fact that each amicable number generates the other gives them an intimate relationship that played a role in mysticism and superstition through the ages. In 1636, the French mathematician Pierre Fermat discovered a second amicable pair, 17,296 and 18,416. In 1638, René Descartes discovered a third pair, and in 1750, Leonhard Euler found 60 other pairs. In 1866, a 16-year-old Italian, Nicolo Paganini, astounded the mathematical world when he discovered the small amicable pair of 1184 and 1210. Today there are more than 900 known amicable pairs of numbers, and they are still intriguing to mathematicians and computer enthusiasts.

Example 5:

Classify the numbers 18, 28, 31, and 45 as (a) composite or prime and (b) as perfect, abundant, or deficient.

Solution:

18: (a) Composite number because 1 is not the only proper factor.
   (b) Abundant number because the sum of its proper factors (1, 2, 3, 6, 9) equals 21, and 21 > 18.

28: (a) Composite number because 1 is not the only proper factor.
   (b) Perfect number because the sum of its proper factors (1, 2, 4, 7, 14) equals 28.

31: (a) Prime number because its only proper factor is 1.
   (b) Deficient number because its only proper factor is 1, and 1 < 31.

45: (a) Composite number because 1 is not its only proper factor.
   (b) Deficient number because the sum of its proper factors (1, 3, 5, 9, 15) equals 33, and 33 < 45.

Example 6:

Show that the numbers 17,296 and 18,416 found by Pierre Fermat are amicable numbers.

Solution: The proper factors of 17,296 are 1, 2, 4, 8, 16, 23, 46, 47, 92, 94, 184, 188, 368, 376, 752, 1081, 2162, 4324, and 8648. The sum of these factors is 18,416. The proper factors of 18,416 are 1, 2, 4, 8, 16, 1151, 2302, 4604, and 9208. The sum of these factors is 17,296. Thus, 17,296 and 18,416 are amicable numbers. ▪

Notes on π

Another number that has been of interest since ancient times is the ratio of the circumference (C) of a circle to its diameter (D), given by C/D. No matter what size circle is considered, this ratio has the same value. By about 2000 B.C., the Babylonians used a value of 25/8 for this ratio. Many brilliant minds have worked on obtaining approximate values for this ratio. Here are some of them:

Archimedes of Syracuse (200 B.C.): 211875/67441

Astronomer Ptolemy (160): 377/120

Liu Hui (263): 157/50

Āryabhata (499): 626832/200,000

Valentin Otho (1573): 355/113

In 1706, William Jones used the symbol π (the Greek letter pi) to represent the ratio. With usage of this symbol in 1736 by Leonhard Euler, π became a standard. Between 1500 and 1800, others used trigonometry and calculus to approximate π to more than 500 decimal places. In 1766, Johann Lambert proved that π could not be represented by the ratio of two whole numbers and was therefore an irrational number. In the 20th century, calculators and computers have been used to determine π to thousands of decimal places. In 1989, David and Gregory Chudnovsky, mathematicians at Columbia University, established a new record of 480 million digits. If printed in a straight line, the number would be more than 600 miles long. The present-day feat of determining π to millions of digits with a computer is impressive. However, without the use of computers evidence of accurate estimations of π have been noted. For example, in the Great Pyramid of Gizeh in Egypt (2600 B.C.), the ratio of twice the width of the pyramid ($w = 230.364$ m) to the height ($h = 146.599$ m) of the pyramid gives π accurate to the hundredths place ($2w/h \approx 3.14277$).

The first 501 digits of π are as follows:

3.14159 26535 89793 23846 26433 83279 50288 41971 69399 37510 58209 74944 59230
78164 06286 20899 86280 34825 34211 70679 82148 08651 32823 06647 09384 46095
50582 23172 53594 08128 48111 74502 84102 70193 85211 05559 64462 29489 54930
38196 44288 10975 66593 34461 28475 64823 37867 83165 27102 19091 45648 56692
34603 48610 45432 66482 13393 60726 02491 41273 72458 70066 06315 58817 48815
20920 96282 92540 91715 36436 78925 90360 01133 05305 48820 46652 13841 46951
94151 16094 33057 27036 57595 91953 09218 61173 81932 61179 31051 18548 07446
23799 62749 56735 18857 52724 89122 79381 83011 94921   (never stops or repeats)

<table>
<tr><td>

SECTION 1.4

PROBLEMS

</td><td>

1. From the list below, choose the numbers belonging to each category.
$-11, -9.4, -8\frac{2}{9}, -\sqrt{50}, -4, -\sqrt[3]{7.3}, 0, \frac{3}{4}, 1, \sqrt{-2}, \sqrt{2}, 6.1212\ldots,$
$\sqrt{49}, 9, 10.12$

(a) Natural numbers
(b) Whole numbers
(c) Integers
(d) Rational numbers
(e) Irrational numbers
(f) Real numbers
(g) Imaginary numbers
(h) Noninteger rational numbers

</td></tr>
</table>

2. From the list below, choose the numbers belonging to each category.
$-14.785, -7, -\sqrt{64}, -\sqrt{-25}, -\frac{5}{16}, 0, \sqrt[5]{19}, \sqrt{-8}, \sqrt{8}, \pi, 5\frac{7}{8},$
$9.76555\ldots, \sqrt{100}, 19$

(a) Natural numbers
(b) Whole numbers
(c) Integers
(d) Rational numbers
(e) Irrational numbers
(f) Real numbers
(g) Imaginary numbers
(h) Nonradical irrational numbers

3. Answer true or false for each statement. If a statement is false, give an example to show that it is false.

(a) All rational numbers are real numbers.
(b) All real numbers are rational numbers.
(c) All irrational numbers are real numbers.
(d) All real numbers are irrational numbers.
(e) All integers are whole numbers.
(f) All whole numbers are integers.
(g) All rational numbers are irrational numbers.
(h) All irrational numbers are rational numbers.
(i) All imaginary numbers are irrational numbers.
(j) All irrational numbers are imaginary numbers.
(k) All radicals are irrational.
(l) Complex numbers of the form $a + bi$ are real numbers when $b = 0$.

4. List five numbers that satisfy each description.

(a) Real numbers that are not rational
(b) Rational numbers that are not integers
(c) Irrational numbers that are not square roots
(d) Real numbers that are not irrational
(e) Integers that are not natural numbers
(f) Noninteger rational numbers

5. Even numbers are integers that end in 0, 2, 4, 6, or 8, and odd numbers end in 1, 3, 5, 7, or 9. How can even numbers be defined by using the concept of a factor?

6. What are the fifth and sixth pentagonal numbers? Make a sketch of each number.

7. Example 3 showed that there is a pattern going from term to term in the triangular numbers. Find the patterns for the square and pentagonal numbers and use the patterns to find the first ten of each type of number.

8. The first three hexagonal numbers are 1, 6, and 15. Make a sketch of these three polygonal numbers.

9. Why is 2 the only even prime number?

10. Why is every prime number a deficient number?

11. Classify each of the following numbers as (a) prime or composite and (b) perfect, abundant, or deficient.
    (a) 31
    (b) 77
    (c) 145
    (d) 1988
    (e) 8128
    (f) 9000

12. Show that the pair of numbers 1184 and 1210, found by 16-year-old Nicolo Paganini in 1866, is an amicable pair of numbers.

13. Determine whether the following are magic squares.

7	5	3
2	9	4
6	1	8

14	7	11	2
1	12	8	13
4	9	5	16
15	6	10	3

2	21	20	14	8
18	12	6	5	24
25	19	13	7	1
11	10	4	23	17
9	3	22	16	15

14. The following "very" magic 4 × 4 square is found in an Albert Dürer engraving.

16	3	2	13
5	10	11	8
9	6	7	12
4	15	14	1

In parts (a)–(e), verify the following properties of this magic 4 × 4 square.
    (a) The 2 × 2 squares in each corner and the center have the property that the sum of the four numbers in each square is 34.

(b) The sum of the squares of the numbers in the two top rows is the same as the sum of the squares of the numbers in the two bottom rows.

(c) The sum of the squares of the numbers in the first and third rows is the same as the sum of the squares of the numbers in the second and fourth rows.

(d) The sum of the numbers on the diagonals is the same as the sum of the numbers that are not on the diagonals.

(e) The sum of the squares of the numbers on the diagonals is the same as the sum of the squares of the numbers not on the diagonals.

(f) What other groups of four numbers besides the horizontal rows, vertical columns, diagonals, and the 2 × 2 squares mentioned in (a) also have a sum of 34?

15. The ancient Chinese considered even numbers to be female and odd numbers to be male. Using the Lo Shu magic square as a pattern, create the female magic square, using the even integers 2, 4, 6, 8, 10, 12, 14, 16, and 18, and the male magic square, using the odd integers 1, 3, 5, 7, 9, 11, 13, 15, and 17.

16. The three layers shown contain some of the numbers of a 3 × 3 × 3 magic cube. Determine the missing numbers.

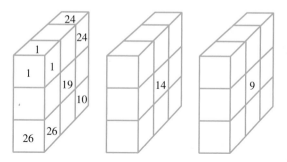

17. An old basic math text stated that $\pi = 22/7$. Why is this statement incorrect? What is the correct relationship between π and 22/7?

*18. There are methods for creating magic squares. Do some research on one of these methods and show how it can be used to generate a magic square.

*19. Explain why the number 1 is not considered a prime number.

*20. The Japanese mathematician Kittoku Isomura (c. 1660) did a great deal of work on magic circles. In these circles, consecutive natural numbers, starting at 1, are placed on the diagram shown. If we add the numbers on any circle and the number in the center of the diagram, we get the same result as the sum of the numbers on each of the diagonals of the circle.

(a) Place the numbers 1 to 9 in the diagram to create a magic circle.

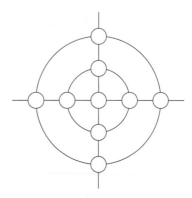

(b) Place the numbers 1 to 19 in the diagram to create a magic circle.

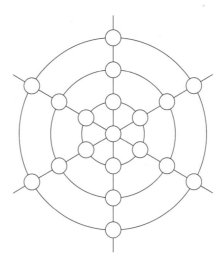

C H A P T E R	1	**SUMMARY**

**KEY TERMS,
CONCEPTS, AND
FORMULAS**

The important terms in this chapter are

Binary: A number system with a base of 2 using the digits 0 and 1.　　p. 23

Complex number: The sum of a real number and an imaginary number.　　p. 36

Composite number: A whole number that has proper factors greater than 1.　　p. 40

Duodecimal: A number system with a base of 12 using the digits 0, 1, 2, 3, 4, 5, 6, 7, 8, 9, A, and B.　　p. 23

Hexadecimal: A number system with a base of 16 using the digits 0, 1, 2, 3, 4, 5, 6, 7, 8, 9, A, B, C, D, E, and F.   p. 23

Imaginary number: A number involving $\sqrt{-1}$ (i).   p. 36

Integer: A number from the set
$\{\ldots -4, -3, -2, -1, 0, 1, 2, 3, 4, \ldots\}$.   p. 34

Irrational number: A number that cannot be represented as the ratio of two integers; as a decimal, it does not terminate or repeat.   p. 34

Magic square: A square array of numbers that has the same sum vertically, horizontally, and diagonally.   p. 38

Natural number: A number from the set $\{1, 2, 3, 4, 5, \ldots\}$.   p. 34

Number: A measure of a quantity or amount.   p. 2

Numeral: A symbol used to represent a number.   p. 2

Octal: A number system with a base of 8 using the digits 0, 1, 2, 3, 4, 5, 6, and 7.   p. 13

Perfect number: A whole number with the property that the sum of its proper factors equals itself.   p. 40

Pi (π): The ratio of the circumference of a circle to its diameter (≈ 3.14159).   p. 42

Place value: The value given to the position a digit holds in a numeral.   p. 11

Polygonal numbers: Numbers based on geometric shapes, such as triangular, square, pentagonal, and hexagonal numbers.   p. 37

Prime number: A whole number that is only divisible by 1 and itself.   p. 40

Proper factor of a natural number N: A natural number less than N that divides evenly into N.   p. 39

Rational number: A number that can be represented as the ratio of two integers; as a decimal it terminates or repeats.   p. 34

Real number: A number that is either rational and irrational; each real number corresponds to a point on a number line.   p. 34

System of numeration: A scheme for representing numbers by using a set of symbols.   p. 2

Tally: A mark used to represent objects being counted.   p. 2

Whole number: A number from the set $\{0, 1, 2, 3, 4, 5, \ldots\}$.   p. 34

After completing this chapter, you should be able to:

1. Explain the difference between a number, a tally, a numeral, and the word used to verbalize a quantity or amount.   p. 2

2. Represent numbers in ancient systems of numeration that use grouping symbols along with:
(a) Addition—Egyptian hieroglyphic system

(b) Addition and subtraction—Roman numeral system
(c) Addition and multiplication—traditional Chinese system, Ionic Greek system
(d) Place values—Babylonian system, Mayan system   p. 6

3. Represent numbers in the Hindu-Arabic system (decimal system), which is a place-value system using a base of 10.   p. 17

4. Show how fractions are formed in the decimal system and in some of the ancient systems of numeration.   p. 18

5. Represent numbers in a place-value system that has any base and be able to convert between decimal numerals and numerals in other bases.   p. 22

6. Convert between binary, octal, and hexadecimal numerals.   p. 27

7. Classify different types of numbers, such as real numbers, complex numbers, numbers based on geometric shapes, and numbers based on factors.   p. 34

SUMMARY
PROBLEMS

1. Represent the tally on the right as a numeral in each of the following systems of numeration:

(a) Egyptian hieroglyphic
(b) Roman numeral
(c) Traditional Chinese
(d) Ionic Greek
(e) Babylonian
(f) Mayan
(g) Hindu-Arabic
(h) Binary
(i) Base 5
(j) Octal
(k) Duodecimal
(l) Hexadecimal

2. Using the symbols → for 1, ← for 5, ↓ for 25, ↑ for 125, ↔ for 625, and ↕ for 3125, design an additive system of numeration. Use that system to represent:

(a) Number of tallies in Problem 1
(b) Number of days in a leap year
(c) Number of feet in a mile
(d) Number of grams in a kilogram

3. Using the letters of the alphabet: a for 1, b for 2, c for 3, d for 4, e for 5, f for 6, g for 7, h for 8, i for 9, and dots placed above a letter to indicate that a certain digit is being multiplied by a power of 10. (. placed above a letter indicates it is being multiplied by 10, .. placed above a letter indicates it is being multiplied by 100, ... placed above a letter indicates it is multiplied by 1000, and so on), form a system of numeration that uses both addition and multiplication. Use that system of numeration to

(a) Find the value of the following numerals:

   (i) e ḋ

   (ii) f̈ ȧ d

  (iii) h⃛ i ḋ e

  (iv) c⃛ a ḃ

   (v) g⃜ a g̈ e

  (vi) a⃜ d̈

(b) Represent the quantities asked for in Problem 2.

4. Devise a method for representing fractions in the system of numeration in Problem 3. Give examples showing how various fractions can be written by using the system.

5. Using the symbols * for 0, / for 1, ✕ for 2, and ▼ for 3, design a base 4 place-value system of numeration. Represent the same quantities in this place-value system as is asked for in Problem 2.

6. Explain the components of a base 7 system of numeration. Show how whole numbers and fractional numbers can be represented in this system. Represent the quantities asked for in Problem 2 as base 7 numerals.

7. The octal ASCII code for the letter S is 123. What are the binary, decimal, and hexadecimal representations of the letter S?

8. The algebraic expression $n^2 - n + 41$ generates prime numbers for $0 \leq n \leq 40$. Find the first nine prime numbers generated by this algebraic expression. Show that this expression generates a composite number when $n = 41$. Find another value for n where this expression generates a composite number.

9. Classify the four numbers 400, 461, 496, and 512 as (a) composite or prime and (b) as perfect, abundant, or deficient.

10. The following four layers contain some of the numbers that form a 4 × 4 × 4 magic cube. Determine the missing numbers.

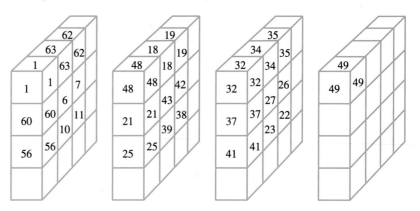

11. A figure is created by placing a number at each intersection point on the lines of a star. If the sum of the numbers along each line of the star is the same as every other such sum in that star, the star is called a magic star. Verify that star (a) is a magic star and determine the missing values in stars (b), (c), and (d) that will make them magic stars.

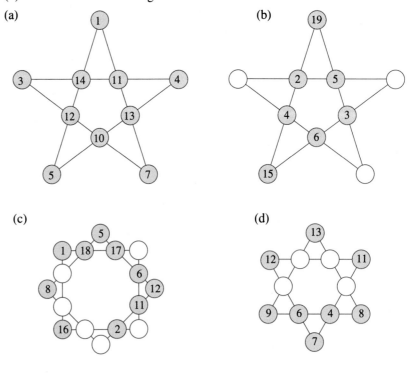

(a)

(b)

(c)

(d)

12. -7.45, $-\sqrt{40}$, -5, $\sqrt[3]{-27}$, $-\frac{5}{9}$, 0, $\sqrt[4]{19}$, π, 3.1416, $4.6161\ldots$, $7\frac{2}{3}$, 13, $\sqrt{-400}$

From the list above determine which of the numbers are:

(a) Imaginary
(b) Integers
(c) Irrational
(d) Natural
(e) Rational
(f) Real
(g) Whole

13. Design a system of numeration using your own symbols and your own scheme to represent numbers. How would you represent fractions in your system? Give examples and explanations of the components of your system.

2

ALGEBRAIC MODELS

Melancholia I by the 16th-century artist Albrecht Dürer shows the contemplation engendered by the study of mathematics. (The Metropolitan Museum of Art)

A SHORT HISTORY OF ALGEBRA

As ancient men and women investigated the geometry of the world around them and used their number systems to count, measure, and calculate, they began to generalize the procedures of arithmetic and apply them to unknown quantities. Anthropologists believe that before 2000 B.C. the Chinese, Persians, Babylonians, and people of India may have begun this process and had some elementary knowledge of what we now call algebra. However, the first definite evidence of algebra is found in the Rhind papyrus (c.1650 B.C.). In this work the Egyptian mathematician Ahmes included problems such as this:

If a ''heap'' and a seventh of a ''heap'' are 19, what is the value of the ''heap''?

The ancient Greeks (650 B.C.–A.D. 200) contributed much to the development of mathematics, but their main concern was geometry, not algebra. This left algebra in a stage where its problems and solutions were stated only in words and used mainly in reference to geometric figures. Around A.D. 250 a major step in the development of algebra occurred with the work of Greek mathematician Diophantus (210–290). He worked out a system of his own to solve problems by using symbols to replace numbers and operations. For example, he used ⟍ for subtraction, (for equals, and (for an unknown quantity. The work of Diophantus made significant contributions to mathematical notation and expanded the scope of algebra. For this he is considered by many to be the father of algebra.

The period after the disintegration of the Roman Empire in the fourth and fifth centuries was called the Dark Ages. These were years of very little progress in the development of algebra in Europe. The main advances came from India and Arabia. Hindu mathematicians like Brahmagupta (c.625) followed the lead of Diophantus by continuing to use symbols in the solution of mathematical problems. Around 825, Al-Khowârizmî, an Arabian teacher of mathematics in Baghdad, used the word we know as algebra in his work *Ilm al-jabr walmuqabalah*, meaning the science of transposition and cancellation. Through his writing, algebra became known as the study of solving equations. The interest in algebra also spread to Persia, where famed poet and mathematician Omar Khayyam (1050–1123) wrote a book on algebra. The Arabian and Indian influence did much to improve number notation and the symbolism of algebra.

As Europe emerged from the Dark Ages, contributions to the development of algebra by Europeans again appeared. Italian merchant Leonardo de Pisa (1202), commonly known as Fibonacci, summarized Arabian algebra and introduced the Hindu-Arabic number system to Europe in his work *Liber Abaci*. John of Holywood (1240) wrote the standard mathematics text that was used for centuries in European universities. In 1247, Ch'in Kiu-shao showed the high degree of sophistication of Chinese mathematics in his works on solving higher-degree equations by numerical methods, a discovery not made in Europe until 1819. In 1303, Chinese scholar Chu Shih-Chieh displayed the binomial coefficients more than 200 years before it was published in Europe. In 1360, Nicole Oresme introduced fractional exponents in his unpublished work *Algorismus Proportionum*.

The Renaissance period that followed in Europe was a time of great progress and creativity in the development of algebra and its notation:

Johann Widmann (1489) used + and − for positive and negative numbers.

Christoff Rudolff (1525) introduced $\sqrt{}$ for square roots.

In 1527, the coefficients for binomial expansions were published.

Scipione del Ferro, Nicolo Fontana Tartaglia, and Girolamo Cardano (1545) found general solutions to cubic equations.

Robert Recorde (1557) used the symbol = to represent equality.

Rafael Bombelli (1572) published the first consistent treatment of imaginary numbers.

Christopher Clavius (1583) initiated the use of a dot for multiplication.

Francois Viète (1591) systematically used letters to represent unknowns.

John Napier (1614) invented logarithms.

Johann Kepler and Henry Briggs (1624) published a table of logarithms.

Probably the most notable contributions to elementary algebra are credited to René Descartes. Even though Pierre de Fermat worked on similar material before Descartes, Descartes was the first to publish his work. In *La Geometrie,* he introduced notation similar to what we find in present-day algebra. He used x, y, and z for unknowns and the superscript (x^3) for cubes. But most significantly, he brought algebra and geometry together by creating the (x, y) rectangular coordinate system. He made it possible for the equations of algebra to be represented graphically, laid the foundation for algebraic geometry (analytic geometry), and made the development of calculus possible.

Following Descartes and Fermat, Sir Isaac Newton (1642–1727) and Gottfried Leibniz (1646–1716) independently developed the calculus, and for the next 200 years mathematicians spent a great deal of effort on calculus and its applications. Along with these advancements, however, came progress in algebra. The major contributors and their contributions were:

Thomas Harriot (1631) introduced the inequality symbols $>$ and $<$.

John Wallis (1655) used algebraic notation very similar to what is currently used, including negative exponents and ∞ for infinity.

Seki Kōwa of Japan (c. 1683) introduced a system of determinants for solving equations some 10 years before Gottfried Leibniz suggested it.

Maria Agnesi (1748) published a widely used math text covering topics from algebra through calculus.

Leonhard Euler (c. 1749) defined algebraic functions and used i to represent $\sqrt{-1}$, e for the base of natural logarithms, and Σ for summations.

Gabriel Cramer (1750) gave a general rule for solving systems of n linear equations in n unknowns.

David Rittenhouse (1799) made America's earliest contribution to mathematics research when he wrote on methods of computing with logarithms.

Carl Friedrich Gauss (1832) initiated the use of the term ''complex number'' for the sum of a real number and an imaginary number.

Carl Jacobi (1841) developed the theory of determinants.

Karl Weierstrass (1841) introduced the absolute value symbol $|\ |$.

Arthur Cayley (1857) formulated the algebra of matrices.

Equations of degree higher than 3 were investigated throughout the 1800s by many mathematicians, such as Niels Abel, L. Ferrari, Evariste Galois, and Peter Roth.

Some mathematicians also examined the underlying structure of algebra. These discoveries opened the door to the study of modern, or abstract, algebra.

Because of the work of such dedicated individuals, we find elementary algebra to be a mathematical system that

a. Has a rich history of development.

b. Uses symbols to represent numbers and operations.
c. Allows us to graphically represent and analyze mathematical concepts.
d. Has a logical foundation.
e. Gives us a powerful problem-solving tool.

This chapter contains problems and concepts from this system of elementary algebra. We will study the use of algebraic functions as models representing various real-life situations.

CHECK YOUR READING

1. Show how to solve the problem on the Rhind papyrus contained in the first paragraph of this section.
2. In 1624, the first English settlement was established in eastern India. What important event occurred in mathematics during this year?
3. The coefficients for the binomial expansion were published in the same year that Sebastian Cabot built the fortifications of Espiritu Santo in Paraguay. What year was this?
4. In 1557, Spain and France went bankrupt. What mathematical symbol was first used during this year?
5. While the Swedish army was occupying Cracow and Warsaw in Poland, what symbol was John Wallis introducing to mathematics?
6. In the late 1740s, Giacobbo Rodriguez Pereire invented a sign language for deaf people. Who wrote the popular mathematical textbook used during this period?
7. From 2500 to 2000 B.C. was a significant period in history. Not only did painted pottery appear in China, papyrus appear in Egypt, and chickens first become domesticated in Babylon, but algebra was being developed in which ancient civilizations?
8. In 1832, the New England Anti-Slavery Society was founded in Boston and Japanese artist Ando Hiroshige published his famous art series, "Fifth-three Stages of the Tokaido." What term did Carl Gauss initiate in this year?
9. Match each of the following names with the appropriate symbol or word.

    (a) Al-Khowârizmî $|\ |$
    (b) Euler $+$ and $-$
    (c) Gauss   Algebra
    (d) Harriot   Complex number
    (e) Napier $=$
    (f) Recorde $<$ and $>$
    (g) Rudolff i and e
    (h) Wallis ∞
    (i) Weierstrass   Logarithms
    (j) Widmann $\sqrt{\ }$

> # RESEARCH QUESTIONS

In order to answer the following questions, you will need to refer to material not contained in the text. Possible sources of information are listed in the bibliography at the end of the text.

1. Many of the mathematicians mentioned in this short history of the development of algebra had other interests besides mathematics. Explain some of these other interests. What anecdotes have been recorded about these mathematicians?
2. Throughout the history of mathematics, there has been controversy over the person given credit for a particular discovery. Discuss one of the following controversies:
   (a) René Descartes and Pierre de Fermat over algebraic (analytic) geometry.
   (b) Scipione del Ferro, Nicolo Fontana Tartaglia, and Girolamo Cardano over the solution of cubic equations.
3. What are Diophantine equations? Give some examples and solutions.
4. What are formulas? Why are they an application of algebra? Cite some areas that use formulas and some of the formulas used in those areas.
5. What was the School Mathematics Study Group (SMSG)? Who were some of the people involved in the group, and what were the objectives of the group?
6. Show how the solution of equations in algebra can be viewed as the science of transposition and cancellation.
7. Descartes developed the (x, y) rectangular coordinate system, but there is another coordinate system used in mathematics, the polar coordinate system. What is the polar coordinate system? How does it differ from the rectangular coordinate system?
8. Algebra is said to have a logical foundation based on certain properties. What are some of these properties and show how they are used in algebra.
9. What were the Dark Ages? Why did mathematics make little progress in Europe during this period?
10. What was the Renaissance? Why did mathematics make great progress in Europe during this period?
11. What is Pascal's triangle? How can it be used to raise the binomial $x + y$ to the fourth power?
12. What is Fermat's Last Theorem? Why has it caused so much interest? What event in 1989 caused renewed interest in Fermat's Last Theorem?

SECTION 2.0

▼

REVIEW

This section contains some of the algebraic facts, terminology, and techniques needed in Chapter 2.

Functions

The concept of a function in mathematics flows naturally from everyday experiences. For example, the size of a projected image on a screen depends on (is a function of) the distance of the projector from the screen. The temperature of a pot of soup on the stove depends on (is a function of) the length of time it has been on the hot burner. In the first example, for each distance from the screen there is one image size. In the second example, for each length of time the soup has a certain temperature. This concept can be summarized into the mathematical definition of a function. A **function** is a collection of values arranged in pairs, usually written as (x, y). In a function, for each value of x there is exactly one value of y. The set of x values is called the **domain**, and the set of y values is called the **range** of the function.

Linear Functions

A **linear function** is one whose graph is a line or part of a line, has a single value that measures the slope of its graph, and has an equation of the form $y = mx + b$. In the equation, the slope is given by m, the coefficient of x. The point where the graph of this line crosses the y axis is called the **y intercept**. In the equation, the location of the y intercept is given by the constant b.

For a line passing through the points (x_1, y_1) and (x_2, y_2), the slope is

Slope

$$m = \frac{\text{change in the } y \text{ values}}{\text{change in the } x \text{ values}} = \frac{y_2 - y_1}{x_2 - x_1}$$

To find the equation of a line and represent it as a function, we use the slope-intercept form.

Equation of a Line

$$y = mx + b \qquad \text{where} \begin{cases} m = \text{slope} \\ b = y \text{ intercept} \end{cases}$$

Example 1:

Graph the linear function $y = 2x - 2$.

Solution: Since there are no restrictions on the domain (x values) of this function, x can be any real number. Since two points determine a line, simply plot two points that satisfy the equation and draw a line connecting both points.

x	y
0	−2
2	2

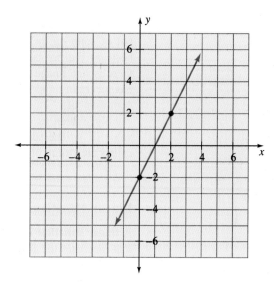

Example 2:

Graph $y = 2x - 2$ where $0 \leq x \leq 4$.

Solution: The restriction on the domain of the function allows us to use only the values from 0 through 4 for x. The graph is only part of a line, a line segment.

x	y
0	−2
4	6

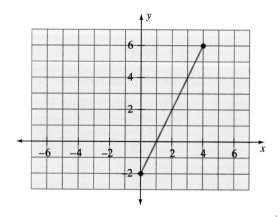

Example 3:

Graph $y = 2x - 2$ where $0 \leq x \leq 4$ and x is a whole number.

Solution: The restriction on the domain of the function here forces us to use only the whole number values from 0 through 4 for x. The graph is a series of five points. It is a discrete graph, not a continuous one.

x	y
0	−2
1	0
2	2
3	4
4	6

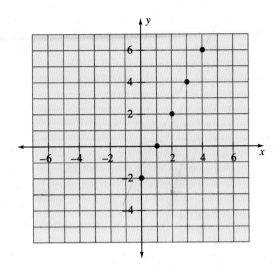

Example 4:

Find the equation of the linear function passing through the points $(2, -3)$ and $(4, 7)$.

Solution: The solution requires two steps. The first step is to find the slope:

$$m = \frac{y_2 - y_1}{x_2 - x_1} = \frac{7 - (-3)}{4 - 2} = \frac{10}{2} = 5$$

The second step is to use the equation for a linear function:

$$y = mx + b$$

$$y = 5x + b \qquad \text{since } m = 5$$

Find b by substituting known values for (x, y), either $(2, -3)$ or $(4, 7)$. Using $(2, -3)$ we get

$$-3 = 5(2) + b$$

$$-3 = 10 + b$$

$$-13 = b$$

Thus, $y = 5x - 13$ is the desired linear function.

Quadratic Functions

A quadratic function is a function whose graph is a parabola and has an equation of the form $y = ax^2 + bx + c$, where $a \neq 0$. To graph a quadratic function it is best to find the vertex (the maximum or minimum point) of the parabola it represents. The x coordinate of the vertex can be determined by the equation

$$x = \frac{-b}{2a} \qquad \text{where} \begin{cases} \text{the parabola opens upward if } a > 0 \\ \text{the parabola opens downward if } a < 0 \end{cases}$$

The y coordinate of the vertex can be found by substituting the value found for x into the quadratic function.

Example 5:

Find the vertex and graph $y = x^2 - 6x + 4$.

Solution:

The x coordinate
of the vertex is

$$x = \frac{-b}{2a} = \frac{-(-6)}{2(1)} = \frac{6}{2} = 3$$

substitute $x = 3$

The y coordinate
of the vertex is

$$y = x^2 - 6x + 4$$
$$y = (3)^2 - 6(3) + 4$$
$$y = 9 - 18 + 4$$
$$y = -5$$

Thus, the vertex is $(3, -5)$. Since $a > 0$, the parabola opens upward and the vertex is a minimum point.

To graph the parabola, calculate and plot points using x values to the left and right of the vertex.

x	y	
0	4	
1	−1	
2	−4	
3	−5	(vertex)
4	−4	
5	−1	
6	4	

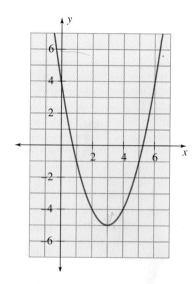

Example 6:

Graph $y = -2x^2 + 5x$.

Solution: Find the vertex.

$$x = \frac{-b}{2a} = \frac{-5}{2(-2)} = 1.25$$

$$y = -2(1.25)^2 + 5(1.25) = 3.125$$

Since $a < 0$, the parabola opens downward and the vertex (1.25, 3.125) is the maximum point on the parabola.

Calculate the plot points, using x values to the left and right of the vertex.

x	y	
-1	-7	
0	0	
1	3	
1.25	3.125	(vertex)
2	2	
3	-3	

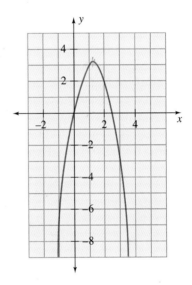

Quadratic Formula

If the y value of a quadratic function is zero, we have the quadratic equation

$$ax^2 + bx + c = 0$$

We can solve for x and find the x intercepts of the graph of the quadratic function by using a calculator and the quadratic formula.

Quadratic Formula

$$x = \frac{-b \pm \sqrt{b^2 - 4ac}}{2a}$$

where $a \neq 0$ and a, b, and c are the constants in the quadratic equation.

If the quantity under the square root in the quadratic formula is negative, the solutions are not real numbers. Since most calculators use only real numbers, your calculator may give you an error message when the square root of a negative number is attempted. The solutions to the quadratic equations in this text are real numbers. Therefore, if the error message occurs, please check your computation.

Example 7:

Solve for x: $x^2 - 5x + 7 = 4$

Solution:

$x^2 - 5x + 7 = 4$

$x^2 - 5x + 3 = 0$ Get a zero on one side by adding -4 to both sides.

$x = \dfrac{-(-5) \pm \sqrt{(-5)^2 - 4(1)(3)}}{2(1)}$ Use the quadratic formula with $a = 1$, $b = -5$, and $c = 3$.

$x = \dfrac{5 \pm \sqrt{13}}{2} \approx 4.30 \text{ or } 0.70$

Exponential Functions

An **exponential function** is a function that contains an exponent that is a variable and a base that is a constant, such as $y = 2^x$, $y = 1.025^x$, $y = e^x$, and $y = 10^x$. The base of an exponential function is greater than 0 and not equal to 1. The equation

$$y = b^x \qquad \text{where } \{b > 0; b \neq 1; x \text{ is a real number}\}$$

defines the basic exponential function. You must understand that there is a significant difference between a quadratic and an exponential function. You can see this difference by examining a chart of values and the graphs of the quadratic function $y = x^2$ and the exponential function $y = 2^x$.

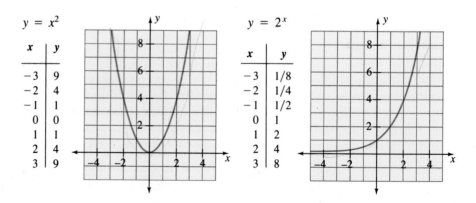

$y = x^2$

x	y
-3	9
-2	4
-1	1
0	0
1	1
2	4
3	9

$y = 2^x$

x	y
-3	$1/8$
-2	$1/4$
-1	$1/2$
0	1
1	2
2	4
3	8

Example 8:

Graph the exponential function $y = 2^{-x} = (\frac{1}{2})^x$.

Solution: Calculating a chart of values for (x, y) and plotting the points, we get

x	y
-3	8
-2	4
-1	2
0	1
1	1/2
2	1/4
3	1/8

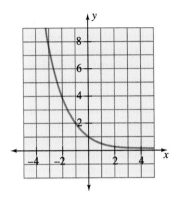

By examining exponential functions of the form $y = b^x$, where $b > 0$ and $b \neq 1$, we can summarize the following properties of an exponential function:

1. Its graph is a continuous curve that has the shape of a "banana" or "hockey stick."
2. Its graph passes through the point $(0, 1)$.
3. Its graph approaches the x axis but never touches it.
4. If $b > 1$, then b^x increases as x increases.
5. If $0 < b < 1$, then b^x decreases as x increases.

In this chapter, we consider exponential functions that include other constants along with the basic exponential form of b^x. We examine exponential functions of the form

$$y = a + c(b)^{kx} \qquad \text{where} \quad \begin{cases} b > 0 \text{ and } b \neq 1 \\ a, c, \text{ and } k \text{ are constants} \end{cases}$$

The constants a, c, and k simply move the basic exponential graph up and down or change the rate at which the y values increase or decrease. No matter what constants are used, the exponential function retains the basic "banana" or "hockey stick" shape. The graph of an exponential function can be determined by calculating and plotting a sufficient number of points that satisfy the function. To perform the computations involved in exponential functions, we use the following keys on a calculator:

If your calculator does not have all of these keys, please check the manual for your calculator or check with your instructor for a possible alternative method of performing calculations involving those keys.

To determine 3^7:

Press   **Display**

   2,187

To determine $8(6.5)^4$:

Press   **Display**

8 × 6 . 5 x^y 4 =   = 14,280.5

To determine $10^{-1.56}$:

Press   **Display**

1 . 5 6 ± 10^x ≈ 0.0275

Note

The ± key on the calculator changes the sign of the number in the window of the calculator.

To determine $9e^{-3.1}$:

Press   **Display**

9 × 3 . 1 ± e^x =   ≈ 0.4054

To determine $e^{0.18(76)}$:

Press   **Display**

. 1 8 × 7 6 = e^x ≈ 873,269.94

Example 9:

Graph $y = 4 + 10^x$.

Solution: With the help of a calculator, determine and plot points that satisfy the exponential function. A sufficient number of points must be determined so that the exponential function can be placed on the graph.

x	y
−3	4.001
−2	4.01
−1	4.1
0	5
1	14
2	104

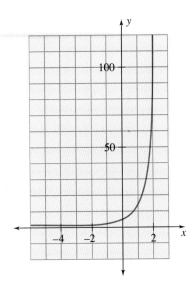

Example 10:

Graph $y = 50e^{0.3x}$.

Solution: With the help of a calculator, determine and plot points that satisfy the exponential function. A sufficient number of points must be determined so that the exponential function can be placed on the graph.

x	y
−3	20.3
−2	27.4
−1	37.0
0	50.0
1	67.5
2	91.1
3	123.0

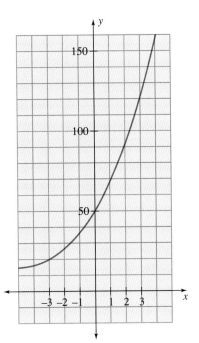

Example 11:

Graph $y = 100 + 250(4)^{-0.3x}$ where $x \geq 0$.

Solution: Using $x \geq 0$, calculate and plot points that satisfy the function.

x	y
0	350
1	264.9
2	208.8
3	171.8
4	147.4
5	131.3
6	120.6
7	113.6
8	109.0
9	105.9
10	103.9

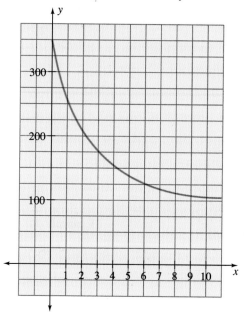

Logarithmic Functions

As you may remember from algebra, inverse functions are functions that have the opposite effect. In arithmetic, multiplication and division are inverses of each other. For example, if you choose a number, say 7, and multiply it by 5, you get an answer of 35. If you then divide that answer by 5, you get back the 7 you started with. In algebra, equations such as $y = 2x$ and $y = \frac{1}{2}x$ are inverse functions. If you choose a number, say $x = 8$, and substitute $x = 8$ into the equation $y = 2x$, you get the answer 16. If you substitute $x = 16$ into the second equation, $y = \frac{1}{2}x$, you get the answer 8, the number you started with.

Similarly, the inverse of the exponential function is the logarithmic function. For example, the inverse of the exponential function $y = 10^x$ is the function $y = \log x$. To see this inverse relationship, choose a number, say $x = 3$. Substituting $x = 3$ into the equation $y = 10^x$ gives us the answer $10^3 = 1000$. Substituting this result for x in the function $y = \log x$ gives us $\log 1000$. To determine this value, we can use a calculator.

To determine $\log 1000$:

Press	**Display**
⬚1⬚ ⬚0⬚ ⬚0⬚ ⬚0⬚ ⬚log⬚	3

Log 1000 = 3 is equivalent to the statement $10^3 = 1000$. The exponential function gives the result of raising 10 to the third power as its answer, whereas the logarithmic function gives the exponent of 10 as its answer. A logarithm is simply an exponent. Although logarithms can be evaluated with different bases, in this chapter we use only **common logarithms** and **natural logarithms**. Common logarithms use the base 10 and are denoted by the LOG (log) button on a calculator. Natural logarithms use base e and are denoted by LN (ln) on a calculator. The logarithmic functions used in the text are

$$y = \log x, \text{ which is equivalent to } x = 10^y$$

$$y = \ln x, \text{ which is equivalent to } x = e^y$$

Since 10 raised to any power or e raised to any power is always a positive quantity, x is always positive. We can, therefore, take the logarithms of only positive quantities.

To determine log 458:

Press	Display
4 5 8 log	≈ 2.66

To determine ln 458:

Press	Display
4 5 8 ln	≈ 6.13

To determine $5 \ln(9 - 3.6)$:

Press	Display
9 − 3 . 6 = ln × 5 =	≈ 8.43

The graph of a logarithmic function has the same basic shape as an exponential function. A logarithmic function can be graphed by calculating and plotting a sufficient number of points to establish its "banana" or "hockey stick" shape.

Example 12:

Graph $y = \ln x$.

Solution: With the help of a calculator, determine and plot points that satisfy the equation. Remember to choose x values greater than 0, since it is not possible to compute the logarithm of a negative number.

x	y
0.5	−0.69
1	0
5	1.61
10	2.3
20	3.0
30	3.4

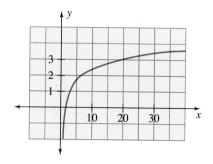

If we include other constants in a basic common or natural logarithmic function, the graph of the logarithmic function can be moved up and down or the rate at which it increases or decreases can be changed. In this chapter we consider logarithmic functions of the form

$$y = a + b \log (x + c) \quad \text{and} \quad y = a + b \ln (x + c)$$

where a, b, and c are constants.

The graphs of these functions have the same basic shape as an exponential function. Logarithmic functions can be graphed by determining and plotting points with the help of a calculator. In this process, you must remember that you cannot take the logarithm of a negative number.

Example 13:

Graph $y = 1.2 \log x$.

Solution: With the help of a calculator, determine and plot points that satisfy the logarithmic function. Since it is impossible to take logarithms of negative numbers, use $x > 0$.

x	y
0.5	−0.36
1	0.00
5	0.84
10	1.20
20	1.56
30	1.77

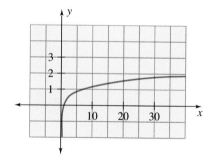

Example 14:

Graph $y = 4.7 + \ln (x - 2)$ where $x \geq 4$.

Solution: With the help of a calculator, determine and plot points that satisfy the logarithmic function, using $x \geq 4$.

x	y
4	5.4
6	6.1
8	6.5
10	6.8
20	7.6

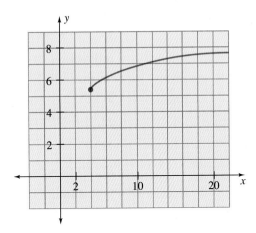

SECTION 2.0

PROBLEMS

1. Graph $y = -2x + 5$.

2. Graph $y = -2x + 5$ where $x \geq -1$.

3. Graph $y = -2x + 5$ where $x \leq 6$ and x is a whole number.

4. Graph $y = \dfrac{1}{4}x - 3.5$

5. Graph $y = \dfrac{1}{4}x - 3.5$ where $4 \leq x \leq 10$

6. Graph $y = \dfrac{1}{4}x - 3.5$ where $4 \leq x \leq 10$ and x is a whole number.

In Problems 7–10, find an equation for the linear function that

7. has a slope of 4 and passes through the point $(3, -5)$

8. passes through the points $(-4, -5)$ and $(8, -1)$

9. passes through the points $(0, 525)$ and $(4, 800)$

10. passes through the points $(1, 2300)$ and $(12, 5900)$

In Problems 11–16, find the vertex and graph each quadratic function.

11. $y = x^2 + 8x - 7$ 12. $y = -x^2 + 6x - 5$

13. $y = -4x^2 - 7x$ 14. $y = -3.2x^2 - 5.6$

15. $y = \dfrac{3}{4}x^2 + 12x + 8$ 16. $y = \dfrac{1}{2}x^2 + 9x$

In Problems 17–20, solve for x using the quadratic formula. Round off answers to the nearest hundredth.

17. $x^2 + 8x - 7 = 0$

18. $-x^2 + 7x - 5 = 0$

19. $3x^2 - 6x + 3 = 4$

20. $2.7x^2 - x - 25.3 = 20$

In Problems 21–28, use your calculator to determine the answers. Round off answers to the nearest thousandth.

21. 5.2^4

22. $1.08 + 10^{-2.56}$

23. $7.6e^{1.3454}$

24. $9(10)^{(47.89 - 45.9)}$

25. $12.7 \log (56.91)$

26. $12.7 + \ln (56.91)$

27. $3000 + 5600 \ln (56.8 - 4)$

28. $4.5 - \log (3.45 - 3.1)$

In Problems 29–34, graph each exponential or logarithmic function.

29. $y = 0.25e^x$

30. $y = 4.2 \ln (x - 2.9)$

31. $y = 32 + 48.5 \log (x + 2)$

32. $y = 500 + 10^x$

33. $y = 100(1.06)^{12x}$

34. $y = -20 + \log (3x + 1)$

35. What does your calculator do when you try to take the common logarithm of a negative number?

36. What does your calculator do when you try to take the natural logarithm of a negative number?

*37. Explain why 10^x and e^x must be greater than zero for all real values of x.

The Australian *Xanthorrhoea quadrangulata* plant can be algebraically described by a set of lines emanating from the same point. (Courtesy of Kurt Viegelmann)

SECTION 2.1
▼
LINEAR MODELS

In algebra, we study a system in which symbols (usually letters) were used to represent numbers. We can use this system to create mathematical models for various kinds of situations. The first model we will look at is one in which the situation can be graphically displayed by a line or part of a line. In this linear model we assume that the rate at which the quantities change (the slope) is constant. Also, we must realize that a model may not give an exact description of the situation and that it may have limitations depending on the situation. Let us look at some situations where a linear function would make an appropriate model.

In Section 2.0 we reviewed how to graph a line. We saw that for a line passing through the points (x_1, y_1) and (x_2, y_2)

Slope

$$m = \frac{\text{change in the } y \text{ values}}{\text{change in the } x \text{ values}} = \frac{y_2 - y_1}{x_2 - x_1}$$

and

Equation of a Line

$$y = mx + b \qquad \text{where} \begin{cases} m = \text{slope} \\ b = y \text{ intercept} \end{cases}$$

We will use these equations to find linear functions that can act as models in various situations.

Example 1:

The equation to convert Celsius (°C) to Fahrenheit (°F) temperature is the linear function

$$F = \frac{9}{5} C + 32$$

(a) Graph this equation.
(b) Find its slope and explain what it tells us about the different temperature scales.
(c) Find the Fahrenheit equivalent of 40°C.

Solution:

(a) To graph a linear function, we need to find and plot two pairs of values that satisfy the equation. Since the values for C (the domain) can be any real number, we draw a continuous line.

°C	°F
0	32
10	50

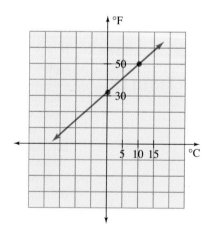

(b) From our equation $F = \frac{9}{5}C + 32$, the slope $m = 9/5$:

$$m = \frac{9}{5} = \frac{\text{change in Fahrenheit (°F)}}{\text{change in Centigrade (°C)}}$$

Thus a 9° change in F corresponds to a 5° change in C.

(c) If $C = 40°$, $F = \frac{9}{5}(40) + 32 = 72 + 32 = 104°$.

Example 2:

Carmen's Coffee Shop had a net loss of $300 in its first month of operation, January. In April it had a net profit of $240. If business continues to grow at this rate, how much profit would the coffee shop make in December? or next April?

Solution: Carmen is looking for a way to predict her monthly profit, assuming that her profit will continue to increase at the present rate. A linear function would satisfy those conditions.

Let t = time in months (t is a whole number greater than 0)

p = net monthly profit

(t, p) = ordered pairs relating time and profit

We are looking for the linear equation that gives us the profit p based on the time t, using the facts:

$$\text{January, loss of } \$300 \rightarrow (1, -300)$$

$$\text{April, profit of } \$240 \rightarrow (4, 240)$$

The equation of a line is normally $y = mx + b$.
The equation of the line, using the ordered pairs (t, p) instead of (x, y), becomes

$$p = mt + b$$

We must now find the slope m and the y intercept b to get the linear function that determines profit based on time.

(a) Find m: $m = \dfrac{p_2 - p_1}{t_2 - t_1}$ (Note: t and p are used instead of x and y)

$$m = \frac{240 - (-300)}{4 - 1} = \frac{540}{3} = 180$$

(b) Find b: $p = mt + b$. Since $m = 180$, $p = 180t + b$. To find b, substitute either known pair for (t, p); $(4, 240)$ is used here.

$$240 = 180(4) + b$$

$$240 = 720 + b$$

$$-480 = b$$

Thus the linear function that determines profit based on time for Carmen's Coffee Shop for any month (t) is

$$p = 180t - 480$$

In December, $t = 12$ and $p = 180(12) - 480 = \$1680$; next April, $t = 16$ and $p = 180(16) - 480 = \$2400$. The graph of Carmen's profit equation is as follows:

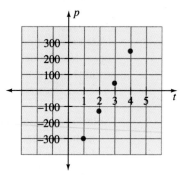

Note:

Since profit is determined at the end of the month, the graph consists of a dot for each month. The graph is a discrete one; it shows that there are no values at fractional parts of months.

This linear model for Carmen's Coffee Shop is based on the assumption that profit will continue to increase at the same rate. Factors such as competition, prices, salaries, weather, advertising, and so on, can affect profit but have not been included in our model. Our model does, however, give us a means of making approximations based on present facts.

Example 3:

The speed of sound has been calculated to be approximately 1090 ft/s when the temperature is 32°F. However, as the temperature rises above 32°F, the speed at which sound travels increases at a constant rate. At 50°F, the speed of sound is about 1110 ft/s. Find the linear equation that relates the speed of sound to the Fahrenheit temperatures and determine the speed of sound at 100°F.

Solution: Let

T = temperature in Fahrenheit where $T \geq 32°F$

s = speed of sound

(T, s) = ordered pairs relating temperature and speed

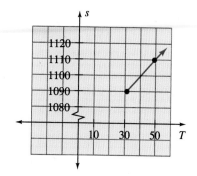

Equations using T and s instead of x and y are

$$s = mT + b \qquad \text{where } m = \frac{s_2 - s_1}{T_2 - T_1}$$

Known pairs for (T, s) are $(32, 1090)$ and $(50, 1110)$.

(a) Find m:

$$m = \frac{s_2 - s_1}{T_2 - T_1} = \frac{1110 - 1090}{50 - 32} = \frac{20}{18} = \frac{10}{9}$$

(b) Find b: $s = mt + b$. Substitute $m = 10/9$ and either known pair for (T, s).

$$1090 = \frac{10}{9}(32) + b \qquad (32, 1090) \text{ is used here}$$

$$1090 = 35.6 + b$$

$$1054.4 = b$$

Thus the linear function that gives the approximate speed of sound based on the Fahrenheit temperature is

$$s = \frac{10}{9}T + 1054.4$$

When $T = 100°F$,

$$s = \frac{10}{9}(100) + 1054.4 = 1165.5 \text{ ft/s}$$

SECTION 2.1
PROBLEMS

1. During the summer, as the temperature gets over 80°F, the chickens on a chicken farm drink more water. This behavior is modeled by the equation

$$W = 25t - 1250 \quad \text{where} \begin{cases} W = \text{number of gallons of water drunk per hour} \\ t = \text{Fahrenheit temperature } (t \geq 80°) \end{cases}$$

(a) Graph this function.

(b) What is the slope of the function and what does it tell us about the situation?

(c) How many gallons of water are used in an hour when the temperature is 100°F?

2. The staff of a local department store notices that there is a direct relationship between the gross revenue (R) in dollars on a given day and the number (n) of customers entering the store. It is determined that the equation $R = 2.3n$ approximates this revenue.

(a) Graph this equation.

(b) What is its slope and what does it tell us about the situation?

(c) If 1500 people enter the store on a given day, what is the approximate revenue?

3. You purchase a new automobile for $16,500. A year later the car is worth only $14,800. If the value of the car continues to depreciate at that rate,

(a) Find the linear equation that determines the value of the car based on the number of years you own it.

(b) When will the car be worth $500?

4. As an object rises in altitude from sea level to 6 miles above sea level, the temperature decreases at a fairly constant rate. If the temperature is 59°F at sea level and 55.5°F at 1000 ft,

(a) Find the linear equation that relates the temperature (t) to the altitude (a).

(b) What is the temperature at an altitude of 24,000 ft?

5. When water turns to ice, its volume increases about 9%. That is, 100 ml of water has a volume of 109 ml after being frozen. Find the linear function that determines the volume of water after it has been frozen.

6. The foundation for a brick wall rises 10 inches above ground level. The bricks used for the wall are 8 inches high.

(a) Find a function that determines the height of the wall in inches based on the number of layers of brick that have been laid.

(b) Graph the function.

(c) Find the equation that would give the height of the wall in feet.

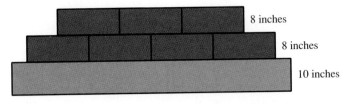

8 inches

8 inches

10 inches

7. A fish tank is setting on a 27-inch-high stand. The tank is 36 inches tall and is being filled with water. The water is rising in the tank at a rate of 3 inches per minute.

(a) Find a function that would determine the distance the water level is above the floor at any given moment.

(b) What is the domain of the function?

(c) Graph the function.

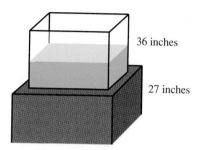

36 inches

27 inches

8. At higher altitudes, water boils at a lower temperature. At sea level, water boils at approximately 212°F. At 2000 ft, water boils at approximately 208°F.

(a) Assuming that this relationship is linear, find the equation that relates altitude to the boiling temperature of water.

(b) Find the boiling temperature of water at the top of Pike's Peak (Colorado), elevation 14,110 ft.

9. The sum of the angles of a triangle is 180°, and the sum of the angles of a quadrilateral (four sides) is 360°.

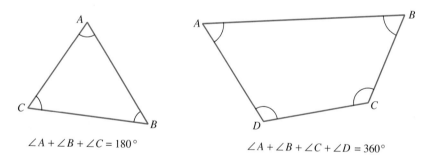

$\angle A + \angle B + \angle C = 180°$ $\angle A + \angle B + \angle C + \angle D = 360°$

The relationship between the sum of the angles of a polygon and the number of sides is linear.

(a) Using the information about the triangle and the quadrilateral, determine the equation to find the sum (S) of the angles of a polygon when the number (N) of sides is known.

(b) For what values of N is the equation valid?

10. Is there a linear relationship between a man's weight and height and a woman's weight and height? The table shows average weights of 20- to 24-year-old Americans by height.

Average Weight in Pounds of 20- to 24-Year-Old Americans

Men		Women	
Height	Weight	Height	Weight
5'7"	153	5'0"	112
5'9"	162	5'2"	120
5'11"	171	5'4"	128

(a) Why does a linear equation fit these lists?

(b) Find the equation that determines the weight for 20- to 24-year-old men and for 20- to 24-year-old women.

(c) Try out the equations on various people. Do the equations work? When? For whom?

11. Wind-chill factor is a combination of the actual temperature and wind speed. The wind makes it feel colder than it really is. Below are the wind-chill Fahrenheit temperatures when the wind speed is 10 miles per hour.

Actual Temperature	Wind-Chill Temperature (at 10 mph)
40°F	28°F
30°F	16°F
20°F	3°F
10°F	−9°F
0°F	−22°F
−10°F	−34°F
−20°F	−46°F
−30°F	−58°F

(a) Explain why a linear function does not exactly fit this chart.

(b) Find a linear equation that relates wind chill to the actual temperature by using the first two pairs of information.

(c) How much error will that equation have in determining the wind-chill temperature when the actual temperature is −30°F?

(d) Plot the given wind-chill data and the graph of the equation from part (b) on the same coordinate system.

(e) How does the linear equation compare to the actual data?

*12. Is there a linear relationship between the length of a woman's foot and her shoe size? Measure the lengths of some women's feet, compare them with shoe size, formulate linear equations to match results, test out equations on other women, and so on. What can you say about the relationship between the length of a woman's foot and her shoe size? Do the same for men and compare the results.

*13. The graph shows the profit of a company based on the number of years the company has been in business.

(a) Why does a linear function seem to be an appropriate model for this graph?

(b) Use the data on the graph to find a linear function that estimates the profit P of the company as a function of time t, where $t \geq 0$.

(c) Use the linear function determined in (b) to estimate the company's profit after 10 years.

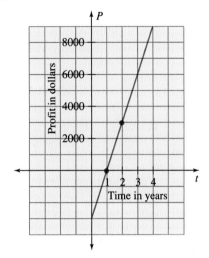

This fireworks display can be algebraically described by a set of parabolas passing through the same point. (Courtesy of Kurt Viegelmann)

SECTION 2.2

▼

QUADRATIC MODELS

The linear function studied in the previous section is only one of many functions that can be used as a mathematical model. There are situations where the appropriate mathematical model is a quadratic function with its parabolic graph, as reviewed in Section 2.0.

As our first example, let us consider Dan'l Webster, the notorious jumping frog of Calaveras County, described in a short story by Mark Twain. That frog could outjump any frog in Calaveras County. One of the feats attributed to Dan'l Webster was his ability to jump from the floor to the top of a counter to catch a fly. If we assume that he took off from a point 2 ft from the counter, that the counter was 3 ft high, and that the apex of his jump occurred at the edge of the counter, it is possible to find the equation of the parabola that approximates the flight of Dan'l Webster.

If we let the origin of a coordinate system $(0, 0)$ be the frog's take-off point, where

x = the length of the jump in feet

y = the height of the jump in feet

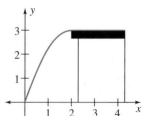

and let the top of the counter (2, 3) be the vertex of the jump, we can find the equation of the parabola by using the general quadratic equation

$$y = ax^2 + bx + c.$$

All we need to do is find the constants a, b, and c. This can be done as follows:

1. Since (0, 0) is on the graph,

$$y = ax^2 + bx + c$$
$$0 = a(0)^2 + b(0) + c$$
$$0 = c$$

2. Since (2, 3) is on the graph and $c = 0$,

$$y = ax^2 + bx$$
$$3 = a(2)^2 + b(2)$$
$$3 = 4a + 2b$$

3. Since the vertex is at (2, 3) and the x coordinate of the vertex can be determined by $x = -b/2a$, we get

$$2 = \frac{-b}{2a}$$
$$4a = -b$$
$$-4a = b$$

4. Now, using the results of parts (2) and (3), we can solve for a and b. Starting with $4a + 2b = 3$ and substituting $b = -4a$ gives

$$4a + 2(-4a) = 3$$
$$4a - 8a = 3$$
$$-4a = 3$$
$$a = \frac{-3}{4}$$

Substituting this result into $b = -4a$ gives $b = 3$.

Thus, assuming the frog's jump follows a parabolic path, the equation for Dan'l Webster's jump to the top of the counter is

$$y = \frac{-3}{4}x^2 + 3x \qquad \text{where} \begin{cases} x = \text{horizontal distance in feet} \\ y = \text{vertical distance in feet} \end{cases}$$

Note

To find the equation of a quadratic function, you can use the coordinates of the vertex and one other point.

With this quadratic model for the jump of Dan'l Webster, we can do some mathematical investigation. Though Mark Twain's narrative does not tell us whether there was a stool in front of the counter where Dan'l Webster leaped, we can determine the possibility of a stool's being there by using the quadratic model discovered above.

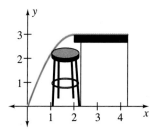

If we assume that a standard stool is 28 inches ($2\frac{1}{3}$ ft) tall and has a circular seat with a diameter of 12 inches, could Dan'l Webster have cleared the stool and made it to the top of the counter? All we need to do is simply find the height of the frog when he is 1 ft from the take-off point, as shown in the figure. If $x = 1$,

$$y = \frac{-3}{4}(1)^2 + 3(1) = \frac{9}{4} = 2\frac{1}{4}\,\text{ft} = 27\,\text{inches}$$

Thus, when Dan'l Webster was 1 ft from his take-off point, he was 27 inches off the ground. Since we assumed the stool to be 28 inches tall, we can conclude that Dan'l would not have cleared such a stool. Since he did make it to the top of the counter, we can logically say that there was no such stool in front of Dan'l Webster in Mark Twain's story.

Example 1:

The 1988 record holder of the annual Calaveras County Frog Jumping Contest held in Angels Camp, California, is Rosie the Ribiter. Her three consecutive jumps totaled 21 ft $5\frac{3}{4}$ inches. If her first jump was 7 ft (84 inches) in length and reached a height of 18 inches at its apex, find the quadratic function that models the parabolic path taken by Rosie on that first of three jumps.

Solution: Let

$$x = \text{length of jump in inches}$$
$$y = \text{height of jump in inches}$$
$$(0, 0) = \text{starting point of jump}$$
$$(84, 0) = \text{landing point of jump}$$

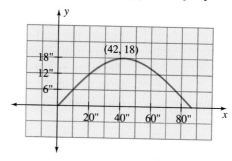

Then, the apex of the jump occurs halfway between $x = 0$ and $x = 84$. So the vertex of the parabola is $(42, 18)$. Now we will again use the general equation for a quadratic function.

1. Since $(0, 0)$ is on the graph,

$$y = ax^2 + bx + c$$
$$0 = a(0)^2 + b(0) + c$$
$$0 = c$$

2. Since $(84, 0)$ is on the graph and $c = 0$,

$$y = ax^2 + bx$$
$$0 = a(84)^2 + b(84)$$
$$0 = 7056a + 84b$$

3. Since $(42, 18)$ is also on the graph,

$$y = ax^2 + bx$$
$$18 = a(42)^2 + b(42)$$
$$18 = 1764a + 42b$$

4. Solve the simultaneous system of equations obtained from (2) and (3).

$$7056a + 84b = 0 \quad \longrightarrow \quad 7056a + 84b = 0$$
$$[1764a + 42b = 18](-2) \longrightarrow -3528a - 84b = -36$$
$$3528a = -36$$
$$a = -1/98$$

Substituting that value for a, we get $b = 6/7$.

Thus, the quadratic function that models the first jump of Rosie the Ribiter in 1988 is

$$y = -\frac{1}{98}x^2 + \frac{6}{7}x$$

As with the quadratic model for Dan'l Webster's jump, this equation can be used to further analyze the jump of the 1988 frog-jumping champion. For example, how far from the take-off was Rosie the Ribiter 10 inches off the ground? By replacing y with 10 inches we can solve for the distance from the take-off point.

$$y = -\frac{1}{98}x^2 + \frac{6}{7}x$$

$$10 = -\frac{1}{98}x^2 + \frac{6}{7}x$$

$$980 = -x^2 + 84x \qquad \text{multiplying both sides by 98}$$

$$x^2 - 84x + 980 = 0 \qquad \text{getting zero to one side}$$

$$x = \frac{84 \pm \sqrt{7056 - 3920}}{2} \qquad \text{using the quadratic formula}$$

$$x = 14 \text{ or } 70$$

Thus, Rosie was 10 inches off the ground at two times in her jump, at 14 inches and 70 inches from her take-off.

Example 2:

Quadratic functions can also be used to analyze objects that are moving under the force of gravity. For example, if you throw a baseball straight upward at 45 mph (66 ft/s) it slows down because of the force of gravity, reaches its highest point, and returns to hand level at approximately the same speed that it left your hand. If we chart the height h that a vertically thrown ball reaches on one axis compared to the time t the ball is in the air on the other axis, we get a graph that is a parabola. The equation for this motion on earth has been determined to be

$$h = -16t^2 + v_0 t + s_0 \quad \text{where} \begin{cases} h = \text{height above the ground in feet} \\ t = \text{time in seconds} \\ v_0 = \text{initial upward velocity in feet/second} \\ s_0 = \text{initial height in feet} \end{cases}$$

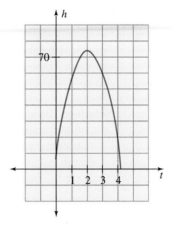

By initial height we mean the height above the ground at which the object began its motion, and by initial velocity we mean the speed at which the object began its motion. Further, as an object moves away from the earth, its velocity is a positive quantity, and as it moves toward the earth its velocity is a negative quantity. The speed of an object is actually the absolute value of the velocity and is measured only as a positive quantity.

Thus, if a vertically thrown ball leaves your hand 6 ft from the ground at 66 ft/s, v_0 is $+66$ ft/s and s_0 is 6 ft. The equation of motion for the thrown baseball is

$$h = -16t^2 + 66t + 6$$

This equation can be used to analyze the path of the ball.

1. What is the maximum height reached by the ball?

2. How long does it take for the ball to return to the ground?

Solution: The ball is at its highest point at the vertex of the parabola. The t coordinate of that point can be found by using $t = -b/2a$.

1. $$t = \frac{-66}{-32} = 2.0625 \text{ s}$$

So the ball reaches its maximum height 2.0625 s after leaving your hand, and the height reached is

$$h = -16(2.0625)^2 + 66(2.0625) + 6 \approx 74 \text{ ft}$$

2. When the ball reaches the ground, $h = 0$.

$$h = -16t^2 + 66t + 6$$

$$0 = -16t^2 + 66t + 6$$

$$t = \frac{-66 - \sqrt{4356 + 384}}{-32} \approx 4.2 \text{ s}$$

Note: In this instance only the negative root gives a positive result.

Example 3:

Suppose a baseball is thrown directly toward the ground from the top of the Sears Tower in Chicago, Illinois, at 60 mph. How far is the ball above the ground after 5 seconds?

Solution: Since the Sears Tower is 1454 ft tall, $s_0 = 1454$. Since our motion formula requires the initial velocity to be in feet per second, we must convert 60 mph to feet per second. The conversion factor for that change is

$$15 \text{ mph} = 22 \text{ ft/s}$$

We can set up a proportion relating mph to ft/s as follows. Let $v_0 =$ the number of ft/s that is equivalent to 60 mph. Then

$$\frac{15}{22} = \frac{60}{v_0}$$

$$15v_0 = 1320$$

$$v_0 = 88$$

Since the object is traveling toward the earth, the initial velocity is negative ($v_0 = -88$). Thus, the equation of the baseball thrown from the Sears Tower is

$$h = -16t^2 + v_0 t + s_0 = -16t^2 - 88t + 1454$$

To determine the height of the ball 5 s after it is thrown, let $t = 5$:

$$h = -16(5)^2 - 88(5) + 1454 = 614 \text{ ft}$$

The quadratic function gives us another tool to use in analyzing problems. The exercises that follow will give you more examples where the quadratic model can be used.

SECTION 2.2

PROBLEMS

1. The path that the pole vaulter's feet take to the top of the crossbar in a successful attempt can be described by the quadratic function $h = -\frac{1}{8}d^2 + 3d$, where $h =$ the height of his feet above the ground measured in feet, $d =$ the horizontal distance from his take-off point to the bar measured in feet, and $0 \leq d \leq 12$.

   (a) Graph the path followed by the vaulter's feet.
   (b) How high did the vaulter's feet get on the vault?

2. At a local frog-jumping contest, Rivet's jump can be approximated by the equation $y = -\frac{1}{6}x^2 + 2x$, and Croak's jump can be approximated by $y = -\frac{1}{2}x^2 + 4x$, where $x =$ the length of the jump in feet and $y =$ the height of the jump in feet.

(a) Which frog jumped the highest? How high did it jump?
(b) Which frog jumped the farthest? How far did it jump?

3. A diver does a swan dive from a platform 20 ft above the water. The path followed by the feet of the diver can be approximated by a parabola, as shown in the figure.

   (a) Find the quadratic equation that gives a mathematical description of the dive.
   (b) How far from the point directly below the take-off point will the diver's feet enter the water?

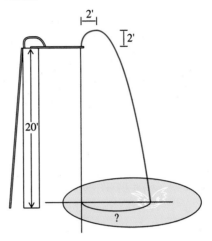

4. The numbers shown below, 1, 3, 6, 10, . . . , are called triangular numbers. The first triangular number has a value of 1, the second nas a value of 3, the third has a value of 6, and so forth. The relationship between the value of the triangular number (V) and its position in the sequence (n) is quadratic.

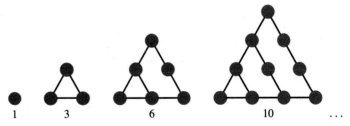

   (a) Find the equation that expresses V in terms of n.
   (b) Find the 100th triangular number.

5. A professional baseball pitcher releases a 139.33-ft/s (95-mph) fastball from a point 9 ft above the ground, sending it on a vertical path upward into the air.

   (a) Find the quadratic function that determines the height of the ball at any given instant.
   (b) Find the maximum height reached by the ball.
   (c) Determine how long the ball remains in the air.

6. A bullet is fired directly upward with a muzzle velocity of 860 ft/s from a height of 7 ft above the ground.

(a) Find the quadratic function that determines the height of the bullet at any given time.

(b) How long does it take the bullet to reach a height of 100 ft?

(c) How long is the bullet in the air?

7. The water from Bridalveil Falls in Yosemite National Park falls 640 ft to a pool at the bottom of the falls. A hiker drops a rock from the top of the falls.

(a) Find the quadratic function that determines the height of the rock above the bottom of the falls at any given time. (*Hint:* $v_0 = 0$)

(b) How far has the rock fallen in 3 seconds?

(c) How long does the rock take to reach the pool at the bottom of the falls?

8. Consider the quadratic function that approximates the leaps of our notorious frogs. They have all been of the form

$$y = -\frac{1}{d} x^2 + bx$$

Suppose $1 \leq d \leq 10$ and $1 \leq b \leq 10$. What values for d and b would produce a jump that is both the longest and highest?

9. The approximate distance it takes to stop a car, based on the speed you are traveling, is given in the table

Miles per Hour	Stopping Distance (ft)
25	62
35	106
45	161
50	195
55	228
65	306

(a) Find a quadratic function based on the stopping distances for 25 mph, 50 mph, and the fact that at 0 mph the stopping distance is 0 ft.

(b) Use that equation to predict the stopping distances for 55 mph and 65 mph and compare them with the distances given in the table.

(c) How accurate is the quadratic function?

(d) If the equation continues to be valid for higher speeds, how many feet would it take to stop a drag racer that reaches a speed of 230 mph?

10. A dog breeder has 260 ft of fencing material to make a kennel for the dogs along the side of a garage, as shown in the figure. If x represents the width of the kennel and y represents the length of the kennel,

(a) Find the equation that represents y in terms of x.

(b) Find the value of x and y that gives the maximum area for the kennel. (*Hint:* Find the vertex of a parabola.)

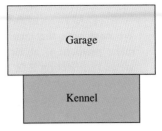

11. To get maximum distance of an arrow shot from a bow, the arrow should be aimed at a 45° angle with the horizontal. The equation of motion for such an arrow can be approximated by

$$y = \frac{-32\,x^2}{v_0^2} + x \qquad \text{where} \begin{cases} x = \text{distance traveled in feet} \\ y = \text{height reached in feet} \\ v_0 = \text{initial velocity of arrow in ft/s} \end{cases}$$

If an arrow leaves the bow with a speed of 192 ft/s,

(a) Find the equation of motion for the arrow.
(b) Find the height reached by the arrow.
(c) Find the distance the arrow travels.
(d) How much higher would the arrow get if it was shot directly upward?

*12. In this section we have looked at the parabola from a purely algebraic point of view. However, there are physical properties of a parabolic-shaped object that make it very useful in many everyday objects. What objects have this parabolic shape, and what property of parabolas makes them useful?

*13. The graph shows the profit of a company based on the number of years the company has been in business.

(a) Why does a quadratic function seem to be an appropriate model for this graph?
(b) Use the data on the graph to find a quadratic function that estimates the profit P of the company as a function of time t, where $t \geq 0$.
(c) Use the quadratic function determined in (b) to estimate the company's profit after 10 years.

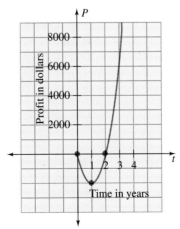

SECTION 2.3

▼

EXPONENTIAL MODELS

We have seen that mathematical models can be used to answer questions and to make predictions about observed events. Exponential functions, which were reviewed in Section 2.0, can also be used as mathematical models of real-life situations and scientific phenomena. Exponential functions can be used as models of situations in which the values for one variable increase at a steady rate while the values for the other variable either

a. Decrease rapidly and then decrease more and more slowly, or
b. Increase slowly and then increase more and more rapidly.

An example of the latter can be seen in the common practice of determining the amount of money in an account after interest is compounded.

Example 1: Compound Interest

Suppose you invest $5000 in an account that earns 1% on the amount in the account each month. If you make no withdrawals from the account and do not deposit any more money into the account, how much will you have in the account at the end of 1 year and at the end of 10 years?

Solution: To determine the amount in the account after 1 year, we could calculate the interest each month by using the formula $I = PRT$ (interest = principle × rate × time). We could then add this interest to the amount in the account to get the new balance in the account at the end of each month as shown below.

Month	Interest	Amount in Account
1	$I = (5000.00)(.01)(1) = \$50.00$	$\$5000.00 + 50.00 = \$5050.00$
2	$I = (5050.00)(.01)(1) = \$50.50$	$\$5050.00 + 50.50 = \$5100.50$
3	$I = (5100.50)(.01)(1) = \$50.51$	$\$5100.50 + 51.01 \approx \$5151.51$ etc.

Such a process could get us the amount in the account after 1 year and after 10 years, but it would take a lot of tedious computation. Luckily, there is an easier method to do this. Let us examine those first three months again.

Month	Amount in Account
1	$5000 + (.01)(5000) = 5000(1 + .01) = 5000(1.01) = \$5050$
2	$5050 + (.01)(5050) = 5050(1 + .01) = 5050(1.01) = \$5100.50$

Since $\$5050 = 5000(1.01)$, $\$5100.50$ could be rewritten as

$$5000(1.01)(1.01) = 5000(1.01)^2$$

The pattern seen in the first two months suggests that the amount in the account at the end of the third month might possibly be determined by $5000(1.01)^3 = 5000(1.030301) \approx \$5151.51$. This result matches our previous total for the third month.

As this discussion suggests, and as we shall see in Chapter 6, if $5000 is invested in an account that pays 1% interest each month with no withdrawals or other deposits, the amount A in the account after n months can be determined by the exponential function

$$A = 5000(1.01)^n$$

Thus, after 1 year (12 months),

$$A = 5000(1.01)^{12} = \$5634.13$$

After 10 years (120 months),

$$A = 5000(1.01)^{120} = \$16,501.93$$

To give you a better understanding of an exponential function let's examine a chart of values and a graph of the exponential function $A = 5000(1.01)^n$.

x	y
0	5,000.00
12	5,634.13
24	6,348.67
36	7,153.84
48	8,061.13
60	9,083.48
72	10,235.50
84	11,533.61
96	12,996.37
108	14,644.63
120	16,501.93

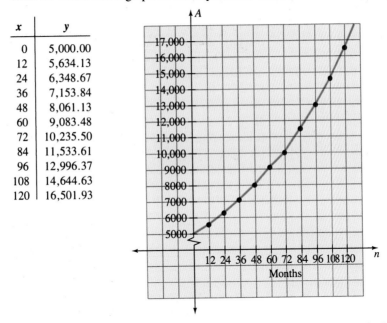

By observing the distances between successive amounts on the vertical scale, you will notice that the amount in the account increases slowly at the start and increases more rapidly as time goes on. For example, in the second year, the account increased by $714.54; in the ninth year, the account increased by $1857.30; and in the 30th year, the account will increase by $22,796.57. As we shall see in the next example, other situations in which a quantity increases by continual multiplication by the same amount lead to other exponential functions.

Example 2: Exponential Growth

Suppose you decide to form a new club that meets every Friday. At the first meeting, just you and a friend show up. The next week, each of you brings a new member to the meeting. Now the club has four members.

The third Friday, each of the four members brings another person to the meeting, making a club of eight people. If every Friday each present member brings a new member to join the club, how many members will the club have after six months?

Solution:

Week	Members
1	2
2	4
3	8
4	16

To answer the question, we could continue the table until we reached the 26th week, but that would be a lot of work. Let's look at that problem more closely. We want to find a relationship between the week (w) the meeting is held and the number of members (M) at the meeting, assuming that every present member always brings a new member to the next meeting. By analyzing the data, we find that the number of members at any meeting is a power of 2 ($2 = 2^1$, $4 = 2^2$, $8 = 2^3$, $16 = 2^4$, etc.), with the exponent being the week of the meeting. So the equation that determines M is $M = 2^w$. If $w = 26$, $M = 2^{26} = 67,108,864$. As you can see, the growth in the membership is astounding. By the 20th week the increase in the number of members per week is over a million. In fact, by the 28th meeting every person in the United States would be a member of your club. This example gives us a good indication of what is meant by a quantity growing exponentially.

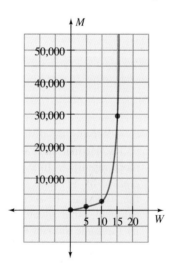

Note: The graph should be a discrete graph consisting of just the dots. The curve was added to make the exponential effect more evident.

Example 3:   Exponential Growth

Population increases when there are more births than deaths. Thomas Robert Malthus (1798) determined a model for predicting population, based on the assumption that the rate of births (B) and the rate of deaths (D) remain constant and no other factors are considered. In this model the population (P) is given by the following exponential function:

$$P = P_0 e^{kt} \qquad \text{where} \begin{cases} P = \text{population at any time} \\ P_0 = \text{initial population} \\ k = \text{annual growth rate } (B - D) \\ t = \text{time in years} \end{cases}$$

In 1960, the population of the United States was 179,323,175, the birth rate was 23.7 per 1000 population, and the death rate was 9.5 per 1000 population. Use this information to predict the number of people in the United States in 1988.

Solution: Using $P_0 = 179{,}323{,}175$, $t = 28$ years, and $k = 23.7/1000 - 9.5/1000 = 0.0142$ in the formula $P = P_0 e^{kt}$ gives

$$P = 179{,}323{,}175 e^{(0.0142)(28)}$$

$$P \approx 266{,}877{,}466$$

The actual population at the end of 1988 was 246,900,000. As you can see, the **Malthusian population model** did not give the exact 1988 population. One of the reasons for this is that both the birth rate and death rate have changed since 1960. The model did, however, give a reasonable approximation based on the facts that were available in 1960.

Example 4:   Atmospheric Pressure

Atmospheric pressure is produced by the weight of air from the top of the atmosphere as it presses down upon the layers of air below it. At sea level, air pressure is about 14.7 lb/in^2. As the distance from the earth's surface increases, the air pressure decreases. This phenomenon can be observed when a sealed bag of potato chips becomes puffed out like a balloon when taken into the mountains. The following exponential function relating air pressure (P) and altitude (a) can approximate the atmospheric pressure at altitudes up to 50,000 ft.

$$P = 14.7(10)^{-0.000018a} \qquad \text{where} \begin{cases} P = \text{pressure measured in lb/in}^2 \\ a = \text{altitude measured in feet} \end{cases}$$

The graph of this function is

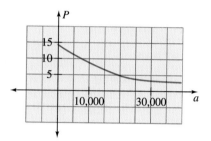

This function can also be used to estimate the air pressure at any altitude up to 50,000 ft. What is the air pressure on the top of the world's tallest mountain, Mount Everest in Nepal-Tibet, which has an altitude of 29,028 ft?

Solution:

$$P = 14.7(10)^{-0.000018a}$$

$$P = 14.7(10)^{-0.000018(29,028)}$$

$$P \approx 4.4\,\text{lb/in}^2$$

This section has attempted to show you that exponential functions can be used as mathematical models for actual occurrences in the world. There are many other places where these functions are used, but many of them are beyond the scope of this book and require a greater knowledge of the area in which they are used. The problems that follow, however, will let you experiment with other exponential functions used as mathematical models.

SECTION 2.3

PROBLEMS

1. In an attempt to promote world peace, you decide to start a chain letter. You send a peace message to five friends and ask each of them to send copies of the message to five of their friends by the end of the week. Suppose this process continues, and every person sends the message on time to five new people. A chart of the number of people receiving messages each week would look like this:

Week	Number of People Receiving Messages
1	5
2	25
3	125
4	625

(a) Find an exponential function relating the number of people (p) that receive the peace message to the number of weeks (w).

(b) How many people would receive the message by the end of 12 weeks?

2. Suppose you are gainfully employed and earn $200.00 a day. You are, however, offered a temporary job doing similar work for three weeks where you will be paid $0.01 the first day, $0.02 the second day, $0.04 the third day, and so on. Your daily wage will continue to double for each of the 21 days. Would it be more profitable for you to take the temporary job or keep your regular job for the three weeks? Justify your answer mathematically.

3. If the $5000 of Example 1 was deposited in a savings account that paid interest daily, the interest rate would be 0.0328767% (12 ÷ 365) each day and the amount A in the account after n days would be given by the exponential function $A = 5000(1.000328767)^n$.

(a) Graph that exponential function.

(b) Find the amount in the account after 1 year.

(c) Find the amount in the account after 20 years.

4. If a principle P is invested at an annual rate r expressed as a decimal and is compounded continuously, the amount A in the account at the end of t years is given by the exponential function $A = Pe^{rt}$. If $5000 is invested at an annual rate of 9%,

(a) Write the exponential function that determines the amount in the account at the end of any year.

(b) Graph that function.

(c) Find the amount in the account after 20 years.

5. The population of the Soviet Union in 1979 was 262,436,000. It had a birth rate of 18.1 per 1000 population and a death rate of 9.6 per 1000 population.

(a) Using the Malthusian population model, determine an estimate of the population in the Soviet Union in 1988.

(b) Use an almanac to find the population of the Soviet Union in 1988.

(c) How do the two values for the population compare?

(d) Give possible reasons for the difference between the two values.

6. Answer the same questions as you did in Problem 5 for Ethiopia. In 1975, Ethiopia had a population of 28,048,000, a birth rate of 49.9 per 1000 and a death rate of 25.4 per 1000.

7. Using the exponential function that gives a model for atmospheric pressure, find the atmospheric pressure on the top of Mount McKinley in Alaska, altitude 20,320 ft.

8. A manufacturing company determines that the profit P for a board game that is on the market for t years is given by the equation

$$P = 6000 + 20,000(3)^{-0.2t}$$

(a) Graph this profit function.

(b) What is the profit after 25 years?

(c) What do the graph and the answer tell us about the profit for the board game?

(d) Is that exponential function a logical model for the profit from a board game? Give reasons for your answer.

9. Suppose you take up the game of golf. You keep a record of your average score (the average number of strokes it takes to complete a round of golf) for each month of playing golf. Explain why an exponential function might make a good mathematical model for your scores in this endeavor.

10. The manufacturing company in Problem 8 is trying to stimulate sales of the board game through 30 days of television advertising in an area that has 250,000 viewers. The number of viewers (V) in thousands who are made aware of the board game after t days of advertising is expected to be $V = 250 - 250e^{-0.04t}$.

(a) Graph this exponential function for the 30 days.

(b) How many viewers were made aware of the board game after one day?

(c) How many viewers were made aware of the board game after two weeks?

(d) How many viewers were made aware of the board game after 30 days?

*11. A queen, wishing to reward a faithful maid, agreed to grant her one wish. The maid replied that she was a very humble woman and only wanted some corn as her reward. The maid requested that the corn be given to her in the following manner: Upon a chessboard, place two kernels of corn on the first square, 4 on the second, 8 on the third, 16 on the fourth, and so on, until the last (64th) square. At first the queen refused, saying that this was not a just reward for such a faithful maid. However, after the maid insisted, the queen ordered a servant to bring in a bag of corn and give the maid her desired reward. How much corn did the maid receive? If 1 lb of corn contains about 3500 kernels, how many pounds of corn did the maid receive?

*12. Exponential functions are also used in other areas, such as in the decay of radioactive material (half-life) and bacterial growth. Do some research on one of these areas and on any other area that uses exponential functions as a mathematical model. Explain how the function is used and give some examples.

*13. The graph shows the profit of a company based on the number of years the company has been in business.

(a) Why does an exponential function seem to be an appropriate model for this graph?

(b) Use the data on the graph to find an exponential function of the form $P = a + be^t$ that estimates the profit P of the company as a function of time t, where $t \geq 0$.

(c) Use the exponential function determined in (b) to estimate the company's profit after 10 years.

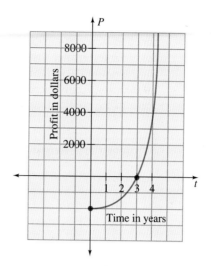

SECTION   2.4

▼

LOGARITHMIC MODELS

As we saw in the previous section, exponential functions can be used as mathematical models of situations in which a quantity experiences a period of gradual increase followed by a period of rapid increase. Logarithmic functions, which were reviewed in Section 2.0, can also be used as mathematical models of real-life situations and scientific phenomena. Some logarithmic functions are inverses of exponential functions, they react in a manner that is opposite to the exponential function. The logarithmic functions we will be studying exhibit a

a. Rapid initial increase followed by a long period of gradual increase, or
b. Rapid initial decrease followed by a long period of gradual decrease.

To help you understand this phenomenon, let's examine the common logarithm function $y = \log x$ by making a chart of values that satisfy the function and sketching its graph.

$y = \log x$

x	y
0.01	-2
0.1	-1
1	0
10	1
50	1.7
100	2
500	2.7
1000	3

As you can see from the chart of values and the graph, the common logarithm function increases rapidly for x values between 0 and 100 and increases very slowly for x values greater than 100. For example, as x increases from 0 to 100, log x increases from very far below zero to a value of 2, and as x increases from 100 to 10,000, log x only increases from 2 to 4. The examples that follow will give you some of the applications of logarithmic functions that behave in a similar manner.

Example 1: Height of Children

A logarithmic function can be used to approximate the change in the height of a child as the child grows older. By age 2, most children have reached 50% of their adult or mature height. It takes approximately 16 years for the child to attain his or her full adult height. A function that allows for a large initial change and then a gradual increase is a logarithmic function. In fact, the mature height of boys aged 0–12 can be approximated by the following function:

$$P = 29 + 48.8 \log (A + 1) \qquad \text{where} \begin{cases} P = \text{percentage of adult height} \\ A = \text{age in years} \end{cases}$$

The graph of that function is

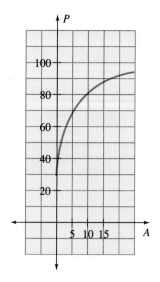

A	P
0	29
5	67
10	80
15	88

We can use that logarithmic model to answer questions about the growth of boys such as

(a) Approximately what percentage of his adult height is a boy at age seven?

(b) If that seven-year-old boy is 52 inches tall, how tall can we expect him to be when he is an adult?

Solution: (a) Substituting $A = 7$ into the formula gives

$$P = 29 + 48.8 \log(A + 1)$$

$$P = 29 + 48.8 \log(7 + 1) \approx 73$$

So, a seven-year-old is 73% of his mature height.

(b) From part (a), the 52-inch boy is 73% of his mature height. So, if $M = $ the mature height,

$$52 = 0.73M$$

$$M = 52 \div 0.73 \approx 71.2 \text{ inches}$$

Thus, we can expect the boy to be a little over 5'11" tall.

Example 2:   Newton's Law of Cooling

From experiments on cooling bodies, Isaac Newton concluded that over moderate temperature ranges, the rate at which an object changes temperature is proportional to the difference between the temperature of the object and the temperature of the surrounding air.

If a cup of 200°F coffee is taken outdoors where the temperature is 35°F, it will begin to cool. If after 1 minute the temperature of the coffee is 170°F, according to Newton's Law of Cooling, the time t it takes for the coffee to reach a temperature x is given by the formula

$$t = 25.5 - 5 \ln (x - 35) \qquad \text{where} \begin{cases} t = \text{time to reach} \\ \quad \text{temperature } x \\ x = \text{temperature of coffee} \\ \quad (35° < x < 170°) \end{cases}$$

Use this function to determine

(a) When the temperature of the coffee is 98.6°F.

(b) When is the temperature of the coffee 40°F?

Solution: (a) Substituting $x = 98.6°$ into the equation gives

$$t = 25.5 - 5 \ln (98.6 - 35) \approx 4.7 \text{ minutes}$$

(b) Substituting $x = 40°$ into the equation gives

$$t = 25.5 - 5 \ln (40 - 35) \approx 17.5 \text{ minutes}$$

This section has attempted to show you that logarithmic functions can be used as mathematical models for actual occurrences in the world. There are other situations in which these functions are used, but many of them are beyond the scope of this book and require a knowledge of the area in which they are used. The problems that follow will let you experiment with other logarithmic functions used as mathematical models.

SECTION 2.4
PROBLEMS

1. At the age of 5, a girl's height is approximately 62% of her full adult height. At age 15 she has reached about 98% of her adult height. The logarithmic function below gives an approximate percentage P of adult height a girl has reached at any age A from 5 to 15 years.

$$P = 62 + 35 \log (A - 4)$$

(a) At the age of 10, what percentage of her height has a girl reached?
(b) If the girl is $4'6''$ at age 10, how tall can she expect to be as an adult?

2. A logarithmic model to approximate the percentage P of adult height a male has reached at any age A from 13 to 18 is

$$P = 16.7 \log (A - 12) + 87$$

(a) Graph this function.
(b) What does the graph tell us about males that have reached the age of 18?

3. A roast, cooking for 2 hours, is taken out of the oven when the meat thermometer reads $140°F$, and is placed in a kitchen that is $68°F$. After 6 minutes the thermometer reads $132°F$. Newton's Law of Cooling states that the time t for the roast to get to a temperature x is given by

$$t = 217.9 - 50.94 \ln (x - 68) \qquad \text{where } 68° < x < 140°$$

(a) In how many minutes will the internal temperature of the roast be $110°F$?
(b) In how many minutes will the internal temperature of the roast be $88°F$?
(c) Graph this function.

4. If $1000 is invested in an account that earns 1% interest each month, the number of months n for the account to grow to an amount A is given by the formula

$$n = -694.2 + 231.4 \log A \qquad \text{where } A \geq \$1000 \text{ and no withdrawals or other deposits are made to the acount}$$

(a) Graph this function.
(b) How many years would it take for the account to grow to $1 million?

5. Suppose you take up the sport of weightlifting. You keep a record of the maximum number of pounds you can lift at the end of each week. Explain why a logarithmic function might make a good mathematical model for predicting the amount of weight you can lift from week to week.

6. If 1000 bacteria are placed in a culture, the time t in hours it takes for the bacteria to grow to an amount A can be approximated by the formula

$$t = -172.7 + 25 \ln A \qquad \text{where } A > 1000$$

(a) Graph this function.
(b) How many hours would it take for the culture to contain a million bacteria?

*7. Logarithmic functions are also used in other areas, such as in the pH (acidity) of solutions, intensity of sound (decibels), and the intensity of earthquakes

(Richter scale). Do some research on one of these areas or any other area that uses logarithmic functions as a mathematical model. Explain how the function is used and give some examples.

*8. The graph shows the profit of a company based on the number of years the company has been in business.

(a) Why does a logarithmic function seem to be an appropriate model for this graph?

(b) Use the data on the graph to find a logarithmic function of the form $P = a \ln t$ that estimates the profit P of the company as a function of time t, where $t \geq 1$.

(c) Use the logarithmic function determined in (b) to estimate the company's profit after 10 years.

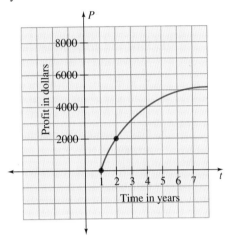

C H A P T E R   2   **SUMMARY**

KEY TERMS, CONCEPTS, AND FORMULAS

The important terms in this chapter are:

Common logarithm: Logarithmic function that uses a base of 10, denoted by log.   p. 67

Discrete graph: A graph consisting of distinct and separate points.   p. 59

Domain: The set of first coordinates of a function.   p. 57

Exponential model: A representation of a situation by an exponential function of the form $y = a + c(b)^{kx}$.   p. 90

Function: A set of ordered pairs such that for each value of the first coordinate there is exactly one value for the second coordinate.   p. 57

Linear model: A representation of a situation by a linear function of the form $y = mx + b$.   p. 71

Logarithmic model: A representation of a situation by a logarithmic function of the form $y = a + b \log (x + c)$ or $y = a + b \ln (x + c)$.   p. 97

Malthusian population model: A method of predicting population growth based on constant birth and death rates.   p. 93

Natural logarithm: Logarithmic function that uses a base of e, denoted by ln.   p. 67

Quadratic model: A representation of a situation by a quadratic function of the form $y = ax^2 + bx + c$.   p. 80

Range: The set of second coordinates of a function.   p. 57

After completing this chapter, you should be able to:

1. Find and graph linear functions that serve as mathematical models for situations in which the rate at which quantities change is constant.   p. 71

2. Find and graph quadratic functions whose parabolic shapes serve as models for given situations.   p. 80

3. Graph and use exponential functions as models to analyze various situations.   p. 90

4. Graph and use logarithmic functions as models to analyze various situations.   p. 97

SUMMARY PROBLEMS

1. Scientists use the Kelvin temperature scale, where the lowest possible temperature (absolute zero) is zero kelvins (0 K). The linear function that relates the Kelvin scale to the Centigrade scale is

$$K = C + 273 \qquad \text{where} \begin{cases} K = \text{temperature on Kelvin scale} \\ C = \text{temperature on Celsius scale} \end{cases}$$

(a) Graph this function.
(b) At what Celsius temperature is absolute zero?
(c) Since water boils at 100°C, at what Kelvin temperature does it boil?

2. If a person walks at 5 mph for an hour, the approximate number of calories burned per hour, based on the person's weight, is given in the table.

Weight in pounds	Calories Burned per Hour
110	440
132	500
154	560
176	620
198	680

(a) Explain why a linear function would be an appropriate model for this data.

(b) Find the linear function that determines the calories (c) burned per hour based on the weight (w) of the person walking at 5 mph.

(c) If you weigh 160 lb and walk at 5 mph, how many calories does your body burn per hour?

3. The first (bottom) row of a huge stack of logs in a lumber yard has 247 logs. The second row has 245 logs, the third row has 243 logs, and so on. If each successive row continues to contain exactly two fewer logs than the previous row,

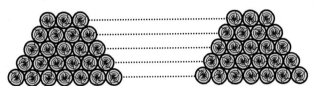

Row 3 → 243 logs
Row 2 → 245 logs
Row 1 → 247 logs

(a) Explain why a linear function could be used to predict the number of logs (L) in any row (r).

(b) Find the linear function that determines the number of logs in any row.

(c) Graph the function found in part (b).

(d) Determine how many logs are in the 50th row.

(e) Determine how many rows of logs the stack contains.

4. At the age of 9, Krista's stamp collection contained 102 stamps. When she entered high school at the age of 14, her collection had grown to 1567 stamps. If Krista continues to collect stamps at that rate,

(a) Find a linear function that, based on her age, predicts the number of stamps she owns.

(b) Predict how many stamps she will have when she graduates from high school at age 18.

(c) Determine at what age her stamp collection would contain more than 10,000 stamps.

5. A rock is thrown vertically upward at 88 ft/s (60 mph) from a sheer cliff in the Grand Canyon, 5000 ft above the Colorado River. A quadratic function that approximates the height of the rock at any time is

$$h = -16t^2 + 88t + 5000$$

(a) Graph this quadratic function for $t \geq 0$.

(b) What is the maximum height the rock reaches?

(c) How long does it take for the rock to reach the Colorado River?

6. In the 1968 Olympics in Mexico City, Bob Beamon of the United States electrified the track and field world with his 29'2.5" leap in the long jump. Assume that the path of the jump can be approximated by a parabola where the highest point occurs at the middle of the jump, and that at that point his feet were 4'6" off the ground.

(a) Find the quadratic function that determines the height of this jump as a function of the length of the jump where distances are measured in inches.

(b) How far past the take-off board was Bob Beamon when his feet were 30″ off the ground?

7. The ancient Greeks studied the pentagonal numbers as shown. The first pentagonal number is 1, the second is 5, the third is 12, the fourth is 22, and so on. The algebraic function that relates the value of a pentagonal number to what term it is in the sequence of numbers is a quadratic function.

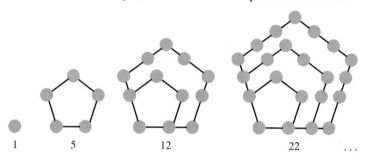

(a) Find the quadratic function that determines the value of a pentagonal number (P) based on what term (t) it is in the sequence.
(b) Graph that function.
(c) Determine the 100th pentagonal number and describe its geometric shape.

8. If the guaranteed rate of return on an investment of $6000 is compounded annually at 10% per year, the exponential function that determines the amount A that investment is worth at time t is given by

$$A = 6000 \ (1.1)^t \qquad \text{where} \begin{cases} A = \text{amount investment is worth} \\ t = \text{time in years} \end{cases}$$

(a) Graph this exponential function for $t \geq 0$.
(b) Determine the value of the investment after 5 years, 10 years, and 30 years.

9. Suppose the total cost for manufacturing a certain toy is given by the equation

$$C = 500 + 400 \ln (x) \qquad \text{where} \begin{cases} C = \text{total cost} \\ x = \text{number of toys and } 1 \leq x \leq 3000 \end{cases}$$

(a) Graph this cost function.
(b) Determine the cost for manufacturing 1000 toys and 2000 toys.
(c) Determine the cost for manufacturing each toy when 1000 toys and 2000 toys are produced. What happens to the cost per toy as the number of toys manufactured increases?

10. The Parker Brothers game of Monopoly™ has a game board of 40 spaces, where your game token can land, and a bank that has $15,140 in play money. Suppose you place $3 on the start (Go), $9 on the next space (Mediterranean Avenue), $27 on the next space (Community Chest), and so on. You keep tripling the amount placed on each space as you go around the board.

(a) Find an exponential function that determines the amount A placed on each space S of the Monopoly™ board.

(b) How much must you place on the ninth space (Vermont Avenue)? Will you have enough money to do that?

(c) The Parker Brothers Company prints about $40 billion in play money each year. With a year's worth of play money would you be able to put the required amount on the 24th space (Illinois Avenue)?

(d) How much play money would you need for the 40th space (Boardwalk)? How many years of play money production by Parker Brothers would you need to put the required amount on Boardwalk?

3

GEOMETRY

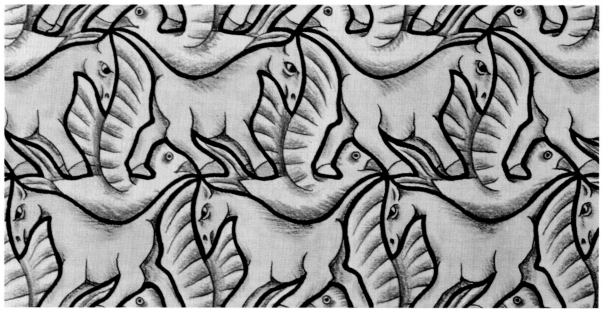

Dutch artist M. C. Escher's *Symmetry Drawing E76* shows the artistic effect that can be achieved with simple geometric tessellations. (M. C. Escher Heirs/Cordon Art-Baarn)

A SHORT HISTORY OF GEOMETRY

The exact origin of geometry is not known, but its roots are believed to date back before recorded history. There is evidence that intuitive concepts of geometry are universal. For example, prehistoric men and women probably realized that the shortest distance between two points is the straight line joining the two points and that the angle at which an arrow is shot affects the distance above the ground the arrow will reach. A basic understanding of geometric shapes is evident in the tools, weapons, and shelters designed by prehistoric men and women. Further, the drawings and handicraft of prehistoric men and women show a concern for spatial relationships. Their pottery, baskets, and weaving display examples of symmetry and sequences of designs. This concern for spatial relationships probably originated in the wonder of the world around them. Perhaps they marveled at the concentric circles formed when a rock is thrown into a pool of water, or the network of hexagons found in a beehive, or the intricate patterns found in snowflakes.

Though we can only speculate on their knowledge of geometry, prehistoric man's interest in geometry seems to have originated from a basic intuition, practical needs, and the aesthetics of order and design.

The first recorded evidence of geometry can be found with the Babylonians and Egyptians (3000 B.C.–300 B.C.). Cuneiform tablets, hieroglyphic papyri, inscriptions on temples and tombs, and construction feats show a variety of practical uses of geometric concepts. Since both civilizations were largely agricultural, much of their geometry was developed to parcel out land, determine areas and perimeters, and calculate volumes of their granaries. In Egypt, the periodic overflows and flooding of the Nile River made surveying the land for reestablishment of boundary lines a necessity. With the use of ropes, Egyptian surveyors, called "rope-stretchers," accurately redetermined agricultural plots in the Nile Valley after the annual flooding had subsided. The Egyptians also showed their skill at measurement in the construction of their pyramids. For example, the Great Pyramid of Gizeh has a square base with sides that are about 756 ft long. Amazingly, the difference in the lengths of the these sides is less than two-thirds of an inch. Babylonian irrigation canals and their beautifully constructed temples, such as the Hanging Gardens of Babylon, also showed practical uses of geometric concepts. The Egyptians and Babylonians are credited with the formation of a geometry that consisted of practical uses of measurement techniques. Their knowledge of geometry was based on intuition, experimentation, and approximation. Tablets and papyri, however, contain only specific, concrete problems in geometry and show no evidence of general formulations, logical proofs, or mathematical abstraction. Thus, their geometry is considered as an empirical or experiential geometry.

The Chinese were also early pioneers in the study of geometry as seen in *K'iu-ch'ang Suan-shu* or *Arithmetic in Nine Sections*, which was probably prepared by Chóu-kung around 1100 B.C. However, since in 213 B.C. Emperor Shï Huang-ti of the Chin dynasty ordered all books to be burned, it is believed that Ch'ang Ts'ang collected writings of the ancients and wrote the version of *K'iu-ch'ang Suan-shu* that has been passed down through history. In this book, the Chinese showed an understanding of determining areas and volumes of geometric objects, finding lengths of sides of figures, and using what is now called the Pythagorean theorem some 500 years before the time of Pythagoras.

Around 700 B.C. the Greeks took the empirical geometry of the Babylonians and Egyptians and began to show that geometric truths could be abstracted from the practical situations in which they arise. In fact, the word "geometry" comes from the Greek words *gē*, "earth," and *met'ron*, "measure." However, the Greeks took the study of geometry far beyond measurement. They developed a geometric system based on logic in which geometric facts follow from generally accepted statements called axioms or postulates. The position of the Greeks on the method and importance of geometry is summarized in quotes from two Greek scholars. Anaxagoras (499–427 B.C.) stated, "Reason rules the world," and Plato (430–347 B.C.) stated, "God eternally geometrizes."

Major contributors and their contributions to the development of Greek geometry are as follows:

Thales (624–547 B.C.) gave logical proofs for geometric relationships and is considered one of the founders of mathematical science.

Pythagoras (572–501 B.C.), a pupil of Thales, formed a society devoted to the study of arithmetic, music, astronomy, and geometry. He and his followers proved many new theorems about triangles, circles, solids, and proportions. He is credited with discovering a geometric proof of what is now called the Pythagorean Theorem (see Section 5.0).

Philosophers Socrates (468–399 B.C.), Plato (430–347 B.C.), and Aristotle (385–322 B.C.) emphasized the need for making clear assumptions, formulating accurate definitions, and using sound logic in studying geometry.

Euclid of Alexandria (c. 300 B.C.) wrote *The Elements*, a collection of 13 books of which the first 6 and the last 3 are devoted to geometry. In *The Elements*, Euclid logically developed and summarized the geometry known up to that time. This "Euclidean" model dominated the study of geometry until about 1700 and is still the basis of many geometry courses taught at the secondary level.

Archimedes (287–212 B.C.) made contributions to finding the areas and volumes of geometric figures.

Apollonius of Perga (262–190 B.C.) wrote on conic sections and named them ellipse, parabola, and hyperbola.

The Greeks also spent much time on three famous construction problems. Using a straight edge and a compass, they attempted to:

1. Divide any angle into three equal angles (trisect an angle)
2. Draw a square equal in area to that of a given circle (square a circle)
3. Draw a cube the volume of which is twice that of a given cube (double a cube)

Greek mathematicians such as Anaxagoras (c. 440 B.C.), Antiphon of Athens (c. 430 B.C.), Hippocrates of Chios (c. 460 B.C.), Hippas of Elis (c. 425 B.C.), Archytas of Tarentum (c. 400 B.C.), Eudoxus (c. 370 B.C.), and Eratosthenes (c. 230 B.C.) worked on these construction problems. Although it was proved in the 19th century that these constructions are impossible, the attempts to solve them led to the investigation of many other important mathematical topics. Because of their extensive contributions to the study of geometry, the Greeks can be considered the founders of geometry.

After Apollonius of Perga, the development in geometry began to stagnate. With the decline of the Greek city-states and the rise of the Roman Empire, during the next 600 years, the centers of mathematical thought in Alexandria and Athens did not experience the advancements that were found in previous centuries. The only significant work of this period was the mathematical treatise *Collection* by Pappus of Alexandria (c. 320). In it, Pappus introduced some of his original work in geometry, but, more significantly, he provided a historical record of parts of Greek mathematics that would otherwise be unknown to us. The death of Hypatia (c. 415) in Alexandria, the execution of Boethius (c. 524) in Athens, and the fall of the Roman Empire (c. 476) brought an end to the Greek period in mathematics.

From the disintegration of the Roman Empire until about 1000, Western Europe experienced a period where intellectual pursuits were at a low. These five centuries are called the Dark Ages by historians. The study of mathematics during this period moved to the East, to India and Arabia. The Hindus and Arabs made advancements in systems of numeration, algebra, and trigonometry, but their contributions to geometry were limited to a few theorems by Āryabhata (c. 510), Brahmagupta (c. 628), Tâbit ibn Qorra (c. 870) and Bhāskara (c. 1150), among others. However, while the Arabs and Hindus did not contribute much to the development of geometry, they did preserve and keep alive the mathematics of the Greeks.

As Europe emerged from the Dark Ages (c. 1000), interest in geometry began to reappear. Mathematical works written in Arabic were translated into Latin. Among these were Adelard of Bath's translation of Euclid's *Elements* (c. 1120), Robert Chester's translation of al-Khowârizmî's algebra (c. 1140), and Johannes Campanus's widely published translation of Euclid's *Elements* (c. 1260). Creative work in geometry was also given impetus by the establishment of universities in Europe such as the University of Paris in 1200, Oxford in 1214, and Cambridge in 1231. During the Renaissance period of the 14th century, the geometry of Euclid was expanded by Leonardo Fibonacci (c. 1220) in *Practica geometriae* and Jordanus Nemorarius (c. 1225) and Regiomontanus (c. 1464) in *De triangulis*. Henry Billingsley (c. 1570) also translated Euclid's *Elements* from Latin into English, and in 1607, Jesuit missionary Matteo Ricci and Chinese scholar Hsü translated the first six books of *Elements* into Chinese. With this start the major advancements in geometry settled into four distinct categories: analytic/algebraic geometry, projective/descriptive geometry, non-Euclidean geometry, and differential geometry.

Analytic/Algebraic Geometry

In about 1629, Pierre de Fermat began applying methods of algebra to geometric objects. His work included the determination of equations for lines, circles, ellipses, parabolas, and hyperbolas. However, his work was not published until after his death in 1679. In 1637, *La Geometrie*, a discourse by René Descartes on analytic geometry, was published. In this discourse, Descartes introduced the *xy* coordinate system and allowed for the graphic representation of geometric curves given by equations. Because the work of Descartes was published first, he is credited with founding analytic (algebraic) geometry. In the Descartes-Fermat scheme, points became pairs of numbers and curves became sets of points generated by algebraic equations. Geometry became ''arithmetized.''

Projective/Descriptive Geometry

In the 15th and 16th centuries, a focus of geometry was to obtain the correct perspective in representing what one sees. Architects Filippo Brunelleschi (c. 1400) and Leon Alberti (c. 1435), along with artists Pietro Franceschi (c. 1490), Leonardo da Vinci (c. 1500), and Albrecht Dürer (c. 1525) worked on representing three-dimensional objects on a two-dimensional surface. This interest in projecting a space figure onto another surface led to the development of projective and descriptive geometry. The mathematics of these geometries was initiated by Girard Desargues (c. 1640) and Blaise Pascal (c. 1650) and developed by Gaspard Monge (c. 1795), Victor Poncelet (c. 1822), Jacob Steiner (c. 1832), K. G. C. von Staudt (c. 1847), and Felix Klein (c. 1871). The work of these architects, artists, and mathematicians led to an understanding of perspective, became the foundation of architectural and mechanical drawing, and initiated investigations of topology.

Non-Euclidean Geometry

Euclid's fifth postulate has been the source of much thought and mathematical investigation. In Euclid's *Elements* we find the fifth postulate.

> *That, if a straight line falling on two straight lines makes the interior angles on the same side less than two right angles, the two straight lines, if produced indefinitely, meet on that side on which the angles are less than two right angles.*

A simpler and more intuitive equivalent of the postulate was formulated by John Playfair in 1795.

> *Through a given point only one parallel can be drawn to a given straight line.*

Mathematicians felt that this postulate could be shown to be true as a result of logical deductions from Euclid's nine other postulates. In an attempt to do this, the efforts of Girolamo Saccheri (c. 1733), Johann Lambert (c. 1788), Adrien Legendre (c. 1794), János Bolyai (c. 1794), Carl Friedrich Gauss (c. 1816), Nicolai Lobachevsky (c. 1829), and Georg Riemann (c. 1854) led to what is known today as Lobachevskian geometry and Riemannian geometry. Lobachevskian geometry is based on a postulate that more than one parallel line can be drawn to a given line through an external point, while Riemannian geometry employs a postulate that no parallel line can be drawn through the point. Some of the details of these geometries will be discussed in Section 3.2.

The logical conclusions reached by assuming the Lobachevskian or Riemannian postulate contradicted Euclid's results. To the scholars of the 19th century, this was very perturbing since, for 2000 years, Euclidean geometry had been accepted as giving unquestionable truth about the real world. The study of non-Euclidean geometry did, however, lead to three conclusions:

1. Euclid's fifth postulate cannot be logically deduced from his other postulates.
2. Non-Euclidean geometries could be used to describe space just as Euclidean geometry did.
3. Mathematics does not give absolute truths about the physical world.

Differential Geometry

Differential geometry is essentially the technique of applying calculus to the study of curves and surfaces. The development of this branch of geometry can be credited to the study of "infinitesimals" by Johann Kepler (c. 1604) and Bonaventura Cavalieri (c. 1635); to the application of the "derivative" and the "integral" to curves by Isaac Newton (c. 1680) and Gottfried Leibniz (c. 1682); to the investigation of "neighborhoods" of a point on a curve or surface by Carl Friedrich Gauss (c. 1827); and to the "methods of analysis" of Georg Riemann (c. 1850) and Jean Gaston Darboux (c. 1890).

We can see from this short history of geometry that many mathematicians from many cultures contributed to its development. We will look at some of the geometric topics investigated by these mathematicians in this chapter and the next.

CHECK YOUR READING

1. What are the five categories of geometry? Give a brief description of each category.
2. What were the major differences between the geometry of the Greeks and that of the Babylonians and the Egyptians?
3. In about 1200 B.C. Chinese mathematicians were working on magic squares. What were the Egyptian "rope-stretchers" doing at that time?
4. While French traders were settling at St. Louis in about 1637, what was French mathematician René Descartes doing?
5. What contributions did the Hindus and the Arabs make to geometry during the Dark Ages?
6. Why did the study of the non-Euclidean geometries cause controversy?
7. While Abraham Ortelius (Antwerp) was producing the first modern atlas with 53 maps in 1570, what was Henry Billingsley (England) doing?
8. While commonplace things like the use of black-lead pencils and pocket handkerchiefs came in to use in the early 1500s, what were artists like Franceschi and da Vinci doing in geometry?
9. What role did artists play in the development of geometry?
10. What were the three famous construction problems of geometry?
11. In 1829, Andrew Jackson was inaugurated as the seventh president of the United States. What was the Russian professor Nikolai Lobachevsky doing at that time?
12. In 1854, the Republican party was formed in the United States. What geometric propositions were being formulated by Georg Riemann?
13. Match each of the following names with the correct mathematical discovery, event, or concept.
    (a) Appollonius $a^2 + b^2 = c^2$ named after him
    (b) Archimedes   Artist involved in perspective
    (c) Billingsley   Edited *Arithmetic in Nine Sections*
    (d) Ch'ang Ts'ang   Famous geometrician who wrote the book *Elements*
    (e) Descartes   Found area and volume formulas
    (f) Dürer   A founder of mathematical science

(g) Euclid	Named the conic sections
(h) Lobachevsky	Devised non-Euclidean geometry with more than one parallel
(i) Plato	Devised non-Euclidean geometry with no parallels
(j) Pythagoras	Stated, ''God eternally geometrizes.''
(k) Riemann	Translated *Elements* into English
(l) Thales	Devised the *xy* coordinate system

RESEARCH QUESTIONS

In order to answer the following questions, you will need to refer to material not contained in the text. Possible sources of information are listed in the bibliography at the end of the text.

1. Many of the mathematicians mentioned in this short history of geometry are known for other mathematical endeavors or had other interests besides mathematics. Do some research on two of the mathematicians mentioned in this section. Tell something about their lives, their achievements, and their interests.

2. One of the reasons for the creation of geometry was its use in the measurement of lengths, perimeters, areas, and volumes. Given some examples of how these practical applications of geometry are still used today.

3. The pyramids of Egypt are early examples of practical geometry at work. Discuss the geometry involved in the construction of the pyramids.

4. Do some research on the geometry of the ancient Chinese.

5. Some credit for the advances of the Greeks in mathematics is given to the Greek schools. The most noted schools of mathematics were the Alexandrian School of Mathematics and the Platonic Academy in Athens. What were these schools like? How was mathematics taught in these schools? Who were some of the teachers in these schools?

6. What were Euclid's first four postulates? Make sketches of each and explain them in your own words. What were Euclid's five common notions?

7. Who were the Pythagoreans? What did this society do, and what were some of their beliefs?

8. Who was Hypatia of Alexandria? What is she famous for?

9. What were the Dark Ages, and what factors contributed to the stagnation of intellectual pursuits during that period?

10. What was the Renaissance, and what factors contributed to the rebirth of intellectual pursuits during that period?

11. Do some research on perspective and projections. Give examples of the different types of perspective and projections.

12. What are the ''infinitesimals'' studied by Johann Kepler, Bonaventura Cavalieri, and others? How were they used in the development of geometry?

13. What is the meaning of the statement "The world is Euclidean"? Explain how the non-Euclidean geometries caused people to question that statement.

14. What are some of the major conclusions of the non-Euclidean geometries? How do they differ from Euclidean geometry?

15. What is topology? What are some of the objects studied in topology, and what are some of the practical applications of topology?

16. Discuss the controversy over the founding of analytic geometry by Pierre de Fermat and René Descartes and of non-Euclidean geometry by Carl Gauss, János Bolyai, and Nicolai Lobachevsky.

17. Who was M. C. Escher? What were his contributions to geometry?

18. Do some research on geometric designs or the use of geometry in art.

Bruce Cohen's *Blue Table with Many Tulips* uses familiar geometric shapes from Euclidean geometry. (Courtesy of the artist)

SECTION 3.1

▼

EUCLIDEAN GEOMETRY

The geometry you have been exposed to in elementary and secondary schools has been a geometry based on the system of geometry contained in *Elements*, a book written by the Greek mathematician Euclid in about 300 B.C. This work summarized much of the geometry known up to that time and presented the first systematic treatment of geometry which used deductive reasoning to justify geometric propositions. Starting with definitions, postulates, and common notions, Euclid proceeded to prove numerous propositions of a geometry now called **Euclidean geometry**. The intent of this section is not to cover all of Euclidean geometry but to make you aware of the development of this mathematical system and to summarize some of the basics of Euclidean geometry that we will need in the text.

Undefined Terms

One of the most important features of a mathematical system is that the terms used in the system must have clear definitions. We must know precisely what a term refers to. When making a definition, you should use terms that are simpler than the term being defined. If you then try to define those terms by still simpler terms and so on, the process could conceivably go on forever or you could return to the same term you were trying to define. There comes a time when a definition must use a term whose meaning is assumed to be clear. Such terms are called **undefined terms**. They are used to begin the process of defining new terms. We will begin our study of Euclidean geometry by considering the simplest geometric objects—points, lines, and planes—as our undefined terms. We will rely on our intuitive ideas of what they mean.

A **point** can be described as a location or position. It can be represented by a dot and is usually named by a capital letter. A **line** may be considered as the set of points arranged along a straight path. It extends indefinitely in two opposite directions and can be named by either a single lowercase letter or by two points on the line with a double-headed arrow placed above the letters. A **plane** can be described as the set of all points that form a completely flat surface extending indefinitely in all directions. It can be represented by means of a parallelogram and named by a capital letter placed in one corner of the parallelogram.

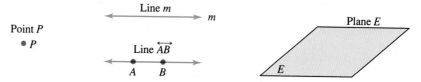

The preceding paragraph merely gives an intuitive description of a point, a line, and a plane. These are not considered definitions. Point, line, and plane are not defined in our system. However, as we proceed in the development of our geometric system, we will become more aware of the properties of these three basic geometric objects. The figures in Euclidean geometry can be visualized by placing them on a plane. The plane is considered the model for Euclidean geometry.

Definitions

With the use of the undefined terms we can now give meanings to other terms and expressions of geometry. The definitions we will need are:

D1:

A **line segment** is the set of points on a line consisting of two points, called endpoints, and all the points in between those two points.

Example:

The line segment joining the points A and B is written $\overline{AB}$.

D2:

A **ray** is the figure formed by extending a line segment in only one direction.

Example:

The ray with end point P extending through point Q is written $\overrightarrow{PQ}$.

D3:

An **angle** is the figure formed by two rays with the same end point.

Example:

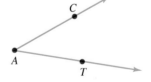

$\angle CAT$ has its vertex at the end points of rays $\overrightarrow{AC}$ and $\overrightarrow{AT}$. $\angle CAT$ has a measure from $0°$ to $180°$, as will be stated in Postulate 6.*

---

*Angles are measured in degrees with $360°$ (read ''360 degrees'') forming a full circle.

D4:

A **straight angle** is an angle that forms a line and measures 180°.

Example:

∠*TIP* is a straight angle.
∠*TIP* measures 180°.
∠*TIP* forms line *k*.

D5:

A **right angle** is an angle that measures 90°; an **acute angle** measures between 0° and 90°; an **obtuse angle** measures between 90° and 180°.

Example

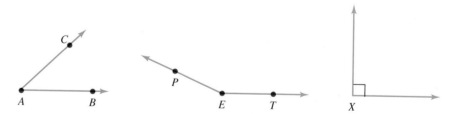

∠*CAB* is an acute angle   ∠*PET* is an obtuse angle   ∠*X* is a right angle

D6:

Two lines, rays, or line segments are **perpendicular** if they intersect and form a right angle.

Example:

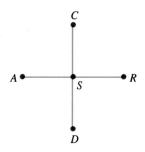

$\overline{AR}$ is perpendicular to $\overline{CD}$ at point S. It is written $\overline{AR} \perp \overline{CD}$.

D7:

A **triangle** is a figure consisting of three line segments determined by three points that are not on the same line.

Example:

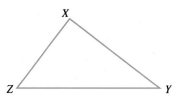

$\triangle XYZ$ has three vertices, the points at X, Y, and Z. It has three sides, $\overline{XY}$, $\overline{YZ}$, $\overline{ZX}$. It has three angles $\angle ZXY$ or $\angle X$, $\angle XYZ$ or $\angle Y$, and $\angle YZX$ or $\angle Z$. ▪

D8:

An **exterior angle** is an angle formed outside a triangle by one side of the triangle and the extension of another side of the triangle.

Example:

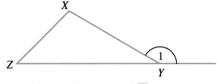

$\angle 1$ is an exterior angle for $\triangle XYZ$. ▪

D9:

Two lines are **parallel** if they lie in the same plane and do not intersect.

Example:

Line *m* and line *n* are parallel, written $m \| n$.

D10:

A **transversal** is a line or line segment that intersects two other lines or line segments.

Example:

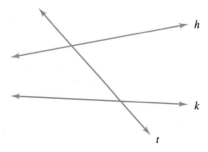

Line *t* is a transversal to line *h* and line *k*.

When two lines are cut by a transversal, the following sets of angles are formed:

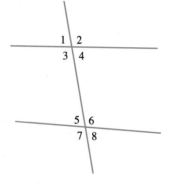

alternate interior angles:
∠3 and ∠6, ∠4 and ∠5
corresponding angles:
∠1 and ∠5, ∠2 and ∠6,
∠3 and ∠7, ∠4 and ∠8

There are many more terms that we could define, but these are all we will need in our brief excursion into geometry.

Axioms and Postulates

If we are to develop a deductive system of geometry, each conclusion must logically follow from true premises. We must have initial statements to start with that can serve as premises leading to conclusions. We simply cannot deduce all statements. Hence, in our system of geometry, we will start with some propositions that are assumed to be true. These propositions are called **axioms** or **postulates**. Though these terms are used interchangeably, historically, axioms referred to assumptions from arithmetic or algebra, whereas postulates referred to assumptions from geometry. Axioms and postulates are sometimes called self-evident truths. However, we shall see in our study of non-Euclidean geometry that this is not necessarily the case. We will start our study with axioms and postulates based on those proposed by Euclid.

Axioms

A1:

A quantity may be substituted for its equal in any expression.

Example:

If $\angle A + \angle B = \angle C$ and $\angle A = 90°$, then $90° + \angle B = \angle C$.

A2:

If quantities are equal to the same quantity, then they are equal to each other.

Example:

If $A = C$ and $G = C$, then $A = G$.

A3:

If equal quantities are added to or subtracted from equal quantities, the results are equal.

Example:

If $\angle A = \angle R$ and $\angle B = \angle K$, then

$$\angle A + \angle B = \angle R + \angle K \quad \text{and} \quad \angle A - \angle B = \angle R - \angle K$$

A4:

If equal quantities are multiplied by the same quantity or divided by the same nonzero quantity, the results are equal.

Example:

If $x = y$, then $5x = 5y$ and $x \div 7 = y \div 7$.

A5:

A whole quantity is equal to the sum of its parts and is greater than any one of them.

Example:

$AD = AB + BC + CD$ and $AD > AB$, $AD > BC$, $AD > CD$, $AD > AC$, $AD > BD$.

Postulates

P1:

Through two given points, one and only one line can be drawn.

Example

Through the points A and C only one line can be drawn.

P2:

A line segment can be extended indefinitely in both directions.

Example

The line segment $\overline{PQ}$ can be extended into line $\overleftrightarrow{PQ}$.

P3:

If two points of a line lie in a plane, then the line through the two points lies in the plane.

Example:

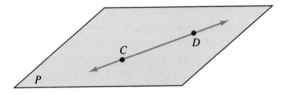

Points C and D lie in plane E. Therefore, the entire line passing through C and D lies in plane E.

P4:

To every pair of points there corresponds a unique positive number called its distance.

Example:

The line segment $\overline{PQ}$ has a unique distance; $PQ = 4$ cm.

P5: Parallel Postulate:

Through a given point, only one parallel can be drawn to a given line.

Example:

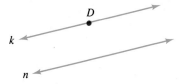

Through point D, line k is the only line that can be drawn parallel to line n.

P6:

To every angle there corresponds a unique number between 0 and 180 called the measure of the angle.

Example:

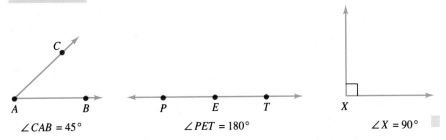

$\angle CAB = 45°$ $\angle PET = 180°$ $\angle X = 90°$

With the establishment of axioms, postulates, and definitions in this section and an understanding of deductive reasoning, we can demonstrate the logical development of and prove some propositions of Euclidean geometry. Such proven propositions are called **theorems**. The **proof** of a theorem consists of a series of statements that logically show a proposition follows from its hypothesis. The premises of a proof are based on axioms, postulates, definitions, and other proven theorems. One of the objectives of this text is to give you a flavor of the role of deductive reasoning in justifying mathematical propositions. We will be looking at the logical structure exhibited in a chain of propositions in hope of gaining an understanding of the nature of proof in mathematics. We will look at the proofs of the following theorems from Euclidean geometry in Chapter 4.

Theorems

T1: If a line segment lies in a plane, then the line containing the segment lies in the plane.

T2: If two distinct lines intersect, they intersect in at most one point.

T3: If two lines in the same plane are parallel to the same line, then they are parallel to each other.

T4: An exterior angle of a triangle is greater than either nonadjacent interior angle.

T5: If two lines m and n are cut by a transversal t such that the alternate interior angles are equal, then $m \| n$.

T6: If two parallel lines m and n are cut by a transversal t, the alternate interior angles are equal.

T7: The sum of the measures of the angles of a triangle is 180°.

SECTION 3.1
PROBLEMS

1. Euclid defined a point as "that which has no part." Do you think this is a good definition? Why or why not?

2. Euclid's defined a line as "breadthless length." Do you think this is a good definition? Why or why not?

3. Using a standard dictionary, show how giving the definition of the word "dimension" can lead you to a circular path; that is, continuing to define the words of previous definitions could lead you back to the word you began with.

4. Find at least two words in which using a standard dictionary could lead you in a circular path, just as defining the word "dimension" did in Problem 3.

5. Explain why it is necessary to have undefined terms and postulates in the development of a deductive system of geometry.

6. Show how Axiom A3 can be used to solve for x in the equation $5x - 3 = 4x + 9$.

7. Show how Axioms A3 and A4 can be used to solve for x in the equation $5 + 6x = 4x - 11$.

8. Explain why the figure to the right is not possible for lines m and n in Euclidean geometry.

9. Explain why the figure to the right is not possible for points A and B and the line through A and B in plane E.

10. Explain the difference between a postulate and a theorem in geometry.

11. The transitive property of equality states that if $a = b$ and $b = c$, then $a = c$. Explain why this is equivalent to Axiom A2.

12. Explain why the following definition of parallel segments is faulty: "Two segments are parallel if they do not intersect." Give a good definition for parallel segments.

13. Draw three sets of two parallel lines. Cut each set of parallel lines by a transversal. Use a protractor to measure each set of corresponding angles. What seems to be true about these angles? Formulate a precise statement of your conjecture.

14. Draw three sets of two parallel lines. Cut each set of parallel lines by a transversal. Use a protractor to measure each set of alternate interior angles. What seems to be true about these angles? Formulate a precise statement of your conjecture.

15. Draw three large triangles and an exterior angle for each triangle. Use a protractor to measure the exterior angle and the interior angles of each triangle. Using your results, make some conjectures about exterior angles and interior angles of a triangle.

In Problems 16–23, make sketches satisfying the following conditions:

16. Obtuse $\angle FUN$, where $\overline{UF}$ and $\overline{UN}$ are line segments.

17. Acute $\angle RUN$, where points R, U, and N lie in plane M

18. Line j and line k, where transversal r makes a right angle with line j

19. Line j and line k, where transversal r is perpendicular to both line j and line k.

20. $\overline{FX} \perp \overrightarrow{FG}$, line $y \parallel \overline{FX}$, and all objects are in the same plane.

21. Right angle $\angle HER$ lying in plane F with $\overline{HE} \perp \overline{ER}$.

22. Right angle $\angle HER$ lying in plane F with $\overline{BE}$ making an angle less than 90° with $\overline{HE}$.

23. $\triangle RAD$ with an exterior angle at each vertex.

In Problems 24–30, use specific points, lines, planes, angles, and the like, as in the examples of the postulates, to:

24. Make a sketch and state the conclusion of Theorem T1.

25. Make a sketch and state the conclusion of Theorem T2.

26. Make a sketch and state the conclusion of Theorem T3.

27. Make a sketch and state the conclusion of Theorem T4.

28. Make a sketch and state the conclusion of Theorem T5.

29. Make a sketch and state the conclusion of Theorem T6.

30. Make a sketch and state the conclusion of Theorem T7.

*31. The seven theorems of geometry stated in this section are a very small selection of the many theorems of Euclidean geometry. Find ten other theorems of Euclidean geometry. Make a labeled sketch of each theorem and state the conclusion of each theorem.

SECTION 3.2

▼ NON-EUCLIDEAN GEOMETRY

Any system of geometry that uses a consistent set of postulates, with at least one that is not logically equivalent to one of Euclid's postulates, is a **non-Euclidean geometry**. In particular, mathematicians wondered if Euclid's parallel postulate was really a postulate. The statement of the postulate by Euclid seemed to lack the clarity and the "self-evident" character of his other postulates. In fact, Euclid did not use the parallel postulate until the proof of his 29th proposition. Mathematicians, therefore, attempted to derive the parallel postulate from Euclid's nine other postulates. These attempts, however, met with little success. It was not until the late 19th and early 20th centuries that mathematicians Eugenio Beltrami (1835–1900), Felix Klein (1849–1929), and Henri Poincaré (1854–1912) finally established that the parallel postulate could not be deduced from Euclid's other postulates. These attempts to prove the parallel postulate did, however, generate some interesting results. The work of the Jesuit priest Girolamo Saccheri (1667–1733) laid the groundwork for the creation of the two principal non-Euclidean geometries that bear the names of the mathematicians who spent a lifetime studying them—Lobachevskian geometry and Riemannian geometry. In this section, we will take a closer look at these two non-Euclidean geometries.

Russian mathematics professor Nicolai Lobachevsky (1793–1856), Hungarian army officer Janós Bolyai (1802–1860), and renowned German mathematician Carl Gauss (1777–1855) accepted the postulates of Euclid but replaced the parallel postulate with the following postulate:

Lobachevskian Parallel Postulate

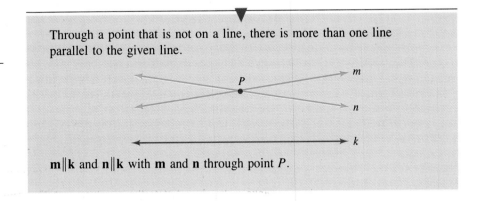

Through a point that is not on a line, there is more than one line parallel to the given line.

m‖**k** and **n**‖**k** with **m** and **n** through point P.

The German mathematician and student of Carl Gauss, Georg Riemann (1826–1866), replaced Euclid's parallel postulate with this:

Riemannian Parallel Postulate

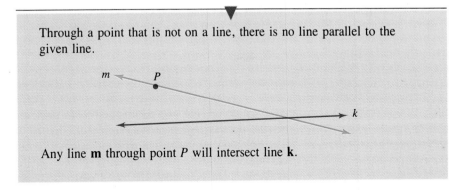

Through a point that is not on a line, there is no line parallel to the given line.

Any line **m** through point P will intersect line **k**.

These assumptions led to the creation of geometries that are logically consistent and contained no contradictions within themselves. However, the theorems deduced from these postulates contradicted some of the well-established theorems of Euclidean geometry. So controversial was the idea that one could deny a postulate of Euclid and arrive at conclusions that contradicted Euclid that even the great Carl Gauss was reluctant to publish his findings. Eventually, these non-Euclidean geometries were accepted by the mathematical community. However, the question of which geometry actually gives an accurate description of physical space remained.

Euclidean geometry was so widely accepted as accurately describing physical space that these non-Euclidean geometries were considered as mere mental exercises. Mathematicians believed that the geometry of the physical world must be Euclidean. While it is true that Euclidean geometry corresponds with our intuitive ideas about our surroundings, we would like to present some models and observations to suggest the possibility that the physical universe could be non-Euclidean.

A Riemannian Model

Besides changing Euclid's parallel postulate, Georg Riemann questioned if lines extended infinitely. He proposed that lines trace back on themselves, like circles. For example, if light in space travels in a circular path, looking into space with a very powerful telescope may enable you to see the back of your head. Further, you could traverse a circle endlessly, but its length is still finite. Thus, Riemann modified Euclid's second postulate, which stated that a line can be extended indefinitely to one that said a line is endless but not necessarily infinite.

Further, do parallel lines never meet? Never? If one looks down a set of railroad tracks, it seems that the tracks get closer together. Maybe lines in space eventually do meet.

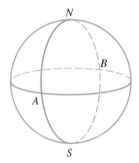

If we accept the two assumptions that lines are endless but not infinite and parallel lines do not exist, we form a different geometry, the geometry of Georg Riemann. Its postulates and theorems cannot be easily displayed on the plane of Euclidean geometry. They can, however, be visualized on the surface of a sphere. In Riemannian geometry, the Euclidean plane becomes a sphere, the Euclidean line becomes a great circle on the sphere, and the Euclidean point becomes a point on the sphere along with its antipodal point (point on the sphere furthest from the first point). For example, while we consider the North and South Poles to be different points, in Riemannian geometry the North and South Poles are considered together as one point. Such a model does not allow us to visualize Euclidean Postulates P2 (A line segment can be extended indefinitely in both directions) and P5 (Through a given point, only one parallel can be drawn to a given line). The great circles of a sphere have a finite length, and any two great circles intersect, so there are no parallel lines. The model, however, can be used to display Euclidean postulates P1, P3, and P4, which we established in Section 3.1:

P1R:

Through two "points" there is only one great circle.

P3R:

If two "points" lie on the sphere, the great circle through those "points" lies on the sphere.

P4R:

To every pair of "points" there corresponds a unique distance, the length of the shortest arc of the great circle through the "points."

Consequences of the Riemannian Parallel Postulate

In Riemannian geometry, all theorems that are not consequences of the parallel postulate (P5) or the infinitude of lines (P2) are exactly the same as the corresponding theorem in Euclidean geometry. For example, Theorems T1–T3 from Section 3.1 remain the same in Riemannian geometry, since they are not based on postulates P2 or P5, but Theorems T4–T7 are changed.

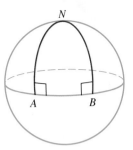

One of the most significant results of the Riemannian parallel postulate is that the sum of the measures of the angles of a triangle is greater than 180° rather than equal to 180°, as found in Euclidean geometry. If we look at the triangle drawn on the spherical model for Riemannian geometry in the figure, we see that $\triangle ANB$ has two 90° angles, so the sum of the angles of $\triangle ANB$ is greater than 180°. We will look at the proof of existence of such a triangle in Section 4.5. For now we note that, in Riemannian geometry,

The sum of the measures of the angles of a triangle is greater than 180°.

The Riemannian parallel postulate causes all the theorems based on Euclid's parallel postulate to change. Here are some other logical consequences of the Riemannian parallel postulate.

1. Every line has a finite length.
2. The exterior angle of a triangle may be less than or equal to the nonadjacent interior angles of the triangle.
3. The sum of the measures of the angles of a triangle varies with the area of a triangle and approaches 180° as the area of the triangle approaches zero.
4. Triangles that have equal angles have the same area.

A Lobachevskian Model

In Riemannian geometry, we were introduced to the possibility that lines are not necessarily straight. The same holds true in Lobachevskian geometry. In fact, scientists believe that space is curved. A ray of light traveling through space does not take a straight path. According to Einstein's theory of relativity, the path of a ray of light is affected by the gravitational field of large objects in space. The gravitational field causes the ray of light to bend. The lines in Lobachevskian geometry also bend, as can be seen in the model in the figure.

The model resembles two attached trumpets with the small ends extending indefinitely, a shape called a pseudosphere. The pseudosphere corresponds to the plane in Euclidean geometry and to the sphere in Riemannian geometry. Lobachevskian lines consist of two symmetric curves meeting at a point at the widest part of the pseudosphere (the bold line in the drawing passing through points A and B). Through point Q there is more than one ''line'' parallel to the ''line'' through A and B. Through point Q on the pseudosphere, you will also notice that ''line'' QB intersects ''line'' AB at point B. The Lobachevskian parallel postulate can be visualized with the help of a pseudosphere. As was true with the Riemannian model, the pseudosphere does allow us to visualize the other Euclidean postulates we established in Section 3.1.

Consequences of the Lobachevskian Parallel Postulate

In Lobachevskian geometry, all theorems that are not consequences of the parallel postulate are exactly the same as the theorem in Euclidean geometry. However, any theorem that uses the parallel postulate in its proof contradicts the Euclidean geometry theorem. In our sequence of theorems in Section 3.1, only T6 and T7 are not Lobachevskian theorems. A notable result of the Lobachevskian parallel postulate is that the sum of the measures of the angles of a triangle is less than 180° rather than equal to 180° (as found in Euclidean geometry) or greater than 180° (as found in Riemannian geometry). If we look at an equiangular triangle drawn on the pseudosphere model, each angle is less than 60° because the sides of the triangle curve inward. The sum of the angles of the triangle is, therefore, less than 180°.

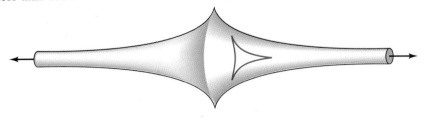

The sum of the measures of the angles of a triangle is less than 180°.

The Lobachevskian parallel postulate would cause all the theorems based on Euclid's parallel postulate to change. Here are some other consequences of the Lobachevskian parallel postulate.

1. Through a point not on a given line there are infinitely many parallels to the given line.
2. In one direction, parallel lines get closer together, and in the other direction they get farther apart.
3. Triangles that have equal angles are congruent and have equal areas.
4. As the area of a triangle approaches zero, the sum of the angles approaches 180°.

Is the World Euclidean, Riemannian, or Lobachevskian?

Before we end our excursion into geometry, we would like to leave you with a possible perspective in answering the question "Is the world Euclidean, Riemannian, or Lobachevskian?" As we live upon the surface of the earth, the earth seems to be flat. As we observe the objects around us from our limited vantage point, the world does seem to be Euclidean. On this page, the line containing the top edge is the only line parallel to the line through the bottom edge. However, if we could follow those two lines by stepping back from the earth and observing them, we might see that they follow the curvature of the earth, intersect, and return to where they started. Airplane navigators, for example, use the great circles of the earth as the path lines for flights. Considerations such as this might lead us to the conclusion that our world is Riemannian. If we considered our world to be all of space and accept the theories and discoveries of our scientists, there could be an infinite number of ''lines'' emerging from space that lie in the same ''plane,'' pass through the top right-hand corner of this page, and are parallel to the line containing the bottom edge of the page. Our world may be Lobachevskian.

We may never know if Euclidean, Riemannian, or Lobachevskian geometry adequately describes our world. Mathematics does not establish truths about the physical world. The physical universe is the way it is, and geometry gives us a set of logical conclusions based on possible perceptions and assumptions about that physical universe. The mathematics of each geometry has an intrinsic beauty and logic. Instead of asking, ''Is the world Euclidean, Riemannian, or Lobachevskian?'' one might wonder, ''Which geometry is the best to apply in a given situation?'' Mankind's experience over thousands of years suggests that when working with measurement, travel, construction, design, and the like, Euclidean geometry seems most useful. On the other hand, advancements in science over the last century suggest that, when investigating the outer space or analyzing the inner space of atoms, properties of non-Euclidean geometries may be more appropriate models.

SECTION 3.2

PROBLEMS

1. Describe the parallel postulates of Euclidean, Riemannian, and Lobachevskian geometries. Explain how they are the same and how they are different.

2. Contrast and compare the triangle-sum theorems of Euclidean, Riemannian, and Lobachevskian geometries.

3. Why would you expect Lobachevskian geometry to have more theorems that are the same as Euclidean geometry theorems than does Riemannian geometry?

4. Why would you expect Riemannian geometry to have fewer theorems that are the same as Euclidean geometry theorems than does Lobachevskian geometry?

5. What does the existence of non-Euclidean geometry tell us about mathematics and the truth about the physical world?

6. The scientific method starts with observation, proceeds to making hypotheses, and uses experimentation to establish laws. Using this method, explain how the ''common man's'' geometry might be Euclidean while the ''research scientist's'' might be non-Euclidean.

7. On the pseudospherical model of Lobachevskian geometry, draw a right triangle, $\triangle LOB$.

8. Use the spherical model of Riemannian geometry to demonstrate a triangle that has two obtuse angles.

9. On the spherical model of Riemannian geometry, draw $\triangle REI$ with three right angles.

10. Make sketches to show that in Lobachevskian geometry for lines h, k, and n, if h is not parallel to k and n is not parallel to k, h may be parallel to n or h may not be parallel to n.

11. Make sketches to show that in Lobachevskian geometry for lines h, k, and n, if $h \| k$ and $n \| k$, then h may be parallel to n or h may not be parallel to n.

A rectangle is a four-sided plane figure that has four right angles.

12. Explain why rectangles do not exist in Riemannian geometry.

13. Explain why rectangles do not exist in Lobachevskian geometry.

14. Draw a four-sided plane figure with three right angles in Lobachevskian geometry. What type of angle is the fourth angle?

15. Draw a four-sided plane figure with three right angles in Riemannian geometry. What type of angle is the fourth angle?

Using the triangle-sum theorem in Lobachevskian geometry explain why the following are possible:

16. In a right triangle, the sum of the two non-right angles is less than 90°.

17. Each angle of an equiangular triangle is less than 60°.

18. A triangle can have only one right angle or one obtuse angle.

Using the triangle-sum theorem in Riemannian geometry, explain why the following are possible:

19. Each angle of an equiangular triangle is greater than 60°.

20. In a right triangle $\triangle ABC$, if $\angle A$ is a right angle, then $\angle B + \angle C > 90°$.

21. A triangle can have two right angles.

SECTION   3.3

▼

GOLDEN RATIOS AND RECTANGLES

At this point the study of geometry could take various directions. Instead of taking the more traditional route of studying either proofs of theorems or problems involving perimeters, areas, or volumes, in the rest of this chapter we return to Euclidean geometry and study various geometric forms from a more aesthetic point of view. We look at the visual beauty contained in geometric objects and investigate some of the mathematics behind the creation of geometric designs.

Ancient architects, sculptors, and artists used a ratio of distances in their work that they deemed pleasing to the eye. Called the **Golden Ratio**, it is based on the division of a line segment into two parts such that the ratio of the longer piece to the shorter piece is the same as the ratio of the entire line segment to the longer piece. The Greek letter **phi**, ϕ (pronounced fī), was adopted in the early 20th century to represent this ratio because it is the first letter in the name of the Greek sculptor Phidias, who made extensive use of the Golden Ratio in his work.

The Golden Ratio

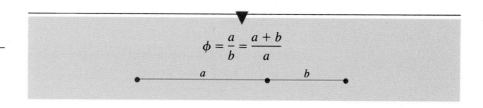

$$\phi = \frac{a}{b} = \frac{a + b}{a}$$

The exact value of the Golden Ratio can be determined by performing some algebraic manipulations on the ratio $a/b = (a + b)/a$. In the derivation that follows, we use the quadratic formula. If you need a review of the quadratic formula, see Section 2.0.

$$\frac{a}{b} = \frac{a + b}{a} \qquad \text{Golden Ratio}$$

$$a^2 = b(a + b) \qquad \text{Cross multiplying}$$

$$a^2 - ba - b^2 = 0 \qquad \begin{array}{l}\text{Subtracting } b(a + b) \\ \text{from both sides}\end{array}$$

$$a = \frac{b \pm \sqrt{b^2 + 4b^2}}{2} \qquad \begin{array}{l}\text{Solving for } a \text{ by the} \\ \text{quadratic formula}\end{array}$$

Therefore,

$$a = \frac{b + b\sqrt{5}}{2} \qquad \begin{array}{l}\text{The length } a \text{ must be} \\ \text{positive.}\end{array}$$

Thus,

$$\frac{a}{b} = \frac{\dfrac{b + b\sqrt{5}}{2}}{b} = \frac{b + b\sqrt{5}}{2}\left(\frac{1}{b}\right)$$

$$\phi = \frac{1 + \sqrt{5}}{2} = 1.618033988 \ldots$$

The Golden Ratio is an irrational number since it contains $\sqrt{5}$. Its decimal representation is a nonterminating, nonrepeating decimal. However, because of errors inherent in measurement and for ease in computation, we will use 1.62 as the value of the Golden Ratio in this chapter.

A **Golden Rectangle** is a rectangle whose sides form a Golden Ratio. The Greeks believed that a rectangle having this ratio was more pleasing to the eye than was any other rectangle. In 1876, the psychologist Gustav Fechner analyzed the responses of many people about which rectangles they found most pleasing. From his research he concluded that people prefer rectangular shapes that are close to Golden Rectangles. Experiments carried out by Witmer (1894), Lalo (1905), and Thorndike (1917) arrived at similar conclusions.

The Golden Rectangle

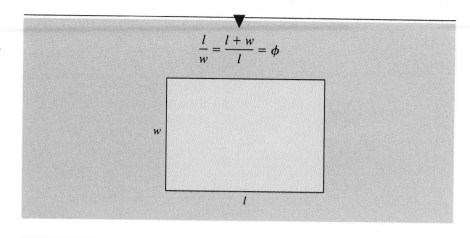

$$\frac{l}{w} = \frac{l+w}{l} = \phi$$

Example 1:

By measuring the rectangles below, determine if they approximate Golden Rectangles.

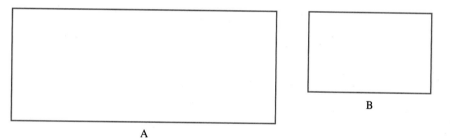

A

B

Solution: Measuring the rectangles, we find the dimensions of rectangle A to be 3 cm and 7 cm, whereas rectangle B has dimensions of 2.1 cm and 3.4 cm. If we take the ratio of the *longer* side to the *shorter* side in each rectangle, we get

A. $7/3 \approx 2.33$, and that is not close to the Golden Ratio of approximately 1.62.

B. $3.4/2.1 \approx 1.62$, which is approximately the same as the Golden Ratio.

Thus, rectangle *A* is not a Golden Rectangle, but rectangle *B* is very close to a Golden Rectangle.

Example 2:

Find a point on $\overline{AB}$ such that $\overline{AB}$ is divided into segments that form a Golden Ratio.

A   B

Solution: Let X be a point that divides $\overline{AB}$ into a Golden Ratio as shown.

According to the Golden Ratio, $a/b = (a + b)/a \approx 1.62$. Since the length of $\overline{AB}$ is 7 cm, $a + b = 7$ and we get

$$\frac{7}{a} \approx 1.62$$

$$1.62a \approx 7$$

$$a \approx 4.3$$

Thus, the point X is 4.3 cm from point A.

The Golden Ratio has an interesting history. Objects that contain Golden Ratios have been studied and admired through the ages. In the rest of this section we investigate some situations in which Golden Ratios occur.

Example 3:

The pentagram, which dates back to ancient Babylonian and Greek cultures, was the mystic symbol and badge of the Society of Pythagoras. The pentagram contains many Golden Ratios. By actual measurement, find two Golden Ratios in the pentagram in Figure 3.3.1.

FIGURE 3.3.1

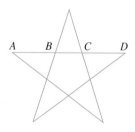

Solution: The ratios of AC to CD and BD to AB are approximately 1.62.

The Golden Ratio can also be found in the measurements of buildings of antiquity such as the Parthenon on the Acropolis in Athens. You can verify that the ratio of the length to the width of the overall dimensions of the Parthenon is approximately a Golden Ratio by measuring the scale drawing of the Parthenon in Figure 3.3.2.

FIGURE 3.3.2

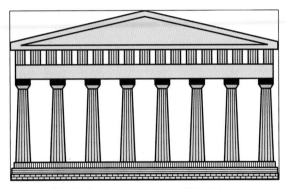

The Parthenon on the Acropolis in Athens

In *Geometry of Art and Life*, the author, Matila Ghyka, shows that the "perfect" human face can be viewed as sequences of Golden Ratios.

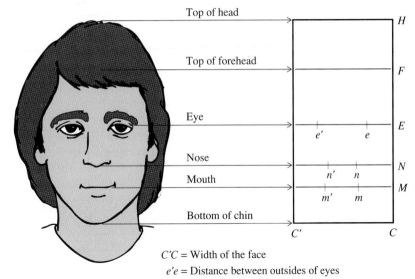

$C'C$ = Width of the face
$e'e$ = Distance between outsides of eyes
$n'n$ = Distance between outsides of nostrils
$m'm$ = Distance between ends of mouth

$$\frac{HC}{C'C} = \frac{HE}{FE} = \frac{EC}{NC} = \phi \qquad \frac{FE}{EN} = \frac{EM}{EN} = \frac{NC}{MC} = \phi \qquad \frac{C'C}{e'e} = \frac{e'e}{m'm} = \frac{m'm}{n'n} = \phi$$

Example 4:

Consider a "perfect" face that measures 2.5 inches between the outside edges of the eyes. How wide and how long is such a face?

Solution: In the figure, $C'C$ represents the width of the face, HC represents the height of the face, and $e'e$ represents the distance between the eyes.

The following Golden Ratios can be used:

$$\frac{C'C}{e'e} = \frac{C'C}{2.5} \approx 1.62 \qquad\qquad C'C \approx 2.5(1.62) \approx 4.05$$

$$\frac{HC}{C'C} = \frac{HC}{4.05} \approx 1.62 \qquad\qquad HC \approx 4.05(1.62) \approx 6.56$$

Thus, such a face has a width of about 4 inches and a height of little more than $6\frac{1}{2}$ inches. ▨

Leonardo Fibonacci (c. 1200) studied sequences of numbers in which each successive number is the sum of the two previous numbers, 1, 1, 2, 3, 5, 8, 13, 21, 34, 55 . . . . In 1877, Edward Lucas named that sequence of numbers the **Fibonacci numbers**. This sequence has the unique property that the ratio of successive terms gets close to the Golden Ratio.

$$\frac{1}{1} = 1 \qquad\qquad \frac{2}{1} = 2 \qquad\qquad \frac{3}{2} = 1.5$$

$$\frac{5}{3} \approx 1.6666667 \qquad\qquad \frac{8}{5} = 1.6 \qquad\qquad \frac{13}{8} = 1.625$$

$$\frac{21}{13} \approx 1.6153846 \qquad\qquad \frac{34}{21} \approx 1.6190476 \qquad\qquad \frac{55}{34} \approx 1.6176470\ldots$$

Example 5:

Find the ratio of the 15th and 16th Fibonacci numbers. How does this ratio compare to the Golden Ratio?

Solution: The 15th Fibonacci number is 610, and the 16th is 987; $987/610 \approx 1.6180327$. The first six digits of that ratio match those of the Golden Ratio. ▨

The Golden Ratio was referred to by various names over the centuries. Luca Pacioli called it *divina proportione* (divine proportion) in 1509. Johann Kepler called it *sectio divina* (divine section) in 1610. The term ''Golden Ratio'' or ''Golden Section'' came into use around 1840. The Golden Ratio has stimulated mathematical interest for centuries and is still of interest to designers, botanists, sculptors, composers, and artists. The work of artists Georges Seurat, Piet Mondrian, and Juan Gris and some musical compositions by Bela Bartok utilize the Golden Ratio.

We end this section with a beautiful mathematical curve. It is known as the logarithmic spiral and is created by curves formed within Golden Rectangles. The spiral has no ending point. It grows outward or inward indefinitely, but its shape remains unchanged. In nature this spiral can be seen in the successive chambers of the nautilus sea shell.

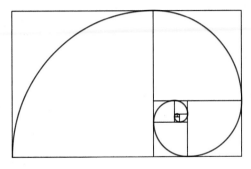

Logarithmic spiral

Nautilus seashell

SECTION 3.3
PROBLEMS

1. Are Golden Rectangles really more pleasing to the eye? To help answer this question, do the following:

   (a) On separate cards cut out rectangles that are 1 by 5 cm, 2 by 5 cm, 3 by 5 cm, 4 by 5 cm, and 5 by 5 cm.
   (b) Place the cards in a random order and ask ten people to select the rectangle that they find the most pleasing or attractive.
   (c) Tabulate your results and calculate the percentage of the people choosing each rectangle.
   (d) Use your results to answer the question posed at the beginning of the problem.

   Note: The 3-by-5-cm rectangle is approximately a Golden Rectangle.

2. Consider a parallelogram whose sides form a Golden Ratio (i.e., 3 by 5 cm). The shape of the parallelogram is determined by the angle between two adjacent sides as shown below.

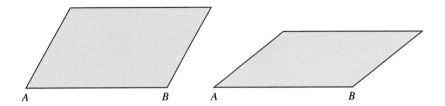

To make the parallelogram even more "golden," let us also make the ratio of the measures of $\angle A$ to $\angle B$ approximately a Golden Ratio. Such a parallelogram would have $\angle A \approx 69°$ and $\angle B \approx 111°$. Is such a "Golden Parallelogram" more pleasing to the eye than other parallelograms? Construct an experiment to answer that question. (See Problem 1.)

Find a point that approximately divides each segment into a Golden Ratio.

3. _____

4. _____

5. _____

6. _____

Determine which of the following rectangles are approximately Golden Rectangles.

7.

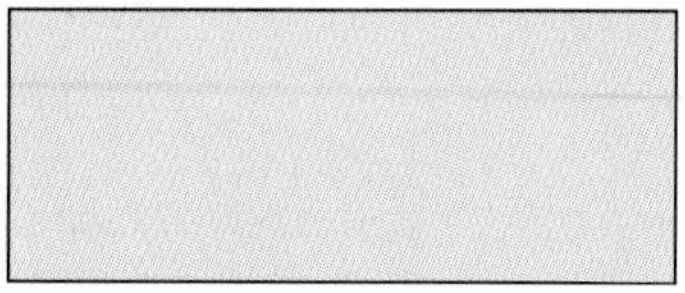

8.

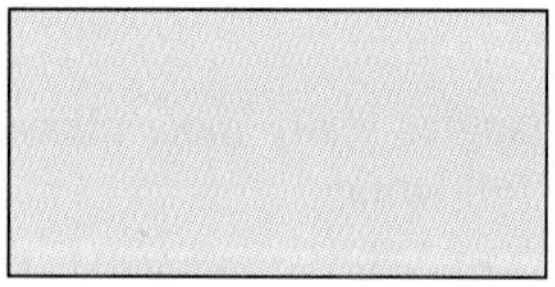

9.

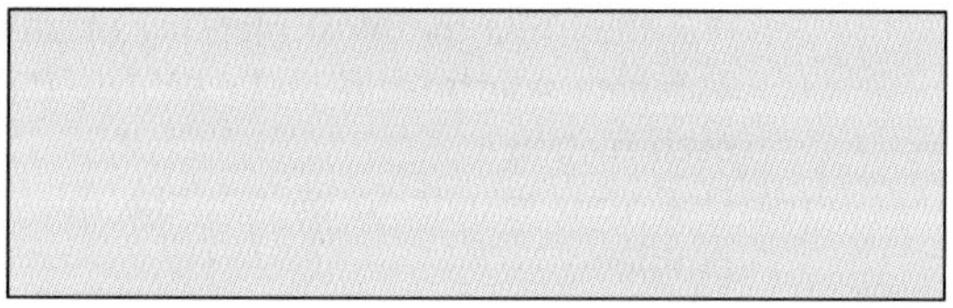

10.

In Problems 11–14, one dimension of a Golden Rectangle is given. Find the two possible values for the other dimension of the Golden Rectangle.

11. 23 ft   **12.** 4.5 mi   **13.** 56.8 m   **14.** 45.5 cm

15. By finding the ratio of the length to the width of ten common rectangular-shaped objects, such as boxes, cards, cushions, doors, appliances, windows, and the like, determine which objects approximate Golden Rectangles and which objects do not approximate Golden Rectangles. Find the average of the ten ratios. How does your result compare to that of psychologist Gustav Fechner, who concluded that the average of the ratios of the sides of common rectangles was approximately the Golden Ratio? Since Golden Rectangles are supposed to be the most pleasing to the eye, why aren't all manufactured rectangular objects Golden Rectangles?

16. A "Golden Can" could be defined as a can that has its height greater than its diameter, where the ratio of its height to its diameter is equal to the Golden Ratio. Measure ten cans of different sizes. Which ones approximate the Golden Ratio, and which do not? Find the average of the ten ratios. How does this average compare to the Golden Ratio? Since the Golden Ratio is supposed to be the most pleasing to the eye, why aren't all cans "Golden Cans"?

17. Do a study of the ratios within the human face shown in Example 4. By analyzing at least two faces or pictures of faces, what can you conclude about the ratios or the average of the ratios?

18. The architect Le Corbusier (c. 1940) developed the *Modular* system of harmonious proportions. In this system, he established that in the visually "perfect" human form,

    (a) The ratio of distance from the bottom of the neck to the navel to the distance from the top of the head to the bottom of the neck is a Golden Ratio.

    (b) The ratio of the distance from the navel to the knee to the distance from the knee to the bottom of the foot is a Golden Ratio.

    Measure people or pictures of people to determine if and when these ratios are golden. Do the average of the ratios you found approximate the Golden Ratio?

19. Psychologist Gustav Fechner, in 1876, also did experiments with ellipses that had the ratio of the length of its major axis to the length of its minor axis approximately equal to the Golden Ratio. Again, he discovered that people found that ellipses close to "Golden Ellipses" were more pleasing to the eye. Use the ellipses shown to test Fechner's findings in present society. (Note: The first ellipse is the "Golden Ellipse.")

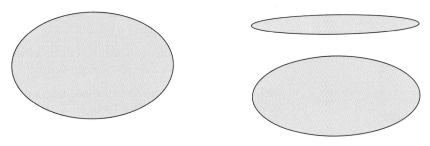

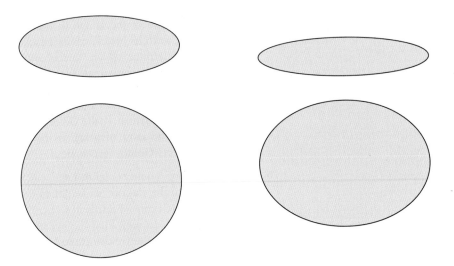

We can define a "Golden Box" as one whose height, width, and length satisfy the Golden Ratio. We are assuming here that the height is the shortest dimension and the length is the longest dimension of the box.

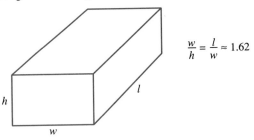

$$\frac{w}{h} = \frac{l}{w} \approx 1.62$$

In Problems 20–25, one dimension of a "Golden Box" is given. Find the dimensions that are not given.

20. $h = 5$ inches

21. $w = 5$ inches

22. $l = 5$ inches

23. $h = 9$ cm

24. $w = 9$ cm

25. $l = 9$ cm

26. Construct a "Golden Box" that has a height of 3 inches.

27. Measure various boxes. Do they form "Golden Boxes," as defined? Find the average of the heights, widths, and lengths of the boxes. Is the ratio of these averages approximately a Golden Ratio?

28. Explain why three consecutive Fibonacci numbers can be used to give approximate dimensions of "Golden Boxes".

*29. Do some research to find a method that determines the exact point that divides a segment into a Golden Ratio.

*30. In Problem 2, find the exact value for $\angle A$ so that the ratio of $\angle A$ to $\angle B$ is a

Golden Ratio. (*Hint*: Use the fact that $\angle A + \angle B = 180°$, and ratio of $\angle B$ to $\angle A$ is $(1 + \sqrt{5})/2$.)

*31. The Golden Ratio ϕ is the only positive number that if decreased by 1 equals its reciprocal. Show algebraically that $\phi - 1 = 1/\phi$.

*32. In Example 5, we showed that the ratio of terms in the Fibonacci sequence approaches the Golden Ratio. Consider any sequence in which we choose any two starting numbers and generate the terms of the sequence by adding two consecutive numbers as in the Fibonacci sequence. For example, if we chose 5 and 2 as the starting numbers, the sequence would be 5, 2, 7, 9, 16, 25, 41, 66, ... Examine the ratio of the terms of any such sequence, as we did for the Fibonacci sequence in Example 5. What do you notice about successive ratios of terms?

*33. Do some research on the occurrence of Fibonacci numbers in nature.

Works of modern artisans employing polygons and stars. (*Left*) Nautical Stars pieced quilt by Judy Mathieson. (*Right*) Ukrainian Easter eggs (Pysanky) by Nancy Eddinger. (Courtesy of the artists)

SECTION 3.4

▼

POLYGONS AND STARS

The Golden Rectangle is just one type of a class of geometric objects called polygons. Polygons and their properties are carefully examined in most treatments of geometry. Instead of doing that in this section, we will spend most of our efforts investigating how polygons can be used to create some interesting geometric designs. A **polygon** is a closed figure in a plane formed by line segments that intersect each other only at their end points. The following are examples of polygons.

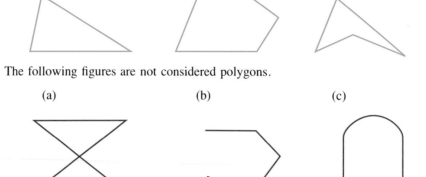

The following figures are not considered polygons.

(a)   (b)   (c)

Example 1:

Explain why each of the figures shown is not a polygon.

Solution: Each figure has a property that contradicts the definition of a polygon.
   (a) The sides intersect at a point other than at the end points.
   (b) It is not a closed figure.
   (c) The top is a curve, not a line segment.

The line segments that form a polygon are called its **sides**, and the points at which the sides meet are called **vertices** (plural of ''vertex''). Polygons are named by the number of sides they contain. Specific names are given to polygons with from 3 to 12 sides. Other polygons are usually referred to as *n*-gons, where *n* represents the number of sides in the polygon. For example, a polygon with 13 sides is called a 13-gon. The following is a list of the first ten polygons and their names.

Number of Sides	Name	I	II	III
3	Triangle			
4	Quadrilateral			

Number of Sides	Name	I	II	III
5	Pentagon			
6	Hexagon			
7	Heptagon			
8	Octagon			
9	Nonagon			
10	Decagon			
11	Undecagon			
12	Dodecagon			

Polygons are classified as concave or convex. A polygon is **concave** if an extension of one of its sides enters the interior of the polygon; a polygon is **convex** if the extensions of its sides do not enter the interior of the polygon. In the previous list, the polygons in column III are concave polygons, and those in columns I and II are convex polygons. Some polygons are classified as **regular polygons**. These polygons have sides of equal length and angles of equal measure. Column I in the previous list contains regular polygons. Some common objects with shapes that are regular polygons are pizza boxes, stop signs, and honeycombs.

Example 2:

In each figure, (a) give its name and classify it as concave or convex and (b) determine if it is a regular polygon.

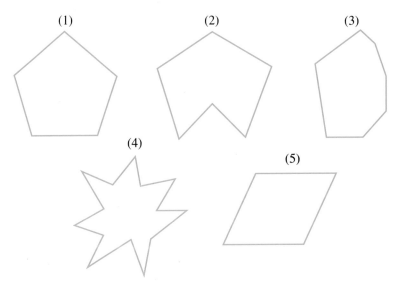

Solution:

(a) (1) Pentagon, convex
    (2) Hexagon, concave
    (3) Heptagon, convex
    (4) 14-gon, concave
    (5) Quadrilateral, convex

For example, Figure 2 is concave since the extension of the side $\overline{AB}$ enters the interior of the hexagon.

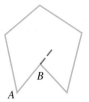

(b) The only regular polygon is Figure 1. Figure 5 is not a regular polygon because its angles are not of equal measure.

We could at this point examine the mathematics of a polygon, such as the sum of its interior angles, the measure of each angle of a regular polygon, or the number of diagonals of a polygon. We will, however, leave that excursion as a research exercise at the end of the section. Instead, we investigate methods for actually drawing polygons and creating designs based on them. Polygons have probably been admired and studied since prehistoric times. These shapes are present in almost every object made by man. The simple beauty and completeness of polygons, especially regular polygons, have stimulated many creative designs over the centuries. Designs using polygons can be found in religious symbols such as the Star of David; in logos such as the pentagon emblem of the Chrysler Corporation; in modern quilts, flooring, and wallpaper; and on wheel covers of cars and trucks. We are confident that this excursion into geometry will enable even the "unartistic" to create some beautiful results.

Drawing Regular Polygons

If you study the regular polygons shown earlier in this section, you will notice that the vertices are equally spaced and that, as the number of sides increases, the regular polygon appears to be more and more like a circle. This suggests a method for actually creating regular polygons.

For example, to draw a regular pentagon, all we need to do is find five equally spaced points on a circle and use those points as vertices of the regular pentagon. We will use the fact that if a ray with its end point at the center of a circle rotates completely around the circle like the second hand of a clock, it passes through 360°. Therefore, to create five equally spaced points on the circle, we simply divide 5 into 360. If we take the answer, 72, and mark off five angles at the center of the circle (central angles) of 72°, we can find the desired points on the circle to use as vertices of the regular pentagon.

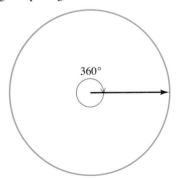

Let's actually draw a regular pentagon. With a compass, draw a large circle. Using a protractor, measure five 72° angles at the center of the circle. Extend the angles until they intersect the circle. Connect the five points marked on the circle in order to form the pentagon.

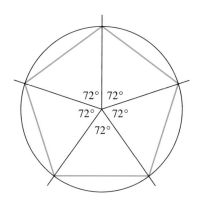

Example 3:

Draw a regular octagon.

Solution: Using the method described in the creation of the pentagon, we should mark off eight central angles of 45° each, since 360 ÷ 8 = 45.

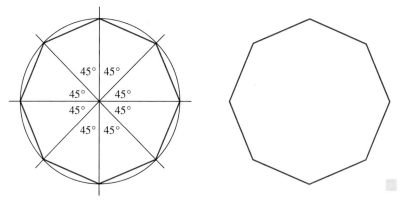

Finding equally spaced points on a circle can also be used to create some interesting geometric "stars." Consider seven equally spaced points on a circle obtained by marking off seven central angles of approximately 51.4° (360 ÷ 7 ≈ 51.423). Instead of connecting each point in order to create a regular heptagon, connect every second point or every third point.

Connecting consecutive points   Connecting every second point   Connecting every third point

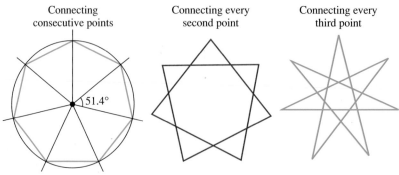

Example 4:

Draw a 12-point star by connecting every fifth point of a regular dodecagon.

Solution: Find 12 equally spaced points on a circle by marking off 12 central angles of 30° (360 ÷ 12 = 30).

Mark off each 30° central angle.   Connect every fifth point.

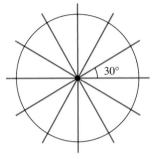

The process of locating equally spaced points on a circle can be used to create regular polygons and a variety of symmetrical stars. That technique combined with others such as those listed below can be used to create some interesting geometric designs.

1. Construct stars using points on a circle that are not equally spaced.
2. Create the illusion of curved lines by marking off equally spaced points on both sides of an angle and systematically connecting points on one side of the angle to points on the opposite side.

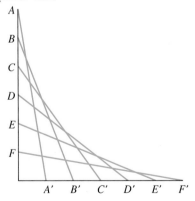

3. Use different colors to systematically shade various regions of the star.
4. Combine different polygons and stars along with various lines in the same design.

The results of experimenting with these and other techniques can produce surprising results. Don't be afraid to let your creative juices flow. Geometry can be beautiful. What follows is an example of a geometric design using some of those techniques.

SECTION 3.4

PROBLEMS

Explain why each of the following is not a polygon.

1.

2.

3.

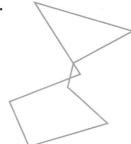

4.

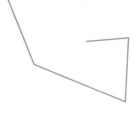

Give the name for the following polygons and classify them as concave or convex.

5.

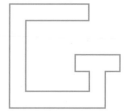

6.

7. 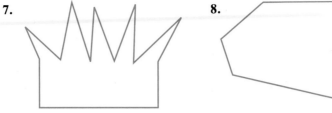   **8.**

Sketch the following polygons.

9. (a) Concave and
   (b) convex 13-gon

10. (a) Concave and
   (b) convex undecagon

11. (a) Concave and
   (b) convex decagon

12. (a) Concave and
   (b) convex dodecagon

13. Complete the following chart to determine the central angle needed to find equally spaced points of a circle.

Number of Points	Central Angle	Number of Points	Central Angle
5	_____	13	_____
6	_____	14	_____
7	_____	15	_____
8	_____	16	_____
9	_____	18	_____
10	_____	20	_____
11	_____	30	_____
12	_____	36	_____

Draw the following regular polygons.

14. Nonagon

15. Octagon

16. 18-gon

17. 20-gon

18. Undecagon

19. 14-gon

Draw the following regular stars.

20. A 12-point star connecting every third point

21. A 12-point star connecting every fourth point

22. A 15-point star connecting every third point

23. A 15-point star connecting every sixth point

24. A 20-point star connecting every ninth point

25. Create an original geometric design using a combination of any techniques suggested in this section.

26. Designs for wheel covers on cars and trucks can be created by using the techniques discussed in this section. Use these techniques to design your own wheel cover.

27. The designs of many wheel covers on cars and trucks use the techniques discussed in this section. Examine and sketch the designs of three different wheel covers, noting the make and model of the vehicle.

*28. What are the formulas used to find the sum of the angles of a polygon, each interior angle of a regular polygon, and the number of diagonals of a polygon? Show how the formulas can be applied to a 30-gon.

*29. What are polyhedra? What are the Platonic solids? What does Euler's formula tell us about polyhedra?

Lithographs by Rick Dula showing the natural tessellation of a cracking street and the manmade tessellation of cobblestones. (Courtesy of Magnolia Editions)

SECTION 3.5

▼

TESSELLATIONS

The study of polygons in the previous section enabled us to create various geometric designs based on placing equally spaced points on a circle. In this section we investigate combining polygons into geometric patterns called tessellations. The word "tessellation" comes from the Latin word *tessella*, which is a small square tile used in Roman mosaics. A **tessellation** is a pattern of one or more congruent shapes that cover an area in a plane without overlapping or leaving any gaps. A

FIGURE 3.5.1

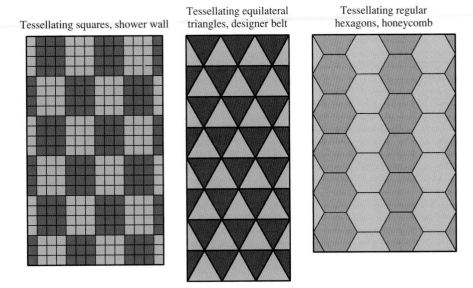

Tessellating squares, shower wall

Tessellating equilateral triangles, designer belt

Tessellating regular hexagons, honeycomb

tessellation actually covers the entire plane if its basic pattern is continued in all directions. However, we will only be concerned with using tessellations to cover a small region in the plane. Simple tessellations or tilings are very common. They can be seen, for example, on walls, on clothing, in beehives, or in works of art (Fig. 3.5.1).

Tessellating "chickens"

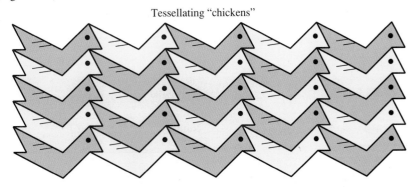

Tesselations were used on window lattices in China; on painted ceilings in Egypt; on the mosques in Granada, Spain; on textile and basket patterns of the native peoples of Peru, India, Ghana, Zaire, America, Mexico, and other countries; and in the decorative arts of the ancient Greeks, Romans, Arabs, Japanese, Persians, and Celts. Tessellations can be observed in nature in the cells of an onion skin, in the design of a spider's web, or in the arrangement of seeds in a sunflower. Tessellations can be seen in our modern society as designs on wallpaper, linoleum, parquet flooring, ceramic tiles, patchwork quilts, crocheted placemats, and lace tablecloths. Tessellations have been made popular by the work of Dutch artist M. C. Escher. Inspired by the ornamental art of the Moors, he created intriguing designs that truly integrate mathematics and art. Tessellations can also be seen in the work of modern kinetic and optical artists such as Bridget Riley and Victor Vasarely and in the intricate tilings of Heinz Voderberg and Roger Penrose. In this section we introduce some of the principles and methods of creating basic tessellations.

Tessellating with a Regular Polygon

The only regular polygons that tessellate the plane are the equilateral triangle, the square, and the regular hexagon, as shown in Figure 3.5.1. Any of the other regular polygons would overlap at a vertex and therefore not tessellate the plane.

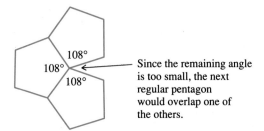

Since the remaining angle is too small, the next regular pentagon would overlap one of the others.

For example, if regular pentagons were placed around one vertex, as shown in the figure, overlapping would occur by the fourth regular pentagon. A similar situation occurs for any other regular polygon with the number of sides other than 3, 4, or 6. Table 3.5.1 will be helpful in verifying that fact. Its proof is given as a starred exercise in this section's problem set.

TABLE 3.5.1   **Regular Polygons**

Number of Sides	Measure of Each Angle	Number of Sides	Measure of Each Angle
3	60 °	11	$147\frac{3}{11}$°
4	90 °	12	150 °
5	108 °	15	156 °
6	120 °	18	160 °
7	$128\frac{4}{7}$°	20	162 °
8	135 °	24	165 °
9	140 °	36	170 °
10	144 °	42	$171\frac{3}{7}$°

Example 1:

Show that it is not possible to tessellate the plane with regular octagons.

Solution:

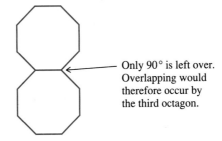

Only 90° is left over.
Overlapping would
therefore occur by
the third octagon.

Since each angle of an octagon is 135°, two octagons placed at the same vertex would have an angle sum of 270°. That would leave 90° around the vertex. Thus, overlapping would occur if another octagon was placed at that vertex.

Tessellating with a Triangle or Quadrilateral

We have seen that only three regular polygons tile the plane. If we allow the use of nonregular polygons, any triangle or quadrilateral can tessellate the plane. The basis for this is the fact that in order to tessellate the plane, there must be no overlapping of polygons and no gaps left by the polygons. Overlapping occurs when the sum of the angles placed around a vertex is greater than 360°, and gaps occur when the sum is less than 360°. Since the sum of the angles of a triangle is 180° and the sum of the angles of a quadrilateral is 360°, as explained in Problem 9 of Section 2.1, triangles and quadrilaterals can be placed around a vertex so that the sum of the angles is exactly 360°. In the case of the triangle, we need to use each angle of the triangle twice. In the case of the quadrilateral, we need to use each angle only once around a vertex.

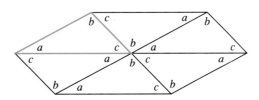

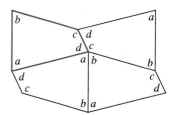

Around the vertex at the center of the figure the three angles of the triangle appear twice. Since $a + b + c = 180°$, the sum of the six angles is exactly 360° and no overlapping occurs.

Around the vertex at the center of the figure the four angles of the quadrilateral appear. Since $a + b + c + d = 360°$, no overlapping occurs.

By actually tessellating the plane with different triangles and quadrilaterals, you will be convinced that any triangle or quadrilateral tessellates the plane by itself.

Example 2:

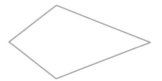

Arrange the angles of the kite-shaped quadrilateral in the figure so that four of them can be placed around a vertex without overlapping each other.

Solution:

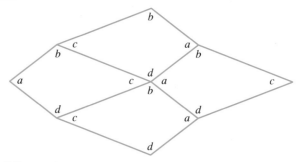

By sliding and turning over the quadrilateral, we can arrange four of them around one vertex as shown.

You are probably wondering how one actually tessellates an area with a triangle or quadrilateral. This process, as you may have guessed, requires some mathematical operations that move geometric figures, translations and reflections.

Translations	Reflections
The triangle is translated a distance that is equal to each of its sides in the direction of each side.	**The triangle is reflected across one of its sides, across a horizontal line, and across a vertical line.**

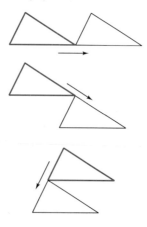

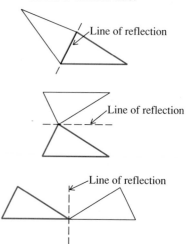

A **translation** slides an object a certain distance in a certain direction. A **reflection** gives the mirror image of an object across a certain line called the line of reflection. A reflection has the effect of turning an object over and placing it on the opposite side of its line of reflection.

Tessellations of a triangle can be formed by using translations or a combination of reflections and translations. Let us examine both methods.

Tessellating a Triangle Using Translations

To tessellate an area with a triangle, we can translate the triangle in the direction of two sides of the triangle a distance that is equal to the sides of the triangle. The tessellation in the figure can be created by repeatedly using two translations.

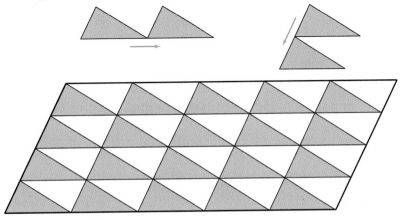

The details of actually creating the tessellation are as follows:

1. Create a primary line of triangles by repeatedly translating the original triangle in the direction of one of the sides of the triangle.

2. Using each triangle in that primary line repeatedly translate in the direction of another side of the triangle.

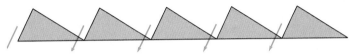

3. Connect any missing lines and the tessellation will be complete. You will notice that in the process blank spaces created half of the triangles.

Example 3:

Using the method shown in the previous example, create a tessellation with the triangle in the figure.

Solution: We can tessellate with the triangle by translating the triangle in the two directions shown.

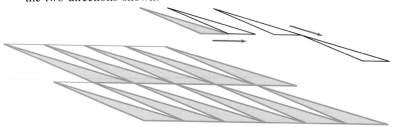

Tessellating a Triangle by Using Translations and a Reflection

A second method of tessellating an area using a triangle involves translations and a reflection. The steps for creating such a tessellation from $\triangle ABC$ are as follows:

1. Reflect the triangle $\triangle ABC$ across line AC, forming quadrilateral $ABCB'$.

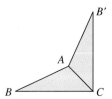

2. Use translations of quadrilateral $ABCB'$ in the direction of its diagonals $\overline{AC}$ and $\overline{BB'}$ as shown.

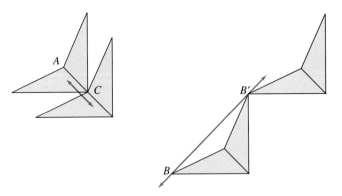

3. Create a primary line of quadrilaterals using the first translation, and then translate each of those quadrilaterals using the second translation. The blank spaces will form quadrilaterals tessellating in a direction opposite to that of ray AC. Create a primary line of quadrilaterals by reflecting quadrilateral $ABCB'$ as shown. (See the left figure on the next page.) Reflect each quadrilateral in the primary line in the direction of the other diagonals shown. (See the right figure on the next page.)

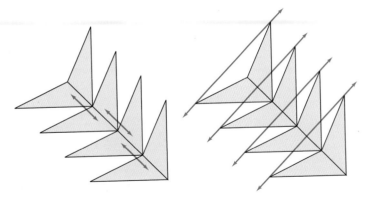

The result of reflecting the original triangle and then translating the resulting quadrilateral will produce a different tessellation than was previously created by using just translations.

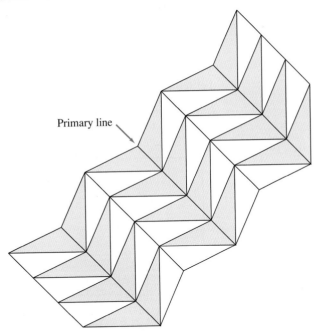

Primary line

This method will also make it possible to tessellate the plane with any quadrilateral. All you need to do is translate the quadrilateral in the direction of its diagonals.

Example 4:

Tessellate an area with the quadrilateral shown.

Solution: To tessellate the plane with the quadrilateral, repeatedly translate the quadrilateral in the direction of both diagonals as shown.

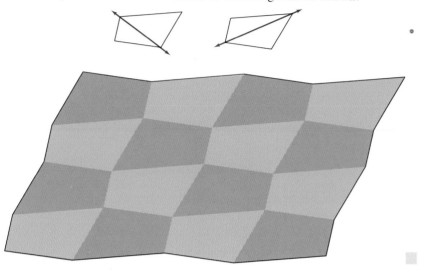

Tessellating with Other Polygons

It is possible to tessellate the plane with certain pentagons and hexagons, but it is impossible to tessellate the plane with single polygons that have more than six sides. Some examples of tessellating pentagons and hexagons follow.

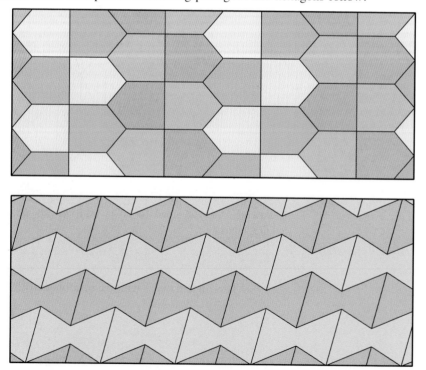

Tessellating with More than One Polygon

The plane can also be tessellated with more than one polygon. There are a multitude of ways to tessellate an area by using nonregular polygons, but there are only 21 possible tessellations using combinations of regular polygons. Remember that for polygons to tessellate the plane, the sum of the angles at any vertex must be exactly 360°. Table 3.5.1, which lists the size of each angle of a regular polygon, will be helpful in determining which combination of regular polygons can be used to tessellate the plane. The tessellations that follow are examples of using more than one polygon to tile the plane.

Example 5:

Explain why it is possible to tessellate a plane by using two regular octagons and one square at each vertex.

Solution: The measure of an angle of a regular octagon is 135°, and the measure of an angle of a square is 90°. The sum of the angles at one vertex of two octagons and a square is 360° (135 + 135 + 90 = 360). With such a sum there will be no overlapping of polygons.

The next tessellation has two regular octagons and one square at each vertex.

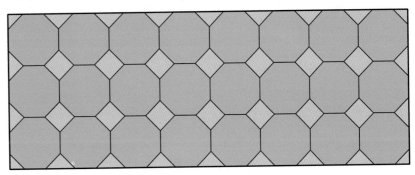

The ways to tessellate the plane with polygons is endless. This section has presented some basic tessellation principles. There is much more to be learned about techniques used in generating other types of tessellations and using tessellations to create Escher-like designs. The purpose of this section was simply to give you a taste of the many possibilities in this area of mathematics. We end this section with two tessellations. The first incorporates stars into a tessellation, and the second shows how simple modifications of a basic tessellation (regular hexagons) can produce some interesting results.

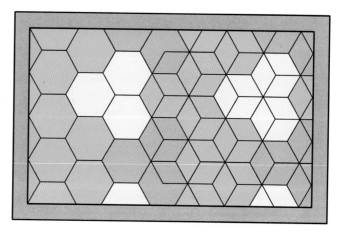

SECTION 3.5

PROBLEMS

1. What is a tessellation?

2. Which three regular polygons can tessellate the plane?

3. Show why it is impossible to tessellate the plane with regular nonagons.

4. Show why it is impossible to tessellate the plane with regular decagons.

In Problems 5–8, tessellate a region with the triangles shown, using only translations.

5.

6.

7.  **8.**

In Problems 9–12, tessellate a region with the triangles shown, using a reflection and translations.

9. 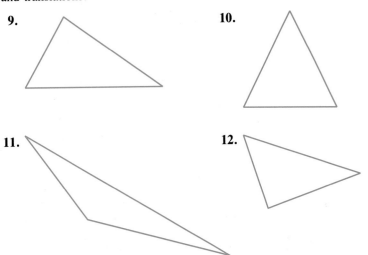 **10.**

11. **12.**

In Problems 13–16, tessellate a region with the quadrilaterals shown.

13. 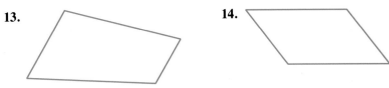 **14.**

15. 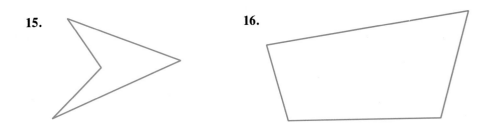 **16.**

17. Explain why it is impossible to tessellate a plane with the following regular polygons located at one vertex: one regular hexagon, one regular pentagon, and one square.

18. Explain why it is impossible to tessellate a plane with the following regular polygons located at one vertex: two dodecagons and one octagon.

19. There are 21 possible combinations of regular polygons that can be placed around a vertex to tessellate the plane. Find at least ten of these combinations. (*Hint:* The sum of the angles around a vertex must be 360°.)

20. Draw sketches of the polygons for the combinations found in Problem 19.

21. Tessellate a region with two regular hexagons and two equilateral triangles at each vertex.

22. Tessellate a region with one regular hexagon, two squares, and one equilateral triangle at each vertex.

23. Using the principles and techniques of the last two sections, create your own tessellation.

*24. Using the fact that each angle (*A*) of a regular polygon can be found by the formula

$$A = \frac{180(n - 2)}{n} \qquad \text{where } n \text{ is the number of sides of a regular polygon}$$

prove that the only regular polygons that tessellate the plane by themselves are the equilateral triangle, square, and regular hexaon. (*Hint:* Work with the expression for 360/*A*.)

*25. Do some research on the methods of creating tessellations and Escher-like designs. Using the information, draw some tessellations.

*26. Do some research on the tessellations associated with the Moslems and the Alhambra in Spain.

(*Left*) A magnified photograph of a resin cast of the airways to the lung (courtesy of C. Quesada). (*Right*) A computer-generated fractal created by Yoichiro Kawaguchi (courtesy of Y. Kawaguchi).

SECTION   3.6

▼

FRACTALS

Since the time of the ancient civilizations, geometry has been used to measure and describe the world in which we live. We have come to believe that much of world can be described by the basic shapes of geometry. Scientists have discovered that the planets and stars are in the shape of spheres and that curved paths such as roads can be measured with straight-line segments. They have also shown that a parabola can be used to describe the path of a thrown object and that the orbits of the planets are elliptical.

As science has progressed, new discoveries have demonstrated that many of our early ideas about using simple geometric shapes to describe natural phenomena are only partially true. The earth is not really a sphere. It bulges along the equator. In addition, although the surface of a sphere is smooth, the surface of the earth is dimpled with craters, canyons, and oceans and has rolling hills and towering mountains jutting from its surface. The simple geometrical models of our predecessors do not accurately describe a world that has since been more carefully observed.

In addition to reexamining old models, scientists are taking a look at phenomena that were previously considered too complex to be described by mathematics. Why are ferns constructed the way they are? Is there a pattern to the branching designs of oak leaves? In an oil spill, what determines the depth to which the oil penetrates the surface? How can the static of a radio transmission be described mathematically? Is there a way to describe the fluctuations of cotton prices over the last 100 years? These phenomena are too complex for the simple geometric models of earlier times. As with the imperfect surface of the earth, a new geometry is needed to accurately describe these details.

Through the use of computers, in the 1970s and 1980s we have seen the arrival of a new area of mathematics called **fractal geometry**. This geometry can model the complex situations mentioned above. The word "*fractal*," coined by the mathematician Benoit Mandelbrot, comes from the same Latin root as does the word "*fraction.*" Mandelbrot uses this term because simple one-, two-, and three-dimensional figures like lines, squares, and spheres cannot describe complex phenomenon. To do so requires objects that have **fractional dimension**. In this section, we give a short history of fractals, describe what is meant by a fractional dimension, describe how fractals can be drawn, and show some examples of one of the most famous fractal sets, the Mandelbrot set.

History

The 19th century was a time when new ideas extended mathematics outside the realm of the observed physical world. Mathematicians such as Georg Cantor, Giuseppe Peano, and David Hilbert used ideas that were at the frontiers of mathematical thought. One such idea was to have a "curve" (a path with length but no thickness) fill a two-dimensional area. One such curve, called Hilbert's curve, has its first four generations shown here.

In each drawing, the boldface curve wraps around the previous generation of the curve, shown in the thinner line. There are two things to notice. First, the basic shape remains the same in each drawing. As the pictures become more detailed, the basic shape is simply drawn at a finer scale. Second, the amount of white space in each drawing is being reduced. Hilbert's remarkable curve eventually fills the entire space!

A question arising from the concept of space-filling curves led to a discovery that became a critical part of Mandelbrot's fractional dimensions. If a curve is a one-dimensional object having length but no thickness, and a square is a two-dimensional object having both length and width, what is the dimension of a space-filling curve? Since it is a curve, it should be a one-dimensional object. However, it fills the two-dimensional space of a square. In 1919, two mathematicians, Felix Hausdorff and A. S. Besicovitch, published a work that answered this question. A space-filling curve has a dimension that is between 1 and 2, with the dimension approaching 2 as the complexity of the curve increases.

A second major factor that influenced Mandelbrot in the development of fractals was the work on iteration of functions* and complex numbers[†] by the French mathematicians Pierre Fatou and Gaston Julia. Their work, along with the availability of the computer, enabled Mandelbrot to make many of his discoveries.

Constructing Snowflakes, Carpets, and Other Fractals

To construct a fractal, we start with a geometric figure and divide it into smaller versions of itself. We then replace some of the smaller versions, as specified by the rule that generates the fractal. First let's look at a few interesting figures from fractal geometry.

The von Koch Snowflake

The von Koch snowflake is constructed by starting with the line segments forming an equilateral triangle, dividing each of the line segments into three equal sections, and replacing the middle section of each segment by two additional sections. Shown here are the first three iterations of this process. If we start with a line segment, the second figure is constructed from four line segments whose lengths are one-third the length of the original line segment. As we repeat this process, notice that all four of the segments of the second diagram have been used to form the third diagram.

Since the initial step in the construction of the von Koch snowflake is to start with an equilateral triangle, we must perform this process on each of the original sides. Doing this on each side of the triangle creates a six-pointed star.

---

*When a function is iterated, it is used repeatedly. For example, suppose we are using the function $f(x) = \sqrt{x}$. If we pick a number, let's say 10, we want to know what happens when the number is put into the function, and that result is in turn put into the function and the process is continued for some time. With our example, $\sqrt{10} \approx 3.1623$, $\sqrt{3.1623} \approx 1.7783$, $\sqrt{1.7783} \approx 1.3335$, etc.

†Complex numbers are of the form $a + bi$, where a and b are real numbers and $i = \sqrt{-1}$.

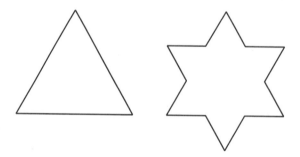

If we repeat this process for each of the 12 sides of the six-pointed star, we obtain a star with 18 points. This, in turn, gives us a 66-point star.

Note

Be sure to notice that the new points are constructed on each segment of the previous diagram.

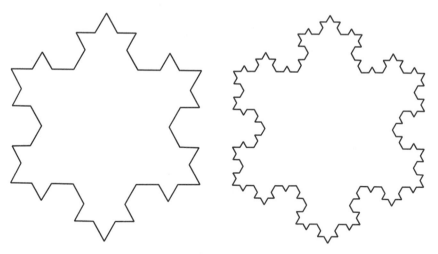

If we continue this process, we arrive at the next two iterations of the von Koch snowflake.

Example 1:

A fractal whose first two iterations are shown in Figures 3.6.1 and 3.6.2 is constructed by dividing each line segment into five equal segments and replacing the middle segment by three new segments, one-fifth the length of the original segment. Draw the next iteration of the fractal.

Solution: In order to construct the next iteration of the fractal, we need to understand the basic construction process. This consists of dividing each line segment into five equal-length sections and constructing a new three-sided figure to replace the middle of the five sections. This must be done for each line segment in the figure. Therefore, starting with one side of Figure 3.6.2, we have the next iteration given in Figure 3.6.3.

FIGURE 3.6.1

FIGURE 3.6.2

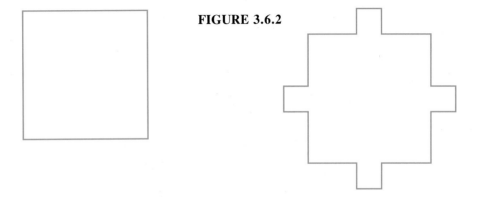

FIGURE 3.6.3

FIGURE 3.6.4

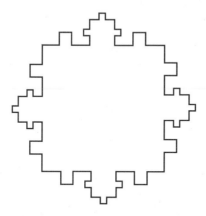

By applying this process to each side of Fig. 3.6.2, we have the third generation of the fractal shown in Fig. 3.6.4.

The Sierpinski Carpet

With the von Koch snowflake and the fractal shown in Example 1, the construction of the fractal was done by working with line segments. The following fractal is created by working with a two-dimensional object, a square. As shown in Fig. 3.6.5, the basic step of the construction is to start with a square, divide it into nine smaller squares of equal size, and remove the center square.

The Sierpinski carpet is shown in Fig. 3.6.6. Starting with a square, it uses the process described above to create a plane region with progressively smaller holes.

FIGURE 3.6.5

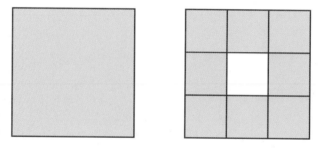

FIGURE 3.6.6

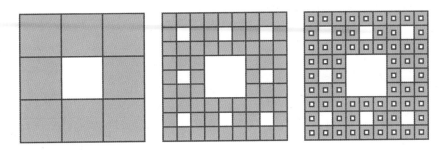

Dimension and Fractals

The formula for the dimension of a fractal is

**The Dimension
of a Fractal**

$$d = \frac{\log N}{\log (1/r)}$$

where

r = ratio of the length of the new object to the length of the original object

N = the number of new objects

Using this formula, we can determine the dimension of the fractals given in the foregoing examples.

Example 2:

Find the dimension of the von Koch snowflake.

Solution: To determine the dimension of the von Koch snowflake, we need to examine the basic construction process, the change that occurs in one step of the construction.

Since each line segment is divided into three equal sections, $r = 1/3$. Because the construction step involves replacing the middle of the three sections by two new sections, the new figure consists of four segments (each of which has a length that is one-third the length of the original

segment); therefore we have $N = 4$. Using the dimension formula gives the dimension of the von Koch snowflake as

$$d = \frac{\log N}{\log (1/r)} = \frac{\log 4}{\log \left(\dfrac{1}{1/3}\right)} = \frac{\log 4}{\log 3} \approx 1.26$$

This result can be found on a calculator by using the following keys:

Press   **Display**

 ≈ 1.26

Example 3:

Determine the dimension of the fractal generated in Example 1.

FIGURE 3.6.7

(a)  (b)

Solution: To determine the dimension of the fractal, we again need to examine the basic construction process. Referring to Figure 3.6.7 and to the directions for creating the fractal, we can see that the fractal is created by dividing each line segment into five equal-length subsections (see Fig. 3.6.7a). Each of the original line segments is replaced by the new shape shown in Figure 3.6.7b. This shape is created from seven of the small subsections. Therefore, using the dimension formula with $N = 7$ and $r = 1/5$, we have

$$d = \frac{\log N}{\log (1/r)} = \frac{\log 7}{\log \left(\dfrac{1}{1/5}\right)} = \frac{\log 7}{\log 5} \approx 1.21$$

Example 4:

Find the dimension of the Sierpinski carpet.

Solution: Since we are replacing one square by eight smaller ones, $N = 8$. Since the length of the side of a square is one-third the length of the side of the previous square, $r = 1/3$. Using the dimension formula gives

$$d = \frac{\log N}{\log (1/r)} = \frac{\log 8}{\log \left(\dfrac{1}{1/3}\right)} = \frac{\log 8}{\log 3} \approx 1.89$$

What Do We Mean by the *Dimension* of an Object?

To understand the concept of a fractional dimension, we first need to examine what we mean when we say that a figure is two-dimensional. Let's look at a square with a side of length 1. The area of the square is given by $A = 1^2 = 1$. Dividing each side of the square by 5 gives 25 minature versions of the original square.

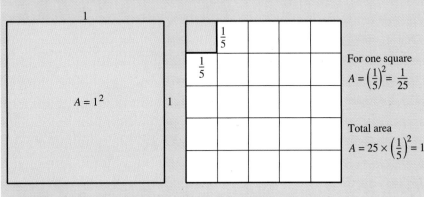

For one square
$$A = \left(\frac{1}{5}\right)^2 = \frac{1}{25}$$

Total area
$$A = 25 \times \left(\frac{1}{5}\right)^2 = 1$$

Each of the 25 new squares has sides of length $1/5$ and an area of $(1/5)^2$. This gives a total area for the 25 squares of
$$A = 25 \times (1/5)^2 = 1.$$

In general, if we let r be the ratio of the length of the new object to the length of the original object, N be the number of new objects, and d be the dimension of the figure, we can say $Nr^d = 1$. For the two-dimensional squares, we have used $N = 25$, $r = 1/5$, and $d = 2$.

To determine a formula for the dimension of an object, we need to solve this formula for d. While doing so is not the intent of the section, this problem is within the abilities of a student who has a firm grasp of logarithms.

$$Nr^d = 1$$

We start by dividing both sides by r^d and using the rules of exponents.

$$N = \frac{1}{r^d}$$

$$N = \left(\frac{1}{r}\right)^d$$

Next, we take the common log of both sides and applying the rules of logarithms.

$$\log N = \log \left(\frac{1}{r}\right)^d$$

$$\log N = d \log (1/r)$$

Finally, dividing by $\log (1/r)$ gives the desired equation.

$$\frac{\log N}{\log (1/r)} = d$$

The Mandelbrot Set

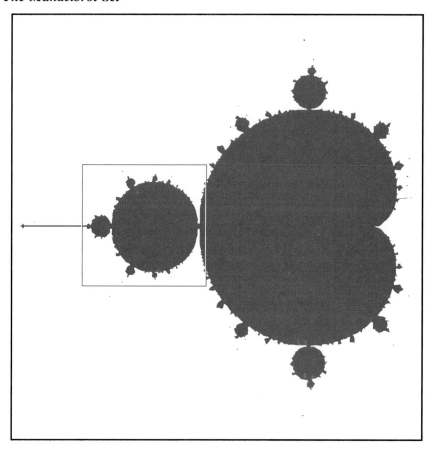

This diagram is called the Mandelbrot set. It is more complex than the fractals discussed earlier, but it still demonstrates the same repetitive patterns exhibited by the other fractals. Notice that the general shape of a circle with a little nob sticking off one side is repeated, at smaller scales, throughout the diagram. If we take the portion of the diagram located in the box and magnify it, we obtain the same structure. This process can be continued indefinitely, with each new iteration showing similar characteristics.

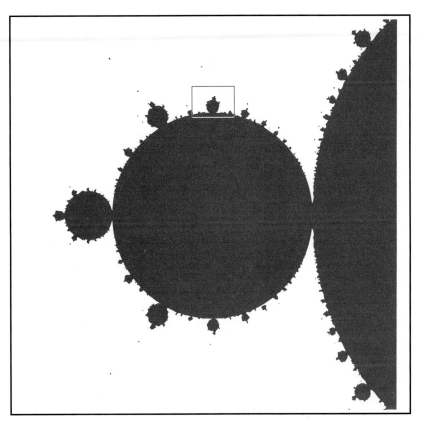

Examining the small nob at the top center of this diagram again gives a new, smaller version of the same diagram.

This set is generated by a very short set of instructions (see page 178), but it provides insights into many physical phenomenon. The idea of a portion of a set being similar to itself (called **self-similarity**) can be seen in the mapping of coastlines. For example, the coastline of California has many small bays and peninsulas. These are usually measured on a scale of thousands of feet. If we examine a small portion of the coastline more closely, the smaller section is also seen to have inlets and peninsulas, this time measured on a scale of hundreds of feet. If this process is continued, we can examine a section of coastline only a fraction of an inch long. In this very small section, we can again see inlets in the form of grains of sand. As we examine the coastline on increasingly more detailed levels, we continue to see the same level of intricacy.

This phenomenon of self-similarity can be seen in many other situations. Cotton prices since 1900 have fluctuated due to the vagaries of supply and demand. Yet, when Mandelbrot and the Harvard economist Hendrik Houthakker closely examined the fluctuations, they found that a decade-by-decade pattern of prices showed the same type of fluctuation as yearly prices or monthly prices. Noise in telephone lines has certain, apparently random, patterns when the signals are examined on an hourly basis. When the same signal is examined at the level of seconds or minutes, the same patterns, at smaller scales, reappear. Like the Von Koch snowflake and the Sierpinski carpet, the same patterns reappear as the situation is examined in finer detail.

The five intricate fractals that follow were created with a computer and a fractal-generating equation.

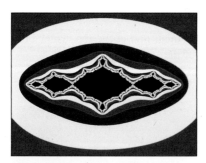

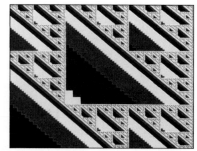

From *Fractals Everywhere* by Michael Barnsley, Academic Press, 1988. (Courtesy of Iterated Systems)

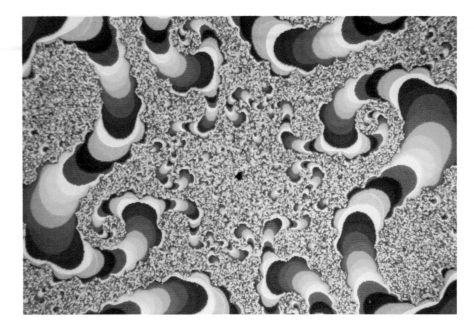

SSS's: These spiraling fractal tubes, based on the Mandelbrot set barely visible at the center, were created with the computer program FracTools™ and then photographed off a computer monitor using a 35-mm camera. (Courtesy of Bourbaki, Inc., and Lloyd W. Black)

BENFORKS: These fractal forks, based on the Mandelbrot set at the center, were created with the computer program FracTools™ and then photographed off a computer monitor using a 35-mm camera. (Courtesy of Bourbaki, Inc., and Lloyd W. Black)

The Mathematics Behind the Mandelbrot Set

In algebra, you may have learned that complex numbers are numbers of the form $a + bi$, where $i = \sqrt{-1}$. You may also have learned that the magnitude of a complex number $z = a + bi$ is given by $\sqrt{a^2 + b^2}$.

The Mandelbrot set is generated by using the equation $z_n = (z_{n-1})^2 + C$, where z_n and C are complex numbers. A complex number z_0 is chosen and substituted into the equation for the z value on the right side of the equation. For each complex number chosen, the equation is used repeatedly until the magnitude of z exceeds 2 or until it is determined that the magnitude of z will probably never exceed 2. If the final result exceeds 2, the starting point z_0 is not in the Mandelbrot set (the white region of the graph). If the final result does not exceed 2, the starting point is in the Mandelbrot set (the black region of the graph).

For example, let's look at $z = 0.75 + 0i$ and assume that the constant $C = 0$. Since the first z value is 0.75, we write $z_1 = 0.75$. This gives the following sequence of values:

$$z_2 = (0.75)^2 = 0.5625$$

$$z_3 = (0.5625)^2 = 0.3164$$

$$z_4 = (0.3164)^2 = 0.1001$$

$$z_5 = (0.1001)^2 = 0.0100, \ldots$$

It is apparent that this sequence of values will approach zero and, hence, is less than 2. Therefore, the starting point $z_1 = 0.75 + 0i$ is in the Mandelbrot set.

If we start with a point such as $z_1 = 0.75 + 1.3i$, we arrive at the following sequence of values:

$$z_2 = (0.75 + 1.3i)^2 = -1.1275 + 1.95i$$

$$z_3 = (-1.1275 + 1.95i)^2 = -2.5312 - 4.3973i$$

$$z_4 = (-2.5312 - 4.3973i)^2 = -12.9293 + 22.2609i$$

Since these numbers are growing quickly, we can see that the magnitude will exceed the limit of 2. Hence, the point $z = 0.75 + 1.3i$ is not in the Mandelbrot set. Although these calculations are tedious, the availability of computers has made the computations and the drawing of the Mandelbrot set and other fractals a reality.

REFERENCES

The reader who is interested in fractals can find a wealth of recent information in the following books. In addition, there are many new books that will have become available by the time you read this. The books marked with an asterisk (*) are what we consider the most readable. We suggest that all readers look at *The Beauty of Fractals* if they can locate a copy in their local or campus library. The mathematics in this book is very technical, but the pictures are stunning.

Michael Barnsley, *Fractals Everywhere,* Academic Press, New York, 1988.
*Martin Gardner, *Penrose Tiles to Trapdoor Ciphers*, W. H. Freeman, New York, 1988.
*James Gleick, *Chaos*, Viking Press, New York, 1987.
Benoit Mandelbrot, *The Fractal Geometry of Nature*, W. H. Freeman, New York, 1982.
H. O. Peitgen and D. Saupe, eds., *The Science of Fractal Images*, Springer-Verlag, New York, 1988.
H. O. Peitgen and P. H. Richter, *The Beauty of Fractals*, Springer-Verlag, New York, 1986.
*Ivars Peterson, *The Mathematical Tourist*, W. H. Freeman, New York, 1988.
Ian Stewart, *Does God Play Dice?*, Basil Blackwell, New York, 1989.

SECTION 3.6
PROBLEMS

1. Examine a leaf of a fern. Explain why the parts of a leaf have properties of fractals.

2. Explain why cirrus clouds can be more accurately depicted by fractals rather than by standard geometric shapes.

3. Create a fractal by starting with a square, dividing each line segment into three equal lengths, and replacing the middle third of each side with three line segments whose lengths are one-third the length of the original segment. The first iteration is shown here. Repeat this process and draw the next iteration of this fractal.

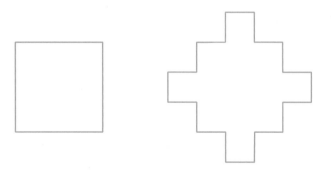

4. Create a fractal by starting with a square, dividing each line segment into five equal sections, and replacing the second and fourth sections of each segment with three line segments whose lengths are equal to the section they are replacing. The first iteration is shown here. Repeat this process and draw the next iteration of this fractal

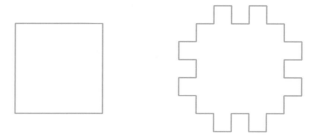

5. Create a fractal by starting with a line segment, dividing the segment into four equal lengths, and replacing both the second and third sections by two segments whose lengths are one-fourth the length of the original segment. The first iteration is shown here. Repeat this process and draw the next iteration of the fractal.

6. Create a fractal by starting with a line segment, dividing the segment into five equal lengths, and replacing both the second and fourth sections by two segments whose lengths are one-fifth the length of the original segment. The first iteration is shown here. Repeat this process and draw the next iteration of the fractal.

7. Create your own fractal by starting with an object and altering it by adding smaller version(s) of the original object. Repeat this process three times.

8. Find the dimension of the fractal in Problem 3.

9. Find the dimension of the fractal in Problem 4.

10. Find the dimension of the fractal in Problem 5.

11. Find the dimension of the fractal in Problem 6.

12. A fractal is created by the following process. A line segment of length 1 is drawn. It is divided into five equal sections. The second and fourth of these sections are then removed. This process is continued indefinitely. What is the dimension of this fractal?

13. A fractal is created by the following process. Start with a regular pentagon. Cut each side into five equal-length sections and replace the middle section with another regular pentagon. This process is continued indefinitely. What is the dimension of this fractal?

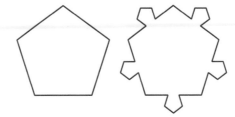

*14. What coastline did Mandelbrot investigate, and what did he estimate as its dimension?

*15. Investigate the resources in the bibliography at the end of this section and determine some of the other areas of study to which fractals are being applied.

*16. What is a Sierpinski gasket? Draw the first three iterations of the gasket.

*17. What is a Cantor dust? In what area of study is it being applied?

CHAPTER   3   **SUMMARY**

KEY TERMS, CONCEPTS, AND FORMULAS

The important terms in this chapter are:

Acute angle: An angle that measures between 0° and 90°.   p. 117

Angle: The figure formed by two rays with the same end point.   p. 116

Axiom: A proposition that is assumed to be true. Historically, axioms referred to propositions of algebra or arithmetic.   p. 120

Concave polygon: A polygon in which an extension of at least one of its sides enters the interior of the polygon.   p. 146

Convex polygon: A polygon in which extensions of its sides do not enter the interior of the polygon.   p. 146

Euclidean geometry: A phrase used to describe a system of geometry based on *Elements* written by the Greek mathematician Euclid.   p. 114

Exterior angle: An angle formed outside a triangle by one side of the triangle and an extension of another side of the triangle.   p. 118

Fibonacci numbers: The sequence of numbers 1, 1, 2, 3, 5, 8, 13, 21, 34, 55, . . . , where each successive number is the sum of the two previous numbers.   p. 138

Fractal: An object with a fractional dimension.   p. 165

Golden Ratio (ϕ): The ratio between distances a and b such that

$$\phi = \frac{a}{b} = \frac{a+b}{a} \approx 1.62$$ p. 133

Golden Rectangle: A rectangle whose sides form a Golden Ratio.   p. 134

Line segment: The set of points on a line consisting of two end points and all the points on the line between those two points.   p. 115

Non-Euclidean geometry: A phrase used to describe a system of geometry that assumes a consistent set of postulates with at least one that is not logically equivalent to Euclid's postulates.   p. 126

Obtuse angle: An angle that measures between 90° and 180°.   p. 117

Parallel lines: Two lines that lie in the same plane and do not intersect.   p. 119

Parallel postulate: A postulate of geometry that establishes the number of lines that are parallel to a given line through an external point.   p. 123

Perpendicular lines: Two lines that intersect and form a right angle.   p. 117

Polygon: A closed figure in a plane formed by the line segments that intersect each other only at their end points.   p. 143

Postulate: A proposition that is assumed to be true. Historically, postulates referred to propositions of geometry.   p. 120

Proof: A series of statements that logically show a conclusion follows from the hypothesis.   p. 123

Ray: The figure formed by extending a line segment in only one direction.   p. 116

Reflection: Movement of a shape in a plane by finding its mirror image across a specified line.   p. 157

Regular polygon: A polygon that has sides of equal length and angles of equal measure.   p. 146

Right angle: An angle that measures 90°.   p. 117

Sides: Line segments that form a polygon.   p. 144

Straight angle: An angle that forms a line and measures 180°.   p. 117

Tessellation: A pattern of one or more congruent shapes that cover an area in a plane without overlapping or leaving any gaps.   p. 152

Theorem: A proven proposition.   p. 123

Translation: Movement of a shape in a plane by sliding it in a certain direction for a specified distance.   p. 157

Transversal: A line or line segment that intersects two other lines or line segments.   p. 119

Triangle-sum theorem: A theorem of geometry that states the results of the sum of the measures of the angles of a triangle.   p. 124

Undefined terms: Terms that have meanings assumed to be clear. Point, line, and plane are undefined terms in geometry.   p. 115

Vertex (pl. **vertices**): The intersection point of sides of a polygon.   p. 144

After completing this chapter, you should be able to:

1. Explain the need for and be able to use undefined terms, definitions, axioms, postulates, and theorems in a system of Euclidean geometry.   p. 114

2. State the differences between Euclidean, Lobachevskian, and Riemannian geometries, including the parallel postulate, model, and triangle-sum theorem of each system.   p. 126

3. Find a point on a line segment that divides it into a Golden Ratio.   p. 133

4. Determine whether a rectangle is approximately a Golden Rectangle and explain the significance of Golden Rectangles in art, architecture, and other areas.   p. 134

5. Design and construct regular polygons and geometric designs.   p. 147

6. Create tessellations of a triangle or quadrilateral, using translations and reflections.   p. 157

7. Recognize basic properties of fractals.   p. 165

8. Given a geometric figure and a method of construction, draw the next iteration of a fractal and determine the dimension of the fractal.   p. 167

SUMMARY
PROBLEMS

1. Explain the difference between
   (a) Undefined terms and definitions
   (b) Postulates, axioms, and theorems

2. Explain why it is necessary to have undefined terms and postulates in a geometric system.

3. Draw $\triangle TRY$ with $\angle T$ an obtuse angle on the model for the plane in Euclidean, Lobachevskian, and Riemannian geometries.

4. Draw lines $h, j,$ and k intersecting at point P on models for the Euclidean plane, Reimannian plane, and the Lobachevskian plane.

5. The sum of the angles of a quadrilateral can be determined by dividing the quadrilateral into two triangles. Using this scheme, determine the sum of the measures of the angles of a quadrilateral in Euclidean geometry, in Riemannian geometry, and in Lobachevskian geometry. Using similar techniques, find the angle-sum for a pentagon and for a hexagon in each geometry. From the results of the four polygons studied, what generalizations can be made?

6. From a point Q that is not on a line m, how many lines can be drawn perpendicular to line m through point Q in Euclidean, Lobachevskian, and Riemannian geometries? Explain your answers.

7. In light of the non-Euclidean geometries, explain the statement ''Mathematics does not state truths about the real world.''

8. If you had to choose only one of the geometries (Euclidean, Lobachevskian, or Riemannian) to describe physical space, which would you choose? Why ?

9. Find a point that approximately divides each segment into a Golden Ratio.

(a) ———————————————   (b)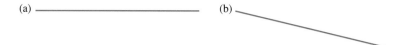

10. If the width of a rectangle is to be 8.5 inches, how long should its length be to make it a Golden Rectangle?

11. A kite is a quadrilateral with two distinct pairs of equal adjacent sides as shown below. Create a definition for a "Golden Kite." Draw some of these "Golden Kites." (*Hint*: There are two different ratios of segments that could be used to make the "Golden Kite.")

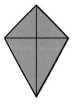 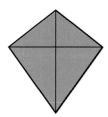

12. Construct the following regular polygons:

(a) dodecagon   (b) 18-gon

13. Construct stars from the regular polygons in Problem 12 by connecting the following points:

(a) Every third point of the   (b) Every fifth point of the
     polygon   polygon

14. Tessellate a rectangular region with the following triangles:

(a) Using only translations   (b) Using reflections and
                                          translations.

 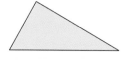

15. Tessellate rectangular regions with the following quadrilaterals:

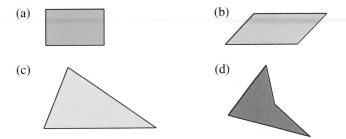

(a)

(b)

(c)

(d)

16. Explain why it is possible to tessellate a plane with a square, regular hexagon, and regular dodecagon placed at each vertex, but it is impossible to tessellate a plane with an equilateral triangle, a regular pentagon, and a regular heptagon placed at each vertex.

17. Construct the tessellation of a rectangular region with a regular hexagon, squares, and equilateral triangles.

18. Use the following procedure to construct a fractal. Start with a rectangle whose length is twice its width. Divide each line segment into four sections of equal length. Replace the center two sections with three sides of a rectangle, as shown in the diagram. The length of the longer of the three added segments should equal one-half the length of the original segment. The length of the other two added segments should be one-fourth the length of the original segment. The first iteration is shown. Repeat this process and draw the next iteration of the fractal.

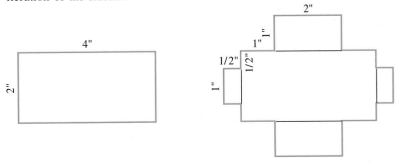

19. Determine the dimension of the fractal discussed in Problem 18. Remember that if the length of the original line segment is 4 inches, the length of the next iteration of that segment is formed by six sections for a total of 6 inches.

LOGIC AND PROOFS

Le Penseur by Tami Whitt-Zenoble: a modern interpretation of a classic representation of the human thinking process. (Courtesy of the artist)

A SHORT HISTORY OF LOGIC

The ability to think logically is an innate human ability. From earliest times human beings have used this power. However, the first systematic study of logic is credited to the Greek philosopher Aristotle (384–322 B.C.). In his work *Organon*, Aristotle systematized principles of reasoning and laws of logic. He is known for his work on arguments consisting of two statements and a conclusion, called syllogisms. The Stoic and Megarian schools in Greece (c. 300 B.C.) continued his study of logic. They formed a logic of propositions and valid inference schemes and were very interested in paradoxes. The most productive of the Stoic-Megarian logicians was Chrysippus.

Logic in the middle ages was marked by several different schools of thought. The Roman philosopher Boëthius (c. 480–520) was instrumental in passing on the logical traditions of the Greeks to European monks. These monks sought to preserve the logic found in classical Greek texts. Meanwhile, the Nyaya schools in India also made contributions to the field of logic during this period. As the Middle Ages came to an end, scholastic logic made its entrance. Scholastic logic was characterized by its use of Latin and the influence of Christian theology. It was developed for discussions of theological questions. Noted contributors in the development of logic during this period were Peter Abelard (c. 1130), Robert Grosseteste (c. 1240), St. Thomas Aquinas (c. 1250), and Petrus Hispanus (c. 1260).

With the Renaissance period in Europe, advances in formal logic again appeared. William of Ockham (c. 1320), in *Summa Logicae*, and Walter Burley (c. 1325), in *De puritate artis logicae*, improved upon Aristotle's logic. Gottfried Leibniz (1666) initiated the study of symbolic and mathematical logic in his essay *De arte combinatoria*. In this work and others over the next 25 years, Leibniz implied that mathematics can be derived from the principles of logic. His work began what is considered the period of mathematical logic. Leonhard Euler (c. 1770) adopted a method of visually checking syllogisms by means of circle diagrams. John Stuart Mill (c. 1843) made contributions to the development of inductive logic. Augustus De Morgan (c. 1850), in *Formal Logic*, and George Boole, in his works *The Mathematical Analysis of Logic* (1847) and *An Investigation of the Laws of Thought* (1854), applied algebraic operations to logic and placed logic on a mathematical basis. John Venn (1880) introduced the Venn diagram, which is a modification of the circle diagrams of Euler. Alfred North Whitehead and Bertrand Russell (1910–1913) published the three volumes of *Principia Mathematica*, which attempted to develop mathematics from only undefined concepts and principles of logic. Jan Lukasiewicz, Emil Post, and Ludwig Wittgenstein between 1920 and 1921 independently introduced truth tables as a means of reaching logical conclusions. Developments in logic continue to the present day. In this chapter we will not look at the details of formal logic, but we will investigate some of the principles of logic and its application to proofs.

CHECK YOUR READING

1. What was studied during the Greek period of logic?
2. What is scholastic logic?
3. In 1912, the first successful parachute jump occurred. What notable attempt was being made by Bertrand Russell and Alfred North Whitehead in that year?
4. Who initiated the study of symbolic and mathematical logic?
5. What three mathematicians introduced truth tables?
6. When Marco Polo was making his journeys c. 1260, what was Petrus Hispanus doing?
7. What were truth tables used for?
8. Match each of the following names with the correct mathematical discovery, event, or concept.

(a)	Aquinas	Applied algebraic operations to logic
(b)	Aristotle	Devised circle diagrams to check syllogisms
(c)	Boole	Modified Euler diagrams
(d)	Chrysippus	Co-authored *Principia Mathematica*
(e)	Euler	Was a scholastic logician
(f)	Lukasiewicz	Was a Stoic-Megarian logician
(g)	Venn	Worked on syllogisms
(h)	Whitehead	Devised truth tables

RESEARCH QUESTIONS

In order to answer the following questions, you will need to refer to material not contained in the text. Possible sources of information are listed in the bibliography at the end of the book.

1. What is the Socratic method? What was it used for? On what principles is it based?
2. What is a paradox? Give some examples. What are some famous paradoxes?
3. What is Boolean algebra? How is it related to logic?
4. What are Euler diagrams? How are they related to Venn diagrams? Give examples of each and show how they are used.
5. What were some of the theological questions the scholastic logicians were trying to answer?
6. Many of the mathematicians mentioned in this short history of logic are known for other mathematical endeavors or had other interests besides mathematics. Do some research on two of the mathematicians mentioned in this section. Tell something about their lives, their achievements, and their interests.

SECTION   4.0

▼

SETS

A **set** is simply a collection of items. Although we have not previously defined sets and their use, we have used and will continue to use the idea of a set throughout the book. For example, our system of numeration uses a set of ten symbols to represent numbers. When we graph an equation, the points on the graph are the set of points that satisfy the equation. In statistics, a collection of data is called a data set. In this section, we want to examine the rules for working with sets and some of their uses. Later in the chapter, we show how sets are used in logic as a method of proof.

Sets and Their Symbols

Set Notation and Members of a Set

To begin our study of sets, we need to discuss the notation used with sets. First we need a name for the items contained in a set. Since a set can contain numbers, words, equations, or even other sets, we need a very general term to describe the items inside a set. In mathematics, we use the word **element**. Each item in a set is an element of the set.

Suppose we want to have a set consisting of all the even integers between 1 and 9. Using the symbols { and } (called braces) to form a set, we can write this in two different ways. Since the even integers between 1 and 9 are 2, 4, 6, and 8, we can write the set by enclosing these numbers inside the braces:

$$\{2, 4, 6, 8\}$$

This method is called the **listing method**. Though it is easy to use, it is not convenient if a set contains a large number of elements.

A second method of writing a set is called the **descriptive method**. When using the descriptive method, simply describe the contents of the set rather than listing every element in the set. Instead of $\{2, 4, 6, 8\}$, we can write

$$\{x \mid x \text{ is an even integer with } 1 < x < 9\}$$

The vertical bar between the x's means "such that." Therefore, the notation is read, "the set of x such that x is an even integer with $1 < x < 9$." Using the descriptive method allows us to write sets with a large number of elements without resorting to the tedium involved in writing out each element.

To indicate that a certain item is an element of a set or is not an element of a set, we use the symbols:

$$\in \quad \text{for "is an element of"}$$

$$\notin \quad \text{for "is not an element of"}$$

Thus, $6 \in \{0, 3, 6, 9, 12, 15, 18\}$, but $8 \notin \{0, 3, 6, 9, 12, 15, 18\}$.

Example 1:

Use set notation to write all the whole numbers less than 13 that are divisible by 3.

Solution: We do this in two ways. If we use the descriptive method, the set is given by

$$\{x \mid x \in \text{whole numbers}, x < 13, \text{ and } x \text{ is divisible by 3}\}$$

If we use the listing method, we have $\{0, 3, 6, 9, 12\}$.

Empty Sets

An **empty set** is a set that does not contain any elements. It can be expressed in two ways. The first way uses the standard set notation of braces. Since the empty set does not contain any elements, the empty set is written as a pair of braces that do not enclose any symbols:

$$\text{empty set} = \{ \ \}$$

The second way to indicate an empty set is to use the symbol $\varnothing$. Thus,

$$\text{empty set} = \varnothing$$

Empty sets can describe impossible events, such as a square circle or a natural number that is even and odd at the same time.

Notation Indicating a Set

To differentiate between sets and other mathematical objects, whenever we are discussing a set we use an uppercase script variable, such as X. This will provide a visual clue that the symbol being used represents a set.

Subsets

Set B is called a **subset** of a set A if every element in the set B is also an element of the set A. The symbol used to indicate that B is a subset of A is $\subset$ ($B \subset A$). For example, if we let $X = \{$ingredients in pizza$\}$ and $Y = \{$ingredients in Italian cooking$\}$, then we can say $X \subset Y$ because every element in the set X is a member of the set Y. To indicate that a set is not a subset of another set, we use the symbol $\not\subset$. Thus for the sets X and Y, since there are some ingredients in Italian cooking that are not used in pizza, Y is not a subset of X. This may be represented as $Y \not\subset X$. An important technical note about the notation for sets is that the subset and element symbols serve different purposes. The subset symbol can only occur between two sets, and the element symbol can only occur between an element and a set. The following example gives correct and incorrect usages for each symbol.

Example 2:

Let $A = \{$all the planets in our solar system$\}$
$B = \{$all the celestial objects$\}$.

Which of the following statements make correct use of the subset and element symbols?

(a) $A \in B$ (b) The earth $\in B$ (c) $B \subset A$ (d) The earth $\subset A$

Solution:

(a) $A \in B$ is an incorrect usage of the element symbol because A is a subset of B, not an element of B. The correct statement is $A \subset B$.

(b) The earth $\in B$ is a correct usage of the element symbol since the earth is one element in the set consisting of all celestial objects.

(c) $B \subset A$ is a correct usage of the subset symbol since both B and A are sets. However, the statement is not true since not every celestial object is a planet. A correct statement is $B \not\subset A$.

(d) The earth $\subset A$ is not a correct usage of the subset symbol since the earth is an element of A, not a subset of it. A correct statement is "The earth $\in A$."

Operations with Sets

There are two set operations that will be used in this text, the operations of union and intersection. The **union** of two sets creates a new set containing all the elements of the two sets. The symbol used to indicate the union of two sets is $\cup$.

Example 3:

Given the sets $\mathcal{A} = \{0, 3, 6, 9\}$ and $\mathcal{B} = \{1, 3, 5, 7, 9\}$, find the union of $\mathcal{A}$ and $\mathcal{B}$.

Solution: The union of $\mathcal{A}$ and $\mathcal{B}$ is given by $\mathcal{A} \cup \mathcal{B}$. Since the union must contain any element that is in either of the original sets, we have

$$\mathcal{A} \cup \mathcal{B} = \{0, 1, 3, 5, 6, 7, 9\}$$

Notice that the elements in the union can be in either of the original sets or in both of the original sets. If there is an element that is contained in both of the original sets, that element is written only once in the union of the two sets. For example, the number 3 was in both of the original sets but was written only once in $\mathcal{A} \cup \mathcal{B} = \{0, 1, 3, 5, 6, 7, 9\}$.

The other set operation is the intersection operation. The **intersection** of two sets is a set consisting of all the elements that are in both sets. The symbol representing the intersection operation is $\cap$.

Example 4:

Find the intersection of the sets $\mathcal{A} = \{0, 3, 6, 9\}$ and $\mathcal{B} = \{1, 3, 5, 7, 9\}$.

Solution: The intersection of $\mathcal{A}$ and $\mathcal{B}$ is given by $\mathcal{A} \cap \mathcal{B}$. Since the intersection contains any element that is in both of the original sets, we have

$$\mathcal{A} \cap \mathcal{B} = \{3, 9\}$$

Translating Words into Set Operations

In algebra, certain key words are translated into mathematical symbols or operations. For example, the word "is" often is represented by the symbol "$=$" when a word problem is translated into mathematical symbols. The same is true for set operations. When the word "**or**" is used, it may be represented in set operations by the union symbol.

Example 5:

Find the set of whole numbers less than 13 that are divisible by 3 or 2.

Solution: The whole numbers less than 13 that are divisible by 3 can be written as the set $\mathcal{A} = \{0, 3, 6, 9, 12\}$. Similarly, the set of whole numbers less than 13 that are divisible by 2 is the set $\mathcal{B} = \{0, 2, 4, 6, 8, 10, 12\}$. Since the question asks for those numbers that are divisible by 3 *or* 2, we want the union of $\mathcal{A}$ and $\mathcal{B}$.

$$\mathcal{A} \cup \mathcal{B} = \{0, 2, 3, 4, 6, 8, 9, 10, 12\}$$

In a similar fashion, the word "**and**" is used to indicate the intersection of two sets.

Example 6:

Find the set of whole numbers less than 13 that are divisible by 3 and 2.

Solution: As before, we let $\mathcal{A} = \{0, 3, 6, 9, 12\}$ and $\mathcal{B} = \{0, 2, 4, 6, 8, 10, 12\}$. Since the question asks for those numbers that are divisible by 3 *and* 2, we want the intersection of $\mathcal{A}$ and $\mathcal{B}$.

$$\mathcal{A} \cap \mathcal{B} = \{0, 6, 12\}$$

Note

It is important to remember that *and* and *or* have very specific meanings when used in connection with sets. In particular, *or* indicates that an element can be in either of the original sets or in both of the original sets. This contradicts the common usage of *or* meaning one set or the other but not both.

Sets and Venn Diagrams

Venn diagrams (named after John Venn, a 19th-century English mathematician) are pictures depicting sets. Typically, Venn diagrams consist of a rectangular region containing several circles. Shown here is a Venn diagram consisting of two intersecting sets, $\mathcal{A}$ and $\mathcal{B}$, depicted by circles. The boundary rectangle is labeled $\mathcal{U}$, for **universal set**. The universal set is a set that contains all elements of the type being discussed in the problem. As we shall see in the following examples, Venn diagrams can be used to help us interpret mathematical problems.

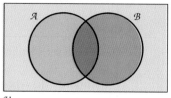

Example 7:

Examine the Venn diagram shown, where $\mathcal{U}$ is the set of all chickens, the circle $\mathcal{W}$ represents chickens with white feathers, and the circle $\mathcal{R}$ represents chickens with red feathers. Determine the type of chickens in each of the regions a, b, c, and d.

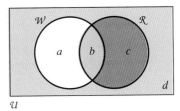

Solution: Region a is inside the circle $\mathcal{W}$ but outside the circle $\mathcal{R}$. Therefore, region a represents those chickens with white feathers but not red feathers. Similarly, region c is inside the circle $\mathcal{R}$ but outside the circles $\mathcal{W}$. Therefore, region c represents those chickens with red feathers but not white feathers.

Region b is inside both the circle $\mathcal{W}$ and the circle $\mathcal{R}$. Therefore, region b represents those chickens with both white feathers and red feathers.

Region d is outside of both circles. Therefore, region d represents those chickens having neither red nor white feathers.

Example 8:

Let $\mathcal{N}$ = the set of natural numbers = $\{1, 2, 3, 4, 5, \ldots\}$.

I = the set of integers = $\{\ldots -3, -2, -1, 0, 1, 2, 3, \ldots\}$

Draw the Venn diagram for these sets and label the regions as was done in Example 7. Use $\mathcal{U}$ = the set of real numbers.

Solution: In this problem, the set $\mathcal{N}$ is a subset of I. Therefore, when we draw the Venn diagram, the set $\mathcal{N}$ should be completely enclosed inside the set I. This gives us the following picture.

The region inside the circle $\mathcal{N}$ is the set of natural numbers. The region labeled a is the set consisting of 0 and negative integers. The region b contains all noninteger real numbers.

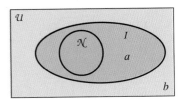

SECTION 4.0

PROBLEMS

1. Write the set of even whole numbers less than or equal to 10, using the
   (a) Descriptive method
   (b) Listing method

2. Write the set of odd whole numbers less than or equal to 12, using the
   (a) Descriptive method
   (b) Listing method

3. Let M = {apples, bananas, peaches, tomatoes} and T = {beans, peas, sprouts, tomatoes}. Determine the following.
   (a) $M \cup T$
   (b) $M \cap T$

4. Let F = {oranges, apples, apricots, peaches} and N = {coconuts, filberts, almonds}. Determine the following.
   (a) $F \cup N$
   (b) $F \cap N$

In Problems 5–16, use the sets T = {3, 6, 9, 12}, F = {5, 10, 15, 20, 25}, I = {all the integers} to determine if the subset and element symbols are used correctly.

(a) If the symbol is being used correctly, is the statement true? If not, write a true statement.

(b) If the symbol is being used incorrectly, write a true statement using the correct symbol.

5. $F \subset I$

6. $I \subset F$

7. $T \subset F$

8. $T \subset I$

9. $5 \subset I$

10. $5 \subset F$

11. $5 \in I$

12. $5 \notin F$

13. $5 \in I$

14. $5 \notin T$

15. $F \in I$

16. $T \notin I$

17. Let U = the set of all people, R = the set of all people with red hair, and W = the set of all women. Draw a Venn diagram for these sets and describe the type of people contained in each region of the diagram.

18. Let $\mathcal{U}$ = the set of all books, $\mathcal{N}$ = the set of all novels, and $\mathcal{P}$ = the set of all books of poetry. Draw a Venn diagram for these sets and describe the type of books contained in each region of the diagram.

19. Let $\mathcal{U}$ = the set of all items in the library, $\mathcal{N}$ = the set of novels in the library, $\mathcal{B}$ = the set of books in the library, and $\mathcal{V}$ = the set of all videos in the library. Draw a Venn diagram for these sets and describe the type of item contained in each region of the diagram.

20. Let $\mathcal{U}$ = the set of all students at your school, $\mathcal{N}$ = the set of new students, $\mathcal{R}$ = the set of returning students, and $\mathcal{V}$ = the set of all students who are veterans. Draw a Venn diagram for these sets and describe the type of people contained in each region of the diagram.

*21. For the set $Q = \{*\}$, there are two subsets, $\{\ \}$ and $\{*\}$.
   (a) How many subsets can you find for the set $\mathcal{A} = \{*, \times\}$?
   (b) How many subsets can you find for the set $\mathcal{B} = \{*, \times, \dagger\}$?
   (c) Suppose a set C contains four elements. How many possible subsets are there?
   (d) Suppose a set $\mathcal{D}$ contains 20 elements. Use the results from the previous parts of this problem to conjecture the total number of possible subsets.

*22. The Venn diagrams presented have been constructed from circles and rectangles, but any shape may be used to construct Venn diagrams. Construct a Venn diagram, containing four sets $\mathcal{A}$, $\mathcal{B}$, C, and $\mathcal{D}$, that has 16 distinct regions representing all possible intersections.

SECTION 4.1
▼
LOGIC, STATEMENTS, AND DEFINITIONS

Even though humans have the ability to think, they do not always reason correctly. The science of correct reasoning and making valid conclusions is called **logic**. An understanding of logic will help you correctly arrange supporting evidence that leads to a conclusion. It will also help you understand the process of proving mathematical facts. This process of proving mathematical propositions is probably one of the most challenging aspects of mathematics. The mathematician wants to be sure that a certain proposition actually follows logically from what has already been accepted or, just as importantly, that a proposition does not follow logically from what has been accepted. To a mathematician, creating an original proof is as gratifying as finishing a painting is to an artist, or as setting a record is to an athlete, or as finding a cure to a disease is to a scientist. In this chapter, we want to let you experience this aspect of mathematics by introducing you to principles of logic, methods of argument, and proofs in geometry.

Statements

The basic components of logic are its statements. Statements in logic must have a clear meaning and be either true or false. Statements cannot be both true and false at the same time. They must have only one truth value—that is, either true or false. In general, questions, commands, or vague sentences cannot be used as statements in logic because they cannot be judged to be true or false. The following list gives examples of some sentences that are statements and some that are not.

Statements	**Nonstatements**
Today is a holiday.	Are we having fun yet?
Pigeons fly.	Do your homework!
The square of 7 is 49.	Don't worry, be happy!
This book contains history sections.	It smells like whatchamacallit.
I did my homework.	This statement is true.

In the study of logic, letters are used to represent statements just as letters are used to represent numbers in algbebra. For example, the letter Q can be used to represent the statement, "All the players on this year's team are over 6 feet tall."

Example 1:

For each of the following, classify S as a statement or nonstatement.

(a) S: All men are mortal.
(b) S: Yea, team!
(c) S: Euclid did not study geometry.
(d) S: Finish your dinner.

Solution:

(a) S is a statement.
(b) S is a nonstatement.
(c) S is a statement.
(d) S is a nonstatement.

Negation of Statements

If you change a statement to one that has the opposite meaning, you form the negation of the statement. The negation of a statement has truth value that is the opposite of the given statement. That is, if a statement is true, then its negation is false. Similarly, if a statement is false, its negation is true. If S represents a statement, then $\sim S$ represents the negation of the statement and is read "not S." For example, if S represents the statement "A triangle has three sides," then $\sim S$ represents the statement "A triangle does not have three sides." Notice that S is true, but its negation $\sim S$ is false. In most statements, forming the negation is simply a matter of changing the action in the statement by adding or deleting the word "not." For example:

Statement	**Negation**
Kai is running.	Kai is not running.
Kristi does not smile.	Kristi does smile.

Statement	Negation
The two amounts are equal.	The two amounts are not equal.
Logic is not a five-letter word.	Logic is a five-letter word.
He is a guitar player.	He is not a guitar player.

In statements that involve the words "all," "every," "some," "none," or "no," forming the negation is not as easy as in the previous examples. For example:

Statement	Negation
All men are mortal.	Some men are not mortal.
Some of the numbers are not positive.	All of the numbers are positive.
No birds are fish.	Some birds are fish.
Some women can swim.	No women can swim.
None of the flashlights worked.	Some of the flashlights worked.

The basic forms for negating statements that involve "all," "every," "some," "none," or "no" can be summarized as follows:

Statement	Negation
All/every	Some . . . not
Some . . . not	All/every
None/no	Some
Some	None/no

Example 2:

Write the negation of the following statements.

(a) My car did not start.
(b) Some of the cars did not start.
(c) None of the cars started.
(d) Every car started.
(e) Some of the cars started.

Solution:

    (a) My car did start.
    (b) All of the cars started.
    (c) Some of the cars started.
    (d) Some cars did not start.
    (e) No car started.

Conditional Statements

A very important type of statement used in logic is the **conditional statement**. It is a complex statement formed by two individual statements joined by the words "if . . . then . . . ." In the conditional statement "If A, then B," the letter A represents the "if" clause or the **hypothesis** or **antecedent**, and the letter B represents the "then" clause or the **conclusion** or **consequent**. For example, in the statement "If you are a student, then you should study," "If you are a student" is the hypothesis and "you should study" is the conclusion. We will see in the next section that conditional statements are used extensively in formulating logical arguments.

The same conditional statement can be written in different ways.

If A, then B	If you are a student, then you should study.
A implies B	Being a student implies that you should study.
$A \rightarrow B$	Being a student $\rightarrow$ one should study.
All A are B	All students should study.

Related to the conditional statement $A \rightarrow B$ are three other basic types of statements.

Converse:	$B \rightarrow A$
Inverse:	$\sim A \rightarrow \sim B$
Contrapositive:	$\sim B \rightarrow \sim A$

These statements are important because they are used in creating valid arguments. It can be shown that if a statement is true, then its contrapositive is always true, and if a statement is false, then its contrapositive is also false. That is, a conditional statement and its contrapositive are logically equivalent. However, if a statement is true, its inverse and converse may be either true or false. A conditional statement and its converse or its inverse are not logically equivalent.

Note

A conditional statement is logically equivalent to its contrapositive. A conditional statement can be replaced with its contrapositive and keep its same truth value. ($A \rightarrow B$ is logically equivalent to $\sim B \rightarrow \sim A$.)

This interrelationship between these statements can be seen by studying the following examples:

Example 3:

Write the converse, inverse, and contrapositive of the true conditional statement below. Determine if each of the statements is true or false.

If it is an IBM PC, then it is a computer.

Solution: Let

A: It is an IBM PC.

B: It is a computer.

$A \rightarrow B$:   the conditional statement.

Converse:	$B \rightarrow A$:	If it is a computer, then it is an IBM PC. (false)
Inverse:	$\sim A \rightarrow \sim B$:	If it is not an IBM PC, then it is not a computer. (false)
Contrapositive:	$\sim B \rightarrow \sim A$:	If it is not a computer, then it is not an IBM PC. (true)

Example 4:

Write the converse, inverse, and contrapositive of the false conditional statement below. Determine if each of the statements is true or false.

If x is an even number, then the last digit of x is 2.

Solution: Let

A: x is an even number.

B: The last digit of x is 2.

$A \rightarrow B$: the conditional statement.

Converse:	$B \rightarrow A$:	If the last digit of x is 2, then x is an even number. (true)
Inverse:	$\sim A \rightarrow \sim B$:	If x is not an even number, then the last digit of x is not 2. (true)
Contrapositive:	$\sim B \rightarrow \sim A$:	If the last digit of x is not 2, then x is not an even number. (false)

Example 5:

Write the converse, inverse, and contrapositive of the true conditional statement below. Determine if each of the statements is true or false.

If two lines are perpendicular, then the two lines form a right angle.

Solution: Let

A: Two lines are perpendicular.

B: Two lines form a right angle.

$A \to B$: the conditional statement.

Converse:	$B \to A$:	If two lines form a right angle, then the two lines are perpendicular. (true)
Inverse:	$\sim A \to \sim B$:	If two lines are not perpendicular, then the two lines do not form a right angle. (true)
Contrapositive:	$\sim B \to \sim A$:	If two lines do not form a right angle, then the two lines are not perpendicular. (true)

In Example 5, notice that the statement and its converse are both true statements; that is, $A \to B$ and $B \to A$ are both true. In such a situation, the two statements are combined into a **biconditional statement**, which is written in the following ways:

A if and only if B

A iff B

$A \leftrightarrow B$

Thus, the results of Example 5 could be written as follows:

Two lines are perpendicular if and only if the two lines form a right angle.

Two lines are perpendicular iff the two lines form a right angle.

Two lines are perpendicular $\leftrightarrow$ the two lines form a right angle.

Definitions

Besides conditional statements, definitions of terms are used as basic building blocks of a mathematical system. A definition states properties of the term being defined, gives us a way of recognizing what is defined, and provides a way of distinguishing what is being defined from other objects. A definition must:

1. Name the term being defined.
2. Use words that have already been defined or already understood.
3. Be biconditional. The statement of the definition and its converse must both be true.

Besides those three necessary properties, a good definition should also:

1. Place the term in the smallest or nearest group to which it belongs.
2. Use the minimum information needed to distinguish the object from other objects.

Example 6:

Explain why the following statements are not examples of definitions.

(a) It is a place where tennis matches are played.
(b) Charity is the act of being eleemosynary.
(c) A mother is a parent of a child.
(d) A social insect is a bee.

Solution:

(a) The term that is being defined is not included.
(b) Charity is being defined by a word that is more difficult to understand and is probably not previously understood.
(c) The statement is not biconditional. The converse statement ''A parent of a child is a mother'' is false.
(d) The definition is not biconditional. The statement is false since a social insect could also be an ant.

Example 7:

Even though the following statements satisfy the three properties of a definition, they are not good definitions. Explain why.

(a) A treasurer is in charge of finances of an organization.
(b) A triangle is a plane figure with three sides, three angles, and three vertices.
(c) A Chevy is a Chevrolet automobile.

Solution:

(a) The group to which a treasurer belongs is not included. A treasurer is a *person* in charge of finances of an organization and not a machine, report, or computer program.
(b) More information is given than is needed to distinguish the object from all other plane figures.
(c) The definition does not place the term into the group to which it belongs. ''Chevy'' is a *slang* term for a Chevrolet automobile.

In this section, we have looked at the various kinds of statements and two ways of combining statements. We should pay particular attention to these concepts:

1. If a statement is true, its negation is false, and vice versa.

2. If a conditional statement is true, then its contrapositive is also true.

3. A definition must be biconditional.

SECTION 4.1
PROBLEMS

Which of the following are considered statements, and which are not considered statements?

1. Don't eat the daisies!

2. My dog is a Dalmation.

3. Do you enjoy reading novels?

4. The jokes are great.

5. Mozart composed classical music.

6. The camera is not a Kodak.

7. This statement is false.

8. Use the quadratic formula on that one.

Write the negation of the following statements.

9. My car is in the shop.

10. Fred did not do his research paper.

11. I hate sitting around doing nothing.

12. The two lines are parallel.

13. That is an example of an exponential equation.

14. No rational number is irrational.

15. All fish can live under water.

16. Every chef knows how to boil water.

17. Some numbers are not prime numbers.

18. Some dogs do not have long tails.

19. Some trees are always green.

20. Some TV shows are boring.

21. None of the numbers are positive.

22. My uncle did not like what you did to his lawn.

For each conditional statement write its converse, inverse, and contrapositive.

23. If you get a busy signal, the phone is in use.

24. If there is a leak in the tube, it will become flat.

25. If it is a point on the circle, then it will be 16 inches from the center of the circle.

26. If a whole number ends in 3, then it is an odd number.

27. When G. H. Mutton speaks, I listen.

28. When I am asleep, nothing bothers me.

29. If the figure has five sides, it is not a hexagon.

30. If it is an ellipse, then its graph is not a circle.

Verify that the following satisfy the three necessary conditions of a definition.

31. A puppy is a young dog.

32. A crook is a person who steals or cheats.

33. A quadratic equation is an equation of the form $ax^2 + bx + c = 0$, where a, b, and c are real numbers and $a \neq 0$.

34. A rational number is a number that can be represented as the ratio of two integers a/b, where $b \neq 0$.

Explain why the following statements are not examples of definitions.

35. A skean is a falchion.

36. To gasconade is to vaunt.

37. It is used to remove the skin of a potato.

38. We call it the period from noon to sunset.

39. An integer is a positive or negative number.

40. An obtuse angle is not a 90° angle.

41. A Toyota is an imported Japanese automobile.

42. A pencil is a writing implement.

If possible, find an example of a conditional statement (P) that satisfies each of the following conditions.

43. P is true and its inverse is false.

44. P is true and its inverse is true.

45. P is true and its converse is true.

46. P is true and its converse is false.

47. P is true and its contrapositive is false.

48. P is true and its contrapositive is true.

49. P is false and its inverse is false.

50. P is false and its inverse is true.

51. P is false and its converse is true.

52. P is false and its converse is false.

53. P is false and its contrapositive is false.

54. P is false and its contrapositive is true.

The works of modern artists Donald Farnsworth (*left*) and David McLaughlin (*right*) show the continuing influence of the Greeks. (*Left* (oil), courtesy of Magnolia Editions; *right* (watercolor), courtesy of the artist)

SECTION 4.2

▼

INDUCTIVE AND DEDUCTIVE REASONING

We can now use the statements discussed in Section 4.1 to formulate arguments. An argument consists of statements of supporting evidence organized to show that a conclusion is true. Two of the reasoning processes used in creating an argument are induction and deduction.

Induction

Induction is the process of reasoning in which conclusions are based on experimentation or experience. When using induction, we make a conclusion about a situation after observing results, analyzing experiences, citing authorities, or presenting statistics. We predict future experiences by extending patterns seen in present experiences.

Example 1:

On a cold winter night there is a fire burning in the fireplace. A baby crawls up to the fireplace and touches the screen covering the fireplace. The baby burns his little hand and cries. A few weeks later, the baby does the same thing and burns his hand again. Because of these experiences, the baby stays away from the fireplace when he sees a fire burning. He has used the process of induction. Based on his experience, the baby has made the conclusion that touching an object heated by a fire will cause his hand to hurt.

Example 2:

In the triangles, use a ruler to measure each side and use a protractor to measure each angle. Is there a relationship between the length of a side and the size of the angle that is opposite that side—that is, between $\angle A$ and side a, $\angle B$ and side b, and $\angle C$ and side c?

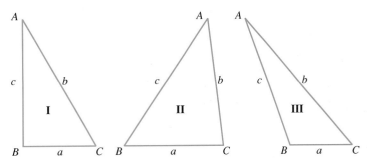

Solution:

Triangle I	Triangle II	Triangle III
$a = 3$ cm $\angle A = 39°$	$a = 4$ cm $\angle A = 40°$	$a = 2.5$ cm $\angle A = 20°$
$b = 5.9$ cm $\angle B = 90°$	$b = 5.1$ cm $\angle B = 56°$	$b = 6.8$ cm $\angle B = 111°$
$c = 5$ cm $\angle C = 51°$	$c = 6.1$ cm $\angle C = 84°$	$c = 5.4$ cm $\angle C = 49°$

From studying the results we can conclude that in each triangle, opposite the longest side is the largest angle or opposite the shortest side is the smallest angle.

Example 3:

Consider the expression $n^2 - n + 11$. It seems to generate prime numbers (see Section 1.4) when whole number values are substituted for n.

$$n = 0 \quad n^2 - n + 11 = 0 - 0 + 11 = 11$$

$$n = 1 \quad n^2 - n + 11 = 1 - 1 + 11 = 11$$

$$n = 2 \quad n^2 - n + 11 = 4 - 2 + 11 = 13$$

$$n = 3 \quad n^2 - n + 11 = 9 - 3 + 11 = 17$$

$$n = 4 \quad n^2 - n + 11 = 16 - 4 + 11 = 23$$

$$\vdots$$

Using inductive reasoning, you might conclude that the expression $n^2 - n + 11$ always generates prime numbers for whole-numbers, n.

This, however, is not true. When $n = 11$, the value of the expression is 121, and 121 is not a prime number. By not investigating a sufficient number of cases, we could have made a false conclusion.

Inductive reasoning is the process of determining a general conclusion by examining individual cases or particular facts. It can show us that there is a good chance that our conclusion is true, but we will not be absolutely certain. For example, if the first ten people you meet at a new school are very helpful and friendly, you may generalize that the people at the school are really nice. However, the next person you meet may be extremely hostile. Based on the first ten people, your conclusion seemed valid. However, the 11th person disproved your conclusion. When reasoning inductively, one has to make sure that there is a sufficient number of facts or specific cases to warrant a conclusion. Scientists, for example, repeat experiments many times before making conclusions. Again, a good inductive argument only gives a high probability that a statement is true or an action should be performed.

Example 4:

Give an inductive argument to persuade your friend Maria to vacation in Hawaii.

Solution: The following list of premises gives an example of an inductive argument.

1. The weather is great in Hawaii, and the beaches are fantastic.
2. My friend has a condo you can rent for only $150 a week.
3. The airlines are having a special on fares to Hawaii this month.
4. I went there last year and had a wonderful time.
5. The people there were friendly and treated me kindly.
6. There are lots of nice guys vacationing there. You'll have a great time and are bound to meet that special man you have been looking for.
7. In a recent travel magazine, 95% of the vacationers polled said they enjoyed their vacation in Hawaii.
8. Anna Holiday, worldwide traveler and economist, in her book *Travels to Paradise*, states that a vacation to Hawaii is the best bet for your travel dollar.

Such an argument shows that vacationing in Hawaii makes good sense. It implies that there is a good chance that Maria would enjoy a vacation in Hawaii based on past experience, statistics, and the opinion of experts. However, even if all the premises of this argument were true. Maria could still have a miserable time in Hawaii.

Even though inductive reasoning does not ensure certainty, it is the basis of many everyday decisions and is used to extend our scope of knowledge by making suppositions based on experimentation. If certainty is desired, we can in some situations use a second reasoning process, deduction.

Deduction

Deduction is the process of reasoning in which conclusions are based on accepted premises. These premises are usually articles of faith, laws, rules, definitions, assumptions, or commonly accepted facts. The conclusions we reach are either explicitly or implicitly contained in the premises.

A deductive argument is a series of statements consisting of premises and a conclusion. The premises are the statements of evidence from which the conclusion is drawn. In deductive arguments, the premises are usually written as conditional statements. Valid arguments may take many different forms. One of the common forms is the **syllogism**. The basic syllogism consists of two statements or premises, and a logical conclusion drawn from them. According to Aristotle, ''a syllogism is a discourse in which, certain things being posited, something else follows from them by necessity.'' In this chapter we use three types of syllogisms: hypothetical syllogisms, affirming the antecedent, and denying the consequent.

Hypothetical Syllogism

If *A, B,* and *C* represent statements, a hypothetical syllogism is constructed from three such statements, the first two lines being the premises and the third being the conclusion. The hypothetical syllogism can be written in three different ways:

$A \rightarrow B$	A implies B.	If A, then B.
$B \rightarrow C$	B implies C.	If B, then C.
$\therefore A \rightarrow C$	Therefore, A implies C.	$\therefore$ If A, then C.

In the hypothetical syllogism, the argument is valid even though one or both of the premises may be false. The truth or falsehood of the premises does not affect the logic of the argument. Logic deals with the relation between premises and conclusion, not the truth of the premises. To say that a deductive argument is **valid** means that the premises are related to the conclusion in such a way that, if the premises are true, the conclusion must be true. A conclusion cannot be false if the logical form is correct and the premises are true.

Note

To reason deductively toward a true conclusion using a syllogism, you must have the correct form and true premises.

The following are examples of valid deductive arguments that use hypothetical syllogisms and lead to true conclusions.

If you live in Palolo, then you live on Oahu.

If you live on Oahu, then you live in Hawaii.

Therefore, if you live in Palolo, then you live in Hawaii.

If a triangle is isosceles, then it has two equal sides.

If a triangle has two equal sides, then it has two equal angles.

Therefore, an isosceles triangle has two equal angles.

Example 5:

Is the following argument a hypothetical syllogism? Why or why not?

If you have a party, you should invite your friends.

If you are graduating from college, you should invite your friends.

Therefore, if you are having a party, you are graduating from college.

Solution: The argument is not a hypothetical syllogism. The premises do not link properly. The conclusion of the first premise should be the hypothesis of the second premise, and no logical rearrangement can accomplish the proper linking of the statements.

Example 6:

Even though the conclusion of this argument is true, explain why the following argument is a poor one.

If you are over 18 years old, then you can read.

If you can read, you can vote.

Therefore, if you are over 18 years old, then you can vote.

Solution: The argument has a valid form so it can be considered a valid argument. However, it is a poor argument, since neither of the premises are true. The argument does not actually prove its conclusion.

Affirming the Antecedent

If *A* and *B* represent statements, an argument that affirms the antecedent has the form

Major premise:	$A \rightarrow B$
Minor premise:	A
Conclusion:	$\therefore B$

The major premise is a conditional statement. The minor premise states that the hypothesis of the major premise is true. This is called **affirming the antecedent**. An example of an argument of this form is as follows.

> If I study for 6 hours, I will pass the exam.
> I studied for 6 hours.
> Therefore, I will pass the exam.

This classical argument is another example of affirming the antecedent.

> All men are mortal.
> Socrates is a man.
> Therefore, Socrates is mortal.

This can be rewritten so that the correct form is apparent.

> If one is a man, then one is mortal.
> Socrates is a man.
> Therefore, Socrates is mortal.

If an argument has the correct form, it is a logically valid argument. However, if it is to be a convincing argument with a true conclusion, its premises must also be true. You can affirm the antecedent to reason deductively if the argument has the correct form and true premises.

Example 7:

Is the following argument a good one? Explain.

> If you want to run a marathon, then you should train for the race.
> Kerry wants to run a marathon.
> Therefore, Kerry should train for the race.

Solution: The argument has the correct form for affirming the antecedent and is, therefore, logically valid. If we take its first premise as true because of commonly accepted notions about the physical stamina needed to run a marathon (26.2 miles), the argument is a good one.

Example 8:

Explain why the following argument is not good.

> All good chess players wear glasses.
>
> Sylvia is a good chess player.
>
> Therefore, Sylvia wears glasses.

Solution: Rewriting the argument into conditional statements, we get the following:

> If one is a good chess player, then one wears glasses.
>
> Sylvia is a good chess player.
>
> Therefore, Sylvia wears glasses.

Even though the argument has the correct form of an argument using the technique of affirming the antecedent, the major premise is not true. Thus, it is logically valid but does not arrive at a true conclusion. You need both the correct form and true premises to ensure true conclusions.

Denying the Consequent

If A and B represent statements, an argument that denies the consequent has the form

Major premise:	$A \rightarrow B$
Minor premise:	$\sim B$
Conclusion:	$\therefore \sim A$

Examples of arguments of this form are as follows:

> If John is at the beach, then he wears sun screen on his nose.
>
> John does not have sun screen on his nose
>
> Therefore, John is not at the beach.

If you pay the bill on time, then you are not charged a penalty.

You are charged a penalty.

Therefore, you did not pay the bill on time.

The major premise is a conditional statement. The minor premise is a denial (negation) of the consequent (conclusion) of the conditional statement. For this reason this argument is called **denying the consequent**. This form of argument is based on the contrapositive principle in which the statement $A \rightarrow B$ is logically equivalent to $\sim B \rightarrow \sim A$. We can therefore see the validity of this form of argument by observing that it is really an application of affirming the antecedent.

$$\begin{array}{llll}
\text{Major premise:} & A \rightarrow B & \text{is equivalent to} & \sim B \rightarrow \sim A \\
\text{Minor premise:} & \sim B & & \sim B \\
\text{Conclusion:} & \therefore \sim A & & \therefore \sim A
\end{array}$$

Example 9:

Is the following argument a good one? Explain.

If a number is not positive, then the number is negative.

Zero is not negative.

Therefore, zero is positive.

Solution: The argument has the form of an argument using denying the consequent, so it is logically valid. However, its first premise is not true, since if a number is not positive it could be either negative or zero. Thus, the argument is faulty.

We can also make valid arguments from premises that do not at first glance seem to be one of our standard logical forms, as in the next example.

Example 10:

Make a valid argument from the following premises.

If P, then $\sim Q$.

If $\sim R$, then Q.

If R, then S.

Solution: To have the correct form of the hypothetical syllogism, the conclusion of one statement must be the hypothesis of the next statement. Since we know that if a statement is true its contrapositive is true, we can use that principle on the second premise.

$$\begin{array}{ll} \text{If } P, \text{ then } \sim Q. & \text{If } P, \text{ then } \sim Q. \\ \text{If } \sim R, \text{ then } Q. \quad \rightarrow & \text{If } \sim Q, \text{ then } R. \\ \text{If } R, \text{ then } \sim S. & \text{If } R, \text{ then } \sim S. \\ & \therefore \text{If } P, \text{ then } \sim S. \end{array}$$

Thus, the valid conclusion of this argument is: If **P**, then ∼**S**.

Even though you can use the contrapositive statement in a valid argument, as in this example, you must be careful not to accept the inverse or converse of a statement to be true in an argument. It is quite easy to fall into an inverse error or a converse error.

Watch out for the following:

Converse: $A \rightarrow B$ does *not* necessarily imply $B \rightarrow A$.

Inverse: $A \rightarrow B$ does *not* necessarily imply $\sim A \rightarrow \sim B$.

Although there are other forms of syllogisms and methods of reasoning deductively, the three forms of syllogisms explained in this section will be adequate in developing the mathematical systems needed to take brief excursions into parts of both Euclidean and non-Euclidean geometry.

The Roles of Induction and Deduction

You have been introduced to two methods of reaching reasonable conclusions, induction and deduction. Both processes play a role in the formulations of the mathematical system of geometry that we will be studying in this chapter. Induction is used to conjecture facts about geometry. Early Egyptians, Babylonians, and Greeks used experience and experimentation to hypothesize relationships about geometric objects. So too, modern mathematicians discover mathematical relationships by looking at specific cases and examples and generalizing their findings into a theorem. After a theorem has been conjectured, the deductive process takes over. It is used to prove or disprove the theorem that has been conjectured. If the theorem is valid, the deductive process shows that the theorem follows logically from what has been previously accepted as true in the mathematical system. This process is sometimes very difficult. For example, it took nearly 2000 years to prove that, in general, it is impossible to trisect an angle with only a straight edge and a compass.

SECTION 4.2

PROBLEMS

1. Example 2 dealt with triangles with sides of unequal lengths. The triangles here have at least two sides with the same length. What conclusions can you induce from analyzing the length of their sides and the measurement of their angles?

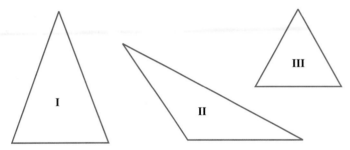

2. Combine the results of Example 2 and Problem 1 to formulate an accurate statement about the relationship between the lengths of the sides of triangles and the angles opposite those sides. Draw a few triangles to check the validity of your statement.

3. Draw any triangle. Find the midpoint of two sides of the triangle and the length of the third side of the triangle. Draw the line segment connecting the two midpoints. Find the length of that segment. State the relationship that seems to exist between the length of the third side and the length of the segment joining the two midpoints. Test out your findings on a few other triangles.

4. Draw any quadrilateral (four-sided figure). Find the midpoint of each of the four sides. Use line segments to join the midpoints (in order) so that another quadrilateral is formed. Repeat this for several other quadrilaterals. What seems to be true about the quadrilaterals formed by connecting the midpoints?

5. Explain how Problems 1–4 are examples of inductive reasoning. Explain what role deduction would play in further analyzing the geometric principles involved in each problem.

6. Use a compass to draw a large semicircle and the diameter of the semicircle. Mark any point on the semicircle and draw line segments joining each end point of the diameter to the point marked on the semicircle. Use a protractor to measure the angle formed by the two line segments. Repeat this for several other points marked off on the semicircle. What seems to be true about the angle formed by the line segments connecting the end points of the diameter to a point on a semicircle?

7. Show that the expression $n^2 - n + 17$ seems to generate prime numbers for whole number values of n. Explain how using induction might cause you to make a false conclusion in this case. What is the first value of n that causes the expression to produce a composite number?

8. Give an inductive argument to convince a friend that he should not vacation in Hawaii.

9. Give both an inductive argument and a deductive argument to convince a friend to quit smoking.

10. Explain what type of argument is used to show that a frying chicken purchased at a local food store weighs less than 4 lb.

(a) Every frying chicken sold over the last 25 years has weighed less than 4 lb. Thus, the chicken you purchased at a local store must surely weigh less than 4 lb.

(b) If a frying chicken weighs 4 lb or more, it is not sold in food stores.
I purchased this frying chicken in a local food store.
Therefore, it must weigh less than 4 lb.

Determine whether or not the following arguments are valid. For those that are not valid, (a) explain what is wrong with the argument; (b) change the minor premise and make a valid argument.

11. When it is midnight, I am asleep.
I was asleep.
Therefore, it was midnight.

12. All NBA basketball players are over 5 ft. tall.
Russell is 6 ft. tall.
Therefore, Russell plays in the NBA.

13. If you are a farmer in Polt County, then you grow corn.
Farmer Ron does not live in Polt County.
Therefore, Farmer Ron does not grow corn.

14. All Rhode Island Red hens lay brown eggs.
My hen, Marguerite, is a Rhode Island Red.
Therefore, Marguerite lays brown eggs.

15. If $ABCD$ is a square, it has four sides.
If it has four sides, then it is a quadrilateral.
Therefore, if $ABCD$ is a square, it is a quadrilateral.

16. If a triangle is equilateral, then it has three equal sides.
$\triangle ABC$ does not have three equal sides.
Therefore, $\triangle ABC$ is not equilateral.

Create valid deductive arguments for the following statements.

17. All even numbers greater than 2 are not prime numbers.

18. If you are a shoplifter, you are dishonest.

19. My teacher, Mrs. Santos, is a nice person.

The deductive arguments based on the hypothetical syllogism have two premises and a conclusion. An argument may, however, have many premises that logically lead to a conclusion. What statement is proven in each of Problems 20–23?

20. $3(x + 4) = 18 \quad \rightarrow \quad 3x + 12 = 18$
$ 3x + 12 = 18 \quad \rightarrow \quad 3x = 6$
$ 3x = 6 \quad \rightarrow \quad x = 2$

21. If you are serious about school, you should be a good student.
   If you are a good student, you should study regularly.
   If you study regularly, you will have less time to watch TV.

22. If A, then B.
   If B, then C.
   If C, then $\sim D$.
   If $\sim D$, then $\sim E$.

23. In Problem 22, find statements for A, B, C, D, and E that will make the argument not only valid but true.

The following premises are not in the exact syllogistic form shown in this section. However, they can be rearranged and/or logically rewritten so that they correspond to one of the types of syllogisms. What valid conclusion follows from these premises?

24. All mice are not birds.
   Some pets are mice.

25. Every integer is a rational number.
   Some numbers are integers.

26. If you can hear, you are not hearing-impaired.
   If you can't hear, I'll use sign language.

27. If the car is full of gasoline, we can drive 300 miles.
   If we haven't reached Yosemite Park, we haven't driven 300 miles.
   If we can't see Vernal Falls, we haven't reached Yosemite Park.

28. $P \leftrightarrow Q$
   $P \rightarrow R$
   $S \rightarrow \sim R$

29. $P \leftrightarrow Q$
   $Q \rightarrow \sim R$
   $S \rightarrow R$

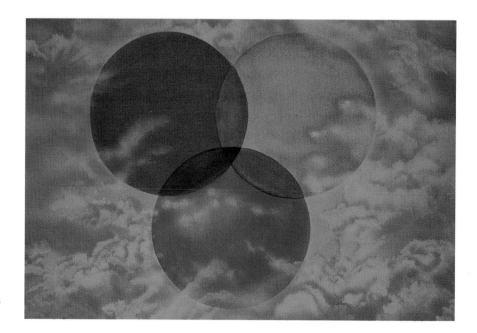

Golden Venn by David
McLaughlin makes use of
Golden Ratios and colorfully
represents the Venn diagram of
three intersecting sets. (Courtesy
of the artist)

SECTION   4.3

▼

USING VENN
DIAGRAMS IN
LOGIC

Along with using inductive and deductive reasoning, there are other ways to solve
problems in logic. One of the ways is to use Venn diagrams. Each region of the
Venn diagram represents one of the possible outcomes of the problem. As each
part of the problem is read, some of the regions are eliminated, leaving only the
solution(s) to the problem. Because this method involves reading and drawing
pictures, it is easy to use. It is limited, however, by the complexity of the pictures
that can be drawn.

Let's examine a case in which we have a Venn diagram containing three circles,
as shown in Figure 4.3.1. A point inside of circle A but outside of circles B and
C indicates that some condition has been satisfied by A but not by B or C. This
region is labeled a, $\sim b$, $\sim c$.

Using this notation, we will demonstrate two types of problems. The first type
shows how to use Venn diagrams to answer specific questions about a situation.

FIGURE 4.3.1

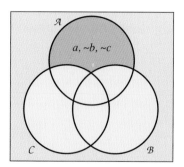

The second type shows how Venn diagrams can be used to take a set of premises and determine a logical conclusion.

Answering Questions

The first problem we consider is the use of Venn diagrams to answer questions about complicated situations. The process is to construct a Venn diagram for the problem and to use this diagram to help understand the problem and determine its solution.

Example 1:

A survey of 200 employees determined that 22 of the employees do not have any medical insurance, while 43 of the employees are covered by the company's policy and an additional policy. If 160 employees are covered by the company's insurance policy, how many employees are covered only by some other policy?

Solution: To determine the solution of this problem, we will use three sets, $\mathcal{U}$, C, and O. $\mathcal{U}$ is the set of the 200 employees in the survey. Let C be the set of employees covered by the company's policy, and let O be the set of employees covered by some other policy. Since 43 employees were covered by two or more policies, there are 43 people in the set $C \cap O$. Since there are a total of 160 employees covered by the company's policy, there must be $160 - 43 = 117$ employees covered only by the company's policy. Also, we know that there are 22 people who do not have any medical insurance. This information can be summarized in the Venn diagram shown here.

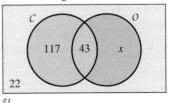

The intersection contains 43 people, the remainder of set C contains 117 people, and there are 22 people not contained in either circle. The number of people who are insured only by some policy other than the company's are represented by x. Since the total number of people surveyed is 200, we have the following equation and solution:

$$22 + 117 + 43 + x = 200$$

$$182 + x = 200$$

$$x = 18$$

Therefore, there are 18 people whose only insurance is not through the company policy.

Example 2:

Out of 600 doctors, 255 accept children as patients, 360 perform surgery, and 370 are general practitioners. If 175 of the general practitioners accept children as patients, 185 of the doctors performing surgery will operate on children, 260 of the general practitioners perform surgery, and there are 135 general practitioners who will perform surgery on children, how many of the 600 doctors are general practitioners who do not perform surgery and do not accept children?

Solution: We let

S = the set of doctors who perform surgery

G = the set of doctors who are general practitioners

C = the set of doctors who accept children as patients

Using the given information in conjunction with the intersection symbol, we have

The number of doctors in C = 255

The number of doctors in S = 360

The number of doctors in G = 370

The number of doctors in $G \cap C$ = 175

The number of doctors in $S \cap C$ = 185

The number of doctors in $G \cap S$ = 260

The number of doctors in $G \cap S \cap C$ = 135

At this point, the only information that can be entered in the Venn diagram is that 135 people are contained in the intersection of the three circles. This gives us the Venn diagram in Figure 4.3.2.

Since we know there are 135 general practitioners who perform surgery on children and there are a total of 260 general practitioners who perform surgery, there must be 260 − 135 = 125 general

FIGURE 4.3.2

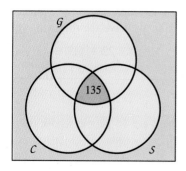

FIGURE 4.3.3

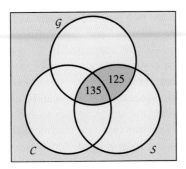

practitioners who perform surgery, but not on children. This provides us with Figure 4.3.3.

Performing similar operations with the intersections $S \cap C = 185$ and $G \cap C = 175$ gives us the third version of the Venn diagram, Figure 4.3.4. The question is to determine how many general practitioners do not perform surgery and do not accept children as patients. This is given by the region labeled x.

Since there are a total of 370 general practitioners, the number of doctors in the four regions of set G must add to 370. Therefore, we have the following algebraic equation and solution:

$$40 + 135 + 125 + x = 370$$

$$300 + x = 370$$

$$x = 70$$

Conjunction and Disjunction

Before proceeding with our discussion of Venn diagrams, we need to introduce two new types of statements. In each of these types, more than one object or action is being described. For example,

Both kittens *and* puppies claw at shoelaces.

Blankets can be made from either wool *or* cotton.

FIGURE 4.3.4

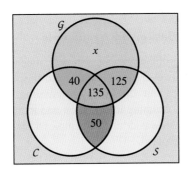

The first example groups two types of animals with the same behavior. The word that provides this information is "and." A **conjunction** is a statement that contains two or more statements that are connected by the word "and." Since a conjunction must have a condition common to all its parts, **a conjunction is true only if all parts of the statement are true**.

The second example states that blankets can be made from either wool or cotton. In this type of statement, the action applies to one or more of the items connected by the word "or." A **disjunction** is a statement that contains two or more statements that are connected by the word "or." Since a disjunction has a property that is held by one or more of its parts, **a disjunction is true if one or more parts of the statement is true**.

Example 3:

Decide whether the following statements are conjunctions or disjunctions and if the statements are true or false.

(a) Dogs and cats have four legs.
(b) Dogs or cats like to chew on rawhide toys.
(c) Portuguese Water dogs and Siamese cats like swimming in rivers.
(d) Dogs or cats have two ears.

Solution:

(a) Since this statement relates to both dogs and cats, it is a conjunction. Both dogs and cats do have four legs so this is a true statement.
(b) Because of the word "or," this statement is a disjunction. Since at least one of the two types of animals (dogs) like to chew on rawhide toys, this is a true statement.
(c) This is a false conjunction since, in general, cats do not like to swim anywhere. In order for a conjunction to be true, all its parts must be true.
(d) This is a true disjunction since at least one of the two types of animals have two ears. An important point to notice is that a disjunction is considered true even if the statement applies to more than one of its parts.

Determining Conclusions to Arguments

The second type of problem gives a series of statements that can be formed into a logical argument. However, no conclusion to the statements is provided. Instead, a question is asked about the given information. This is similar to the actual reasoning process of obtaining information and then developing a conclusion based on that information. As was done in Examples 1 and 2, we will use Venn diagrams to help us with this process.

FIGURE 4.3.5

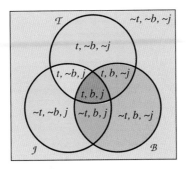

Example 4:

Tom, Jerry, and Bill go to lunch together almost every workday at a truck that sells hot hamburgers and cold sandwiches. Tom and Bill always order the same thing. Either Bill or Jerry, but not both, always orders a hamburger. Either Tom or Jerry, or sometimes both, orders a hamburger. If Jerry orders a hamburger, so does Tom. Who orders the hamburger(s) for lunch?

Solution: Tom, Jerry, and Bill can each be represented by a circle in the Venn diagram. We will let the area inside a circle represent the case in which a hamburger was ordered for lunch. Figure 4.3.5 gives all the possible situations. For example, the region labeled t, $\sim b$, $\sim j$ indicates that Tom ordered a hamburger and that Bill and Jerry did not order hamburgers.

  The first sentence of the problem states that Tom and Bill order the same thing for lunch. This means that the shaded regions in Figure 4.3.6 are not possible solutions, since in each of these Tom and Bill have different lunches. For example, the top region has Tom ordering a hamburger but Bill and Jerry not ordering hamburgers.

  The second statement says that Bill or Jerry, but not both, will have a hamburger for lunch. This eliminates the center region of the diagram, since this region has both Bill and Jerry eating hamburgers. It also eliminates the outside region of the diagram since neither Bill nor Jerry

FIGURE 4.3.6

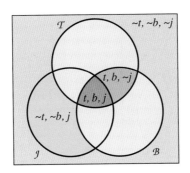

FIGURE 4.3.7

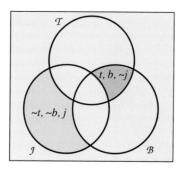

is having a hamburger (see Fig. 4.3.7). This leaves only two regions from which to choose.

The next sentence says that either Tom or Jerry, or sometimes both, orders a hamburger. Since the remaining two regions are $\sim t$, $\sim b$, j and t, b, $\sim j$, this statement does not remove either of the two remaining regions.

The final statement says that if Jerry orders a hamburger, so does Tom. This eliminates the case $\sim t$, $\sim b$, j, leaving only one unshaded region in Figure 4.3.8. From here, we can see that Tom and Bill order the hamburgers and that Jerry orders a cold sandwich. ▪

In this section, we have shown how Venn diagrams can be used to determine the logical solution to a problem. If the problem involves numerical quantities, the Venn diagram can be used to determine the number of items that satisfy the conditions of the set in question. If the problem does not involve numerical values, Venn diagrams can help determine the logical conclusion to a given set of information. The following problems will give you some practice using Venn diagrams in these two types of logical problems.

SECTION 4.3

PROBLEMS

In Problems 1–8, use Venn diagrams to determine the solution to the problem.

1. Given the Venn diagram shown, determine the number of people contained in the intersection if the diagram represents the result of a survey of 300 people.

FIGURE 4.3.8

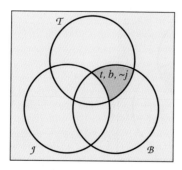

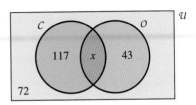

2. Given the Venn diagram shown, determine the number of people contained in the region labeled x if the diagram represents the result of a survey of 500 people.

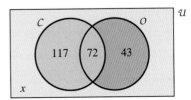

3. Given the Venn diagram shown, what can be said about $A \cap B$?

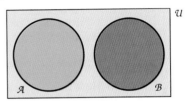

4. Draw a Venn diagram in which A contains a total of 30 elements, B contains a total of 50 elements, and U contains a total of 80 elements. (There are many possible answers.)

5. A survey of 1000 people has found that 625 people drink milk with breakfast, 420 drink coffee, and 130 do not drink coffee or milk. Draw a Venn diagram to represent this information and determine the number of people who drink both coffee and milk for breakfast.

6. Five hundred apples were examined for traces of illegal chemicals. Forty of the apples showed traces of only DDT, 35 showed traces of both DDT and Alar, and 420 showed traces of neither DDT nor Alar. How many showed traces of only Alar?

7. A survey of 1000 people determined the following results about their radio listening habits:

In the morning, between 5:00 and 7:00 A.M., 620 people listen to the radio.

During the evening, between 4:00 and 7:00 P.M., 640 people listen to the radio.

During the day, between 7:00 A.M. and 4:00 P.M., 450 people listen to the radio.

During all three periods, 210 people listen.

During the morning and the evening only, 220 people listen.

During the morning and the day only, 70 people listen.

During the day and the evening only, 130 people listen.

(a) How many people listen only during the morning?
(b) How many people listen only during the day?
(c) How many people listen only during the evening?
(d) How many people do not listen to the radio?

8. A survey of 500 people determined the following results about their exercise habits:

Two hundred forty-two people participate in aerobics.

Two hundred seventy-eight people participate in weight lifting.

Two hundred ninety-eight people participate in running.

Forty-three people participate only in aerobics and weight lifting.

Fifty people participate only in aerobics and running.

Ninety-two people participate only in weight lifting and running.

Seventy-five participate in all three activities.

(a) How many participate only in aerobics?
(b) How many participate only in weight lifting?
(c) How many participate only in running?
(d) How many participate in none of these three activities?

In Problems 9–12, use a Venn diagram to answer the question at the end of each problem.

9. If you are a reformer, then you are an idealist. If you are not a fanatic but you are an idealist, then you are a reformer. If you are not a reformer, then you are not an idealist and you are not a fanatic. Everyone is a fanatic in some ways. What is the conclusion?

10. If you are not working but you are poor, then you are a student. If you are a student, then you are poor or you are working or both. If you are not a student, then you are poor or you are working. If you are not working, then you are not both poor and a student. What is the conclusion?

11. If Audrey and Betty are wealthy, then so is Carla. If Betty or Carla is wealthy, then Audrey is not wealthy. If Audrey is not wealthy, then Betty and Carla are not both wealthy. If at least one of the women is wealthy, how many are wealthy?

12. Arnold or Ben or both went golfing. If Ben went golfing, then Carl went golfing. If Carl did not go golfing, then both Arnold and Ben went golfing. Is this situation possible?

SECTION   4.4

▼

SYMBOLIC LOGIC
AND TRUTH
TABLES

One of the common beliefs about mathematics is that everything can be turned into abstract symbols that must follow certain sets of rules. It is also believed that these rules always lead the mathematician to a correct solution of whatever problem is at hand and that there is no other correct answer. As we have begun to see, this is not always the case. Previous chapters have discussed developments in number systems and geometry systems that have led to different, and sometimes conflicting, systems of mathematics. Which system is best is not easy to say, particularly in the case of geometry. Still, mathematicians often try to systematize their work so that, as often as possible, a certain set of information always leads to one and only one solution.

In this chapter, we have seen several methods of logical thinking. This section covers what is, perhaps, the most mathematical method of logical thinking, symbolic logic. We have seen a small portion of symbolic logic in earlier sections. For example, when sets were discussed in the review section for this chapter, intersections were represented by the symbol ∩. In the section covering statements, the "If A, then B" statement was abbreviated by using the symbols $A \rightarrow B$. In this section, we provide a list of symbols and their meanings, explain how to translate English into these symbols, and show how proofs may be performed using these symbols.

One important note before we start concerns our philosophy about this material. You should treat this material as you did the material in Chapter 1 on ancient numeration systems. We do not expect you to be an expert in symbolic logic. We merely want to expose you to another area of mathematics, to give you a view of one more of the many facets of mathematics. We do not expect you to memorize all the charts and tables in this section. You will need to make frequent references to them to understand the examples and do the problems.

Translating English to Symbols

The following is a partial list of the symbols used in symbolic logic. While looking through the chart, you may have recognized the symbols ∴ and ∼. They are found in earlier sections of this chapter. The remaining symbols have not been used, but some of the English terms for the symbols have been used. For example, when discussing Venn diagrams and sets, we used the symbol ∩ to indicate an intersection of two sets. It represents the common English word "and." In logic, the symbol for "and" is ∧ and it is called a conjunction.

Symbols Used in Logic

English	Symbol	Name
Not	$\sim$	Negation
Therefore	$\therefore$	
Implies: If . . . then	$\rightarrow$	Conditional
Equivalent statements	$\equiv$	Logical equivalency
And	$\wedge$	Conjunction
Or	$\vee$	Inclusive disjunction

From our knowledge of previous material and this list, we can see that not even the logicians and mathematicians always agree on the correct symbol to use. It is for this reason that we encourage you to make repeated referrals to the chart.

Our next step is to see how these symbols can be used to abbreviate English sentences.

Example 1:

Translate the following sentences into symbols.

(a) If it is raining, the skies are cloudy.
(b) If it is a dog and it can run quickly, then it has four legs.
(c) If my grade is not a C and my grade was better than average, then my grade must be an A or a B.

Solution:

(a) This is a conditional statement. If we let R = it is raining and C = the skies are cloudy, we can write

$$R \rightarrow C$$

(b) The premise of this statement involves two conditions, the dog and running quickly. To handle this, we need to use a conjunction as well as the conditional statement. Letting D = dog, R = run quickly, and F = has four legs, we can write

$$(D \wedge R) \rightarrow F$$

We use the parentheses to enclose the portion of the statement that must be considered first.

(c) Like the earlier statements, this is a conditional. It contains a conjunction in the antecedent and a disjunction in the consequent. Letting G = better than average grade and A, B, and C represent those letter grades, we have

$$(\sim C \wedge G) \rightarrow (A \vee B)$$

In our next example, we want to see how an entire syllogism can be translated into symbolic logic.

Example 2:

Translate the following syllogism into symbols.

If I own chickens, I can have fresh eggs for breakfast.
If I have fresh eggs for breakfast, I am in a good mood until lunchtime.
Therefore, if I own chickens, I am in a good mood until lunchtime.

Solution: We will use C = owning chickens, E = having fresh eggs for breakfast, and G = being in a good mood until lunchtime. Using these letters and two of the symbols from the chart, we can write the syllogism as three statements:

$$C \rightarrow E$$
$$E \rightarrow G$$
$$\therefore C \rightarrow G$$

Example 3:

Translate the following paragraph into a set of symbolic logic statements.

If the ground is rocky and the horse needs new shoes, its feet will be sore. However, if the horse does not need new shoes, its feet will not be sore. Therefore, either the ground is not rocky and the horse's feet are not sore, or the horse needs new shoes.

Solution: First, let R = the ground is rocky, N = the horse needs new shoes, and S = the horse's feet are sore. Using these letters, we can abbreviate the paragraph as

If R and N, then S
If $\sim N$, then $\sim S$
Therefore, $\sim R$ and $\sim S$, or N

The problem now looks more approachable. The only difficult part remaining is that the first statement contains both a conjunction and a conditional statement while the third statement contains both a conjunction and a disjunction. To enable us to handle complex statements of this type, we need to use parentheses.

If (R and N), then S
If $\sim N$, then $\sim S$
Therefore, ($\sim R$ and $\sim S$), or N

Now, using our symbols for the conjunction and conditional, we have

$$(R \wedge N) \to S$$
$$\sim N \to \sim S$$
$$\therefore (\sim R \wedge \sim S) \vee N$$

With the completion of this last example, we have seen how a complicated paragraph in English can be reduced to a few short sentences in logic. To complete this section, we need to show how logical arguments can be used to answer questions about complicated situations. We do this by using a mathematical structure called a truth table.

Truth Tables

A **truth table** is a chart consisting of all the possible true and false combinations of the clauses in a statement. Certain sequences of logical statements, such as syllogisms, have been discussed in earlier sections, but we have not been able to handle problems as difficult as the question presented at the end of Example 3. With care and patience, a truth table can provide the answer to even these complicated problems.

The following three truth tables are the basis for all truth tables. They handle the possible situations that can arise in the disjunction, conjunction, and conditional statements.

The Disjunction Statement

A **disjunction** is the logic statement used in connection with the English word "or." As a result, a disjunction is considered true whenever one or both of its clauses are true. Thus, for the disjunction $A \vee B$, we have the following truth table:

Disjunction Truth Table

A	B	$A \vee B$
T	T	T
T	F	T
F	T	T
F	F	F

Notice that the value of $A \vee B$ is true unless both A and B are false. This corresponds to our intuitive idea of the meaning of an *or* statement.

The Conjunction Statement

A **conjunction** is the logic statement used in connection with the English word "and." A conjunction is true only if *both* of its clauses are true. As a result, we have the following truth table for conjunctions:

Conjunction Truth Table

A	B	$A \wedge B$
T	T	T
T	F	F
F	T	F
F	F	F

The Conditional Statement

A **conditional** is the logic statement used when the statement is in the form "if . . . then . . . ." A conditional statement is logically true in three of the four possible cases, as shown here.

Conditional Truth Table

A	B	$A \rightarrow B$
T	T	T
T	F	F
F	T	T
F	F	T

At first, it may seem peculiar that the conditional statement is true even when the first clause (the antecedent) is false. To understand this, we need to realize what is meant by "logically true." Recall from our work on deductive reasoning that if the premise of a syllogism is false, we can prove any statement based on the false assumption. Similarly, if the antecedent of a conditional statement is false, any conclusion is considered logically true. Therefore, the only situation that causes the conditional statement to be false is when the first clause (the antecedent) is true and the second clause (the consequent) is false.

Now that we have these three truth tables, we have the basic building blocks for all truth tables. We can use these tables to determine when a statement is logically true.

Example 4:

Use a truth table to determine the truth values of A and B that make the statement $\sim A \wedge \sim B$ logically valid.

Solution: As in the three previous truth tables, we need to have rows that give all the possible truth values for A and B. In addition, we need to have all the portions of the formula $\sim A \wedge \sim B$ represented as columns in the truth table.

A	B	$\sim A$	$\sim B$	$\sim A \wedge \sim B$
T	T	F	F	F
T	F	F	T	F
F	T	T	F	F
F	F	T	T	T

The first two columns of the truth table give all possible combinations of the truth values of A and B, and the second two columns of the truth table are merely negations of the first two columns. The statement $\sim A \wedge \sim B$ is the conjunction of the two statements $\sim A$ and $\sim B$. Therefore, the only case in which $\sim A \wedge \sim B$ is true is when both A and B are false.

Example 5:

Determine the truth values of A and B that make the statement $\sim(A \vee B)$ logically true.

Solution: As before, we need to have a truth table consisting of four rows. The third column of the truth table gives the truth values for the disjunction $A \vee B$. The fourth column gives the truth values for the negation of the disjunction. Therefore, $\sim(A \vee B)$ is true only when both A and B are false.

A	B	$A \vee B$	$\sim(A \vee B)$
T	T	T	F
T	F	T	F
F	T	T	F
F	F	F	T

Equivalent Statements

Notice that the truth values of $\sim(A \vee B)$ in Example 5 and $\sim A \wedge \sim B$ in Example 4 are identical. Whenever two statements have the same truth values, the statements are said to be **logically equivalent**. Referring to our chart used to convert English to symbols (found at the beginning of the section), we find that the symbol for equivalent statements is $\equiv$. Thus we can write

$$\sim(A \vee B) \equiv \sim A \wedge \sim B$$

Example 6:

Use a truth table to show that a conditional $A \to B$ and its contrapositive $\sim B \to \sim A$ are logical equivalents.

Solution: To do this, we need to construct a truth table containing both $A \to B$ and $\sim B \to \sim A$ and to show that the two statements always have the same truth values. Being careful about the order of $\sim B$ and $\sim A$ in the fourth and fifth columns of the truth table shows us that the truth values of $A \to B$ and $\sim B \to \sim A$ are the same and, therefore, that $A \to B \equiv \sim B \to \sim A$.

A	B	$A \to B$	$\sim B$	$\sim A$	$\sim B \to \sim A$
T	T	T	F	F	T
T	F	F	T	F	F
F	T	T	F	T	T
F	F	T	T	T	T

Verifying Syllogisms

A second use of truth tables is to verify the conclusion of a logical argument. To do this, we need to form a conditional statement. The hypothesis of the conditional will consist of a conjunction of all the premises. The conclusion of the conditional will be the conclusion of the syllogism. A syllogism has a valid conclusion if the conditional formed in this manner is always true.

Example 7:

Use a truth table to verify that the following syllogism has a valid conclusion:

$$P \to Q$$
$$P$$
$$\therefore Q$$

Solution: To verify the syllogism, we need to form a conditional statement whose hypothesis is the conjunction of the premises and whose conclusion is the conclusion of the syllogism. Doing so gives us the statement $[(P \rightarrow Q) \wedge P] \rightarrow Q$. Now we need to construct a truth table with this statement as its last column. If the last column always has a ''true'' value, the syllogism has a true conclusion.

P	Q	$P \rightarrow Q$	$(P \rightarrow Q) \wedge P$	$[(P \rightarrow Q) \wedge P]Q$
T	T	T	T	T
T	F	F	F	T
F	T	T	F	T
F	F	T	F	T

Since the last column of this truth table is always true, the syllogism has a valid conclusion.

Example 8:

Determine whether the following logical argument is valid:

$$P \rightarrow Q$$
$$\sim Q$$
$$\therefore P$$

Solution: To determine whether the argument is valid, we need to form a conditional from the premises and the conclusion of the argument. Doing so gives us the statement $[(P \rightarrow Q) \wedge \sim Q] \rightarrow P$. Now we need to construct a truth table with this statement as its last column. If the last column always has a ''true'' value, the argument is valid.

P	Q	$P \rightarrow Q$	$\sim Q$	$(P \rightarrow Q) \wedge \sim Q$	$[(P \rightarrow Q) \wedge \sim Q] \rightarrow P$
T	T	T	F	F	T
T	F	F	T	F	T
F	T	T	F	F	T
F	F	T	T	T	F

Since the last column of this truth table is not always true, the argument is not valid.

Example 9:

Use a truth table to determine whether the following syllogism has a valid conclusion:

$$S \rightarrow R$$
$$N \rightarrow S$$
$$\therefore N \rightarrow R$$

Solution: If $N \rightarrow R$ is the valid conclusion of $S \rightarrow R$ and $N \rightarrow S$, then the statement $[(S \rightarrow R) \wedge (N \rightarrow S)] \rightarrow (N \rightarrow R)$ must always be true.

Setting up a truth table for this statement requires eight lines since there are three variables: R, N, and S.

S	R	N	$S \rightarrow R$	$N \rightarrow S$	$(S \rightarrow R) \wedge (N \rightarrow S)$	$N \rightarrow R$	$[(S \rightarrow R) \wedge (N \rightarrow S)] \rightarrow (N \rightarrow R)$
T	T	T	T	T	T	T	T
T	T	F	T	T	T	T	T
T	F	T	F	T	F	F	T
T	F	F	F	T	F	T	T
F	T	T	T	F	F	T	T
F	T	F	T	T	T	T	T
F	F	T	T	F	F	F	T
F	F	F	T	T	T	T	T

Since the last column always has a true value, the syllogism must be true.

In summary, this section has presented a few topics from symbolic logic. The important topics are

1. The English to symbol dictionary

English	Symbol	Name
Not	$\sim$	Negation
Therefore	$\therefore$	
Implies, if . . . then . . .	$\rightarrow$	Conditional
Equivalent statements	$\equiv$	Logical equivalency
And	$\wedge$	Conjunction
Or	$\vee$	Inclusive disjunction

2. The three basic truth tables

Disjunction Truth Table			Conjunction Truth Table			Conditional Truth Table		
A	B	$A \vee B$	A	B	$A \wedge B$	A	B	$A \to B$
T	T	T	T	T	T	T	T	T
T	F	T	T	F	F	T	F	F
F	T	T	F	T	F	F	T	T
F	F	F	F	F	F	F	F	T

3. Truth tables can be used to determine whether two statements are logically equivalent and to determine the validity of a logical argument.

SECTION 4.4

PROBLEMS

In Problems 1–10, translate the given English sentence(s) into symbols.

1. If it is midnight, I am asleep.
I was asleep.
Therefore, it was midnight.

2. If a person plays basketball in the NBA, he is over 5 ft tall.
Russell (a person) plays NBA basketball.
Therefore, Russell is over 5 ft tall.

3. If you are a farmer in Polt County, then you grow corn.
Farmer Ron does not grow corn.
Therefore, Farmer Ron does not live in Polt County.

4. If $ABCD$ is a square, it has four sides.
$ABCD$ does not have four sides.
Therefore, $ABCD$ is not a square.

5. If a $\triangle ABC$ is not scalene, then it has either two or three equal sides.
$\triangle ABC$ does not have three equal sides.
Therefore, $\triangle ABC$ has two equal sides.

6. If the correct answer is not yes, then the correct answer is either no or maybe.
The correct answer is not no.
Therefore, the correct answer is maybe.

7. If the animal is a healthy dog, it has four legs and can run quickly, and if the animal is a pig, it has two eyes but very poor eyesight.

8. Bill will study hard and pass the test, or Bill will not study hard and not pass the test.

9. If it gyred or gimbled, then it was a slithy tove or an efficient flibbert.

10. If Joan plays sports or works out, then Joan will not be fat and will not be lazy.

In Problems 11–14, use a truth table to determine the truth values that make each statement true.

11. $(A \rightarrow C) \vee \sim C$

12. $R \rightarrow (C \vee \sim C)$

13. $(\sim F \rightarrow Q) \rightarrow \sim Q$

14. $(V \rightarrow W) \rightarrow \sim W$

In problems 15–16, use a truth table to show that the two statements are equivalent.

15. $\sim(A \wedge \sim B)$ and $\sim A \vee B$

16. $(A \wedge B) \vee (A \wedge \sim B)$ and A

Use truth tables to determine if the arguments in Problems 17–24 are logically valid.

17. $P \rightarrow Q$
P
$\therefore Q$

18. $\sim Q \rightarrow \sim P$
P
$\therefore Q$

19. $\sim A$
$A \rightarrow C$
$\therefore A$

20. B
$B \rightarrow \sim C$
$\therefore \sim C$

21. Chickens do not talk, and my chickens talk. Therefore, if it is a chicken, it is not my chicken.

22. Pigs can find truffles, and my animals cannot find truffles. Therefore, my animals are not pigs.

23. If fish had wings, then eagles would swim. If eagles swam, then eagles would eat fish. Eagles eat fish. Therefore, fish have wings.

24. Money causes all the world's troubles, or money helps the poor. If money helps the poor, it is not the cause of all the world's troubles. Money is the cause of all the world's troubles. Therefore, money does not help the poor.

*25. Determine the validity of the argument in Example 3.

*26. Lewis Carroll, author of *Alice in Wonderland*, was also an accomplished logician. One of his many logic problems was the following.

> No ducks waltz.
>
> No officers ever decline to waltz.
>
> All my poultry are ducks.
>
> Therefore, officers are not my poultry.

If we let D = ducks, P = my poultry, O = officers and W = willing to waltz, the problem becomes

$$D \rightarrow \sim W$$
$$O \rightarrow W$$
$$P \rightarrow D$$
$$\therefore O \rightarrow \sim P$$

Construct a 16-row truth table to give all the possible true-false combinations of D, W, O, and P. Use the truth table to verify the conclusion of the argument.

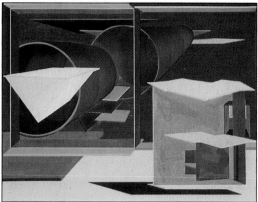

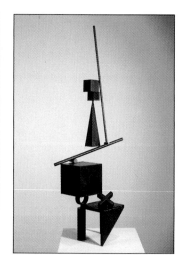

Artists look to geometry as a means of creating visual excitement. (*Upper left*) *Pachinko* by Al Held (courtesy of Crown Point Press). (*Upper right*) *Balanced–Unbalanced Table* by Fletcher Benton (courtesy of the John Berggruen Gallery). (*Left*) *Kastle Keep* by Hassel Smith (courtesy of Magnolia Editions).

SECTION 4.5

▼

PROOFS IN GEOMETRY

As we saw in the short history of geometry in Chapter 3, there are many facets to the study of geometry. Elementary geometry can be classified into three general categories. First, there is the geometry that is practical, which allows us to find distances, perimeters, areas, volumes, and the like. Second, there is the geometry that is a model of space, which gives us a good source of information of spatial relationships in our world. Third, there is the geometry that is a mathematical system in which statements are shown to be true on the basis of valid arguments. In this section, we look at geometry as a mathematical system and show how some geometric facts can be logically deduced using the definitions, axioms, and postulates established in Chapter 3. In this endeavor we will employ both direct and indirect methods of proof.

Direct Proof

A direct proof uses the principles of the hypothetical syllogism and the direct argument of Section 4.2. Such a proof shows that there is a direct and logical path from the hypothesis of a statement to the conclusion of the statement. Our first theorem will give you an example of such a proof.

T1: **If a segment lies in a plane, then the line containing the segment lies in the plane.**

To prove that the conclusion is true, we draw a figure to represent the situation and identify what is given to us (the hypothesis) and what we must show to be true (the conclusion). The proof will then demonstrate that with the help of axioms, postulates, and definitions the conclusion follows logically from the hypothesis.

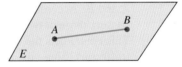

Hypothesis: $\overline{AB}$ lies in plane E

Conclusion: $\overleftrightarrow{AB}$ lies in plane E

Proof: Since $\overline{AB}$ lies in plane E and $\overline{AB}$ contains its end points, A and B must lie in plane E.

$\overline{AB}$ can be extended in both directions to form $\overleftrightarrow{AB}$ (P2, p. 122).

Therefore, $\overleftrightarrow{AB}$ must lie in plane E, since two points of the line lie in E (P3, p. 122).

Indirect Proof

An indirect proof is based on the premise that a hypothesis implies either a certain conclusion or the negation of that conclusion. If a hypothesis does not imply the negation of the conclusion, it must imply the original conclusion. In an indirect proof, we accept the hypothesis of the proposition, but we assume the negation of the conclusion to be true. We then show that this negation leads to a contradiction of the hypothesis, a definition, a postulate, or a theorem. Thus, the negation of the conclusion is impossible and is not true, and the original conclusion is true. We can summarize an indirect proof as follows:

Either $A \rightarrow B$ or $A \rightarrow {\sim}B$.

If $A \rightarrow {\sim}B$ is impossible, then $A \rightarrow B$ is true.

The proof of our second theorem is an example of an indirect proof.

T2: **If two distinct lines intersect, they intersect in at most one point.**

In using an indirect proof for this theorem, we assume that the negation of the conclusion is true and show that this leads to a contradiction of the hypothesis. We assume that the two lines intersect in more than one point.

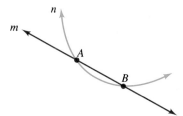

Hypothesis: Lines *m* and *n* are distinct lines that intersect.

Conclusion: Line *m* intersects line *n* in at most one point.

Assumption: Suppose *m* intersects *n* in two points, *A* and *B*.

Proof: Suppose *m* and *n* are two distinct lines that intersect in two points, *A* and *B*. According to P1 (p. 121), there exists only one line passing through two points. Thus, *m* and *n* must be the same line. This contradicts the hypothesis that lines *m* and *n* are distinct (different). Thus, the assumption is false, and the conclusion must be true. Therefore, if two distinct lines intersect, they intersect in at most one point.

The proofs of the two previous theorems were written in paragraph form with an intermingling of statements and the reasons for the validity of the statements. Some readers may prefer another format, the traditional two-column proof, in which statements and the reasons for each statement are placed in separate columns. The proof of our third theorem demonstrates this form of proof.

T3: **If two lines in the same plane are parallel to the same line, then they are parallel to each other.**

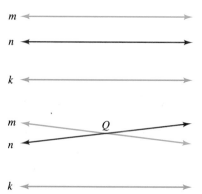

Hypothesis: Lines m and n are in the same plane.

$m \| k$

$n \| k$

Conclusion: $m \| n$.

Assumption: m not $\| n$

Proof:

Statements	**Reasons**
1. Suppose coplanar lines m and n are not $\|$.	**1.** Assumption (indirect proof).
2. $\therefore$ m must intersect n at some point Q.	**2.** Definition of parallel lines (D9, p. 119).
3. But $m \| k$ and $n \| k$.	**3.** Hypothesis.
4. Thus, through point Q there are two lines parallel to line k.	**4.** Result of statements 2 and 3.
5. This contradicts the parallel postulate (P5, p. 123).	**5.** Through a point that is not on a line there is only one parallel.
6. $\therefore$ The assumption is false and $m \| n$.	**6.** Steps 1 to 5.

Now that we have established the methods of proof to be used in this section, we apply them to the proofs of selected theorems that lead to a proof of one of the most astounding theorems of elementary Euclidean geometry: The sum of the measures of the angles of any triangle equals 180°. To prove this result, we need the next three theorems.

T4:

Exterior Angle Theorem

An exterior angle of a triangle is greater than either nonadjacent interior angle of the triangle.

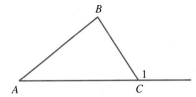

Hypothesis: $\angle 1$ is an exterior angle. $\angle A$ and $\angle B$ are nonadjacent interior angles of $\triangle ABC$.

Conclusion: $\angle 1 > \angle A$.

$\angle 1 > \angle B$.

Proof: The proof involves the development of congruent triangles, which will not be included in this short investigation into Euclidean geometry. Hence, we will accept this theorem without its proof. Research into the proof of the exterior angle theorem would be a worthwhile project for the interested student.

T5:

If two lines *m* and *n* are cut by a transversal *t* such that the alternate interior angles are equal, then *m* ‖ *n*.

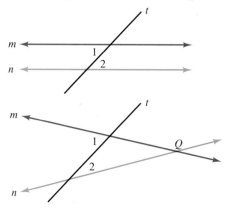

Hypothesis: lines *m* and *n* cut by transversal *t* with ∠1 = ∠2.

Conclusion: *m* ‖ *n*.

Assumption: *m* not ‖ *n*.

Proof: Suppose lines *m* and *n* are cut by transversal *t* and ∠1 = ∠2, but *m* is not parallel to *n*. Therefore, by the definition of parallel lines, *m* and *n* must intersect at some point *Q*. In the triangle that is formed, ∠1 is an exterior angle and ∠2 is a nonadjacent interior angle. By the exterior angle theorem (T4), ∠1 > ∠2. This contradicts the hypothesis that ∠1 = ∠2. Therefore, the assumption is false and *m* ‖ *n*.

T6:

If two parallel lines *m* and *n* are cut by a transversal *t*, the alternate interior angles are equal.

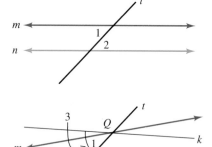

Hypothesis: *m* ‖ *n*.

Conclusion: ∠1 = ∠2.

Assumption: ∠1 ≠ ∠2.

Proof:

Statements	Reasons
1. Suppose *m* ‖ *n* and ∠1 ≠ ∠2.	1. Assumption (indirect proof).
2. Let *Q* be the intersection of *m* and *t*.	2. Two lines intersect in one point (T1, p. 237).

3. Let line k pass through P such that $\angle 3 = \angle 2$.

4. $\therefore k \| n$.

5. But $m \| n$ and passes through Q.

6. $\therefore$ Through Q there are two lines parallel to n.

7. This contradicts the parallel postulate (P5, p. 123).

8. $\therefore$ The assumption is false and $\angle 1 = \angle 2$.

3. Each angle has a unique measure (P6, p. 123).

4. If the alternate interior angles are equal, the lines are parallel (T5, p. 240).

5. Hypothesis and step 3.

6. Steps 1 to 5.

7. Through a point that is not on a line there is only one parallel.

8. Steps 1 to 7.

Euclidean Triangle Sum

T7:

The sum of the measures of the angles of a triangle is 180°.

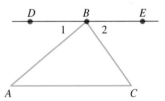

Hypothesis: $\triangle ABC$

Conclusion: $\angle A + \angle B + \angle C = 180°$.

Proof:

Statements	Reasons
1. Let $\overleftrightarrow{DE}$ pass through B so that $\overrightarrow{DE} \| \overrightarrow{AC}$.	1. Through a point that is not on a line only one parallel can be drawn (P5, p. 123).
2. $\angle DBE$ is a straight angle and $\angle DBE = 180°$.	2. Definition of a straight angle (D4, p. 117).
3. $\therefore \angle 1 + \angle B + \angle 2 = \angle DBE$.	3. A whole equals the sum of its parts (A5, p. 121).
4. But $\angle 1 = \angle A$ and $\angle 2 = \angle C$.	4. If two lines are parallel, the alternate interior angles are equal (T6, p. 240).
5. $\therefore \angle A + \angle B + \angle C = 180°$.	5. Quantities may be substituted for their equals (A1, p. 120).

As we saw in Chapter 3, the triangle-sum theorems in the non-Euclidean geometries are quite different from Euclid's theorem. In Riemannian geometry the sum of the angles of a triangle is greater than 180°, whereas in Lobachevskian geometry that sum is less than 180°. We can show the existence of a triangle that has an angle sum greater than 180° in Riemannian geometry by using a deductive proof.

Riemannian Triangle Sum

T7R: **There exists a triangle that has an angle sum greater than 180°.**

Proof: Let line h form a 90° angle with $\overline{AB}$ at point A, and let k form a 90° angle with $\overline{AB}$ at point B. By the Riemannian parallel postulate, h and k intersect at some point C. Now, $\angle 1 \neq 0$, since, if it did, h and k would coincide.

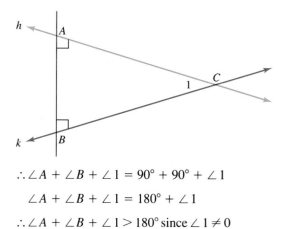

$$\therefore \angle A + \angle B + \angle 1 = 90° + 90° + \angle 1$$

$$\angle A + \angle B + \angle 1 = 180° + \angle 1$$

$$\therefore \angle A + \angle B + \angle 1 > 180° \text{ since } \angle 1 \neq 0$$

Let's conclude our brief excursion into geometric proofs by looking at the triangle-sum theorem in Lobachevskian geometry. Though we will not give a formal proof of that theorem, we will demonstrate the existence of a triangle in Lobachevskian geometry that has angles with a total measure less than 180°.

Lobachevskian Triangle Sum

T7L: **There exists a triangle that has an angle sum less than 180°.***

Proof: Let $r \perp m$ and $q \perp m$. $\therefore q \| r$ (two lines $\perp$ same line are parallel). But the Lobachevskian parallel postulate assumes there is another line s that is also parallel to r ($s \| r$). Call the angle between q and s, $\angle 1$. Let C be a point on line r such that $\angle 4 = \angle 1$. Label $\angle 2$,

---

*It can be proved that all triangles in this geometry have this property.

∠3, and ∠5 as shown in the figure. (Note: ∠2 ≠ 0, since if ∠2 = 0, then line *BC* coincides with line *s*, line *BC* is parallel to *r*, and point *C* would not exist.)

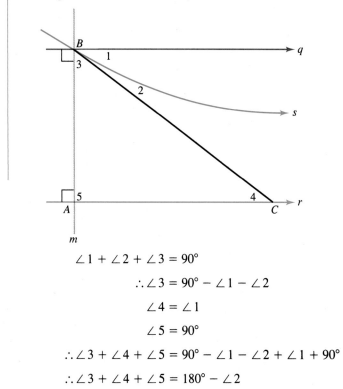

$$\angle 1 + \angle 2 + \angle 3 = 90°$$

$$\therefore \angle 3 = 90° - \angle 1 - \angle 2$$

$$\angle 4 = \angle 1$$

$$\angle 5 = 90°$$

$$\therefore \angle 3 + \angle 4 + \angle 5 = 90° - \angle 1 - \angle 2 + \angle 1 + 90°$$

$$\therefore \angle 3 + \angle 4 + \angle 5 = 180° - \angle 2$$

Thus, the sum of the measures of the angles of △*ABC* is less than 180°.

Many other theorems can be proven by the triangle-sum theorems from each geometry. Some of these are exercises in the problem set at the end of this section.

SECTION 4.5

PROBLEMS

1. Explain the difference between a direct and an indirect proof.

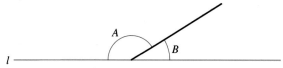

Use the fact that the sum of ∠*A* and ∠*B* along the straight line *l* is 180°, together with T6 and T7, to determine all the angles in Problems 2 and 3.

2. If *m*‖*n* and *p*‖*q*, determine the angles created by the line segments in the figure.

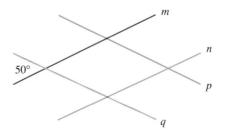

3. If $m\|n$, determine the angles created by the line segments in the figure.

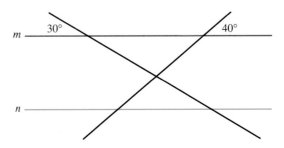

Problems 4–13 involve proofs of the theorems from Euclidean geometry.

4. Use an indirect proof to prove the following theorem: If two lines are cut by a transversal such that the corresponding angles are equal, then the lines are parallel.

5. Write an indirect proof for the following theorem: If two parallel lines are cut by a transversal, then the corresponding angles are equal.

6. Prove: If the measure of one angle of a triangle is equal to the sum of the measures of the other two angles, the triangle must contain a right angle.

7. Prove: At least one angle of a triangle must have a measure that is greater than or equal to 60°.

8. Prove: A triangle can have only one right angle or obtuse angle.

9. Prove: If a triangle has a right angle or an obtuse angle, the other two angles must be acute angles.

10. Prove: If a triangle is equiangular, each angle measures 60°.

11. Prove: If two angles of one triangle are equal to two angles of another triangle, the third angles of each triangle are equal to each other.

12. Prove: The measure of the exterior angle of a triangle is equal to the sum of the nonadjacent interior angles.

13. Prove: From a point not on a line, at most one perpendicular can be drawn to the line.

Prove the following theorems in Lobachevskian geometry.

14. In a right triangle, the sum of the two non-right angles is less than 90°.

15. Each angle of an equiangular triangle is less than 60°.

16. A triangle can have only one right angle or one obtuse angle.

17. An exterior angle of a triangle is greater than the sum of the nonadjacent interior angles.

Prove the following theorems in Riemannian geometry.

18. Each angle of an equiangular triangle is greater than 60°.

19. In a right triangle $\triangle ABC$, if $\angle A$ is a right angle, then $\angle B + \angle C > 90°$.

20. An exterior angle of a triangle is less than the sum of the nonadjacent interior angles.

C H A P T E R   4   SUMMARY

KEY TERMS, CONCEPTS, AND FORMULAS

The important terms in this chapter are:

Affirming the antecedent: A deductive argument of the form

> If A, then B.
>
> A.
>
> Therefore, B.   (p. 209)

Biconditional statement: If A and B represent statements, the biconditional statement combines both the statement "If A, then B" and the statement "If B, then A" into one statement, "A if and only if B."   (p. 200)

Conclusion: The "then" clause of a conditional statement, also called the consequent.   (p. 198)

Conditional statement: A complex statement formed by two individual statements joined by the words "If . . . , then . . . ."   (p. 198)

Conjunction: A statement in which categories are connected with the word "and." A conjunction is true whenever a quality applies to both categories.   (p. 220)

Contrapositive: If A and B represent statements, the contrapositive of the conditional statement "If A, then B" is the statement "If not B, then not A."   (p. 198)

Converse: If *A* and *B* represent statements, the converse of the conditional statement "If *A*, then *B*" is the statement "If *B*, then *A*." (p. 198)

Deduction: The process of reasoning in which conclusions are based on general principles.   (p. 207)

Denying the consequent: A deductive argument of the form

> If *A*, then *B*.
>
> Not *B*.
>
> Therefore, not *A*.   (p. 211)

Descriptive method: The technique of writing a set by giving a rule for its elements.   (p. 189)

Disjunction: A statement in which categories are connected with the word "or." A disjunction is true whenever a quality applies to one or both categories.   (p. 220)

Element: An item in a set.   (p. 189)

Empty set (∅ or { }): A set that does not contain any elements.   (p. 189)

Hypothesis: The "if" clause of a conditional statement; also called the antecedent.   (p. 198)

Hypothetical syllogism: A deductive argument of the form

> If *A*, then *B*.
>
> If *B*, then *C*.
>
> Therefore, if *A*, then *C*.   (p. 207)

Induction: The process of reasoning in which conclusions are based on experience or experimentation.   (p. 204)

Intersection: An operation with two sets that creates a set containing elements common to both sets.   (p. 191)

Inverse: If *A* and *B* represent statements, the inverse of the conditional statement "if *A*, then *B*" is the statement "if not *A*, then not *B*." (p. 198)

Listing method: The technique of expressing a set by writing all its elements in braces.   (p. 189)

Logic: The science of correct reasoning.   (p. 195)

Set: A collection of items.   (p. 188)

Subset: A set whose elements are contained in another set.   (p. 190)

Symbolic logic: A system of logic that uses symbols to represent statements.

The symbols used in this chapter are:

Symbol	English	Name
~	Not	Negation
∴	Therefore	
→	Implies, if . . . then . . .	Conditional
≡	Equivalent statements	Logical equivalency
∧	And	Conjunction
∨	Or	Inclusive disjunction (p. 226)

Truth table: A chart used to check the validity of a series of logic statements.   (p. 228)

Union: An operation with sets that creates a set containing all the elements of both sets.   (p. 191)

Universal set: A set that contains all elements of a certain category.   (p. 192)

Venn diagrams: Pictures used to depict sets.   (p. 192)

After completing this chapter, you should be able to:

1. Distinguish between different types of conditional statements and use the contrapositive as the logical equivalent to a given statement.   (p. 198)

2. Recognize and write good definitions.   (p. 200)

3. Distinguish between inductive and deductive reasoning.   (p. 204)

4. Make valid deductive arguments, using hypothetical syllogisms, affirming the antecedent, and denying the consequent.   (p. 209)

5. Use Venn diagrams to arrive at the conclusion for a logical argument.   (p. 216)

6. Use truth tables to determine the validity of an argument or determine the equivalency of statements.   (p. 228)

7. Prove theorems of Euclidean and non-Euclidean geometry using both direct and indirect proofs.   (p. 236)

SUMMARY

PROBLEMS

1. For the conditional statement "I am in bed if it is after midnight,"

(a) State its hypothesis and conclusion.
(b) Write its converse.
(c) Write its inverse.
(d) Write its contrapositive.

2. What are the three necessary components of a definition? What additional properties are needed for a good definition? For each of the following, state what is wrong with the "definition" and change it to make it a good definition.

(a) Perpendicular line segments are segments that intersect each other.
(b) Microscopic: that which can only be seen through a microscope.
(c) Natural numbers are numbers that are greater than zero.

3. Write a statement that is true but whose converse and inverse are false.

4. Explain the difference between an inductive argument and a deductive argument. Give both an inductive argument and a deductive argument to persuade a friend to help you build a fence.

5. Rewrite the following in correct syllogistic form and state a valid conclusion from the premises.

(a) $X \rightarrow Y$
$Z \rightarrow \sim Y$
$\sim Z \rightarrow P$

(b) If the geometry is Riemannian, then there are no parallel lines.
If the geometry is Euclidean, then parallel lines exist.
If the geometry is non-Euclidean, then at least one of Euclid's postulates is changed.

6. Of 400 students, 360 students are taking a math course or an English course. Eighty-five of the students in math classes are also taking an English class. If a total of 190 students are taking a math course, how many are taking an English course but not a math course?

7. If you are a scientist, then you are logical. If you are logical and not organized, then you are a scientist. Everyone is either logical, a scientist, or organized. If you are logical or a scientist, then you are organized. Use a Venn diagram to determine the logical conclusion.

8. Translate the following statements into symbolic logic.

(a) If John has a headache, then John is either grumpy or silent.
(b) If the weather is not good, then we will not play baseball and we will not have a picnic.
(c) If you do not study math and you want a good job, it will be harder to advance in business.

9. Use truth tables to show that $(A \lor B) \land (A \lor \sim B)$ is equivalent to A.

10. Use a truth table to determine if the argument is logically valid.

Parrots can crack walnuts, and if it is my animal, it cannot crack walnuts. Therefore, if it is my animal, it is not a parrot.

11. Use a direct proof to verify the following theorem from Euclidean geometry: If a ray lies in a plane, then the line containing the ray lies in the plane.

12. Use an indirect proof and the triangle-sum theorem to verify the following theorem from Euclidean geometry: Two lines in the same plane that are perpendicular to the same line are parallel.

13. Prove in Riemannian geometry: Two lines in the same plane that are perpendicular to the same line are not parallel.

14. Prove in Lobachevskian geometry: A triangle cannot contain both a right angle and an obtuse angle.

CHAPTER 5

TRIGONOMETRY

The Lighthouse at Honfleur by Georges Seurat. For the navigator at sea, a lighthouse serves as a permanent reference point for charting a course. (National Gallery of Art)

A SHORT HISTORY OF TRIGONOMETRY

As the understanding of numbers, algebra, and geometry developed, ancient scholars turned their attention to a quantitative study of the sun, the moon, the planets, and the stars. This interest in astronomy led to the formation of what is known today as trigonometry. The word "trigonometry" comes from the Greek words *tri′gonon* (triangle) and *met′ron* (measure). It began as the study of the relationship between arcs and chords of a circle as in a bow and a bowstring, progressed to the study of triangles on the surface of a sphere, and is now commonly known as the study of the relationship between the angles and sides of a triangle. The words used to describe these relationships have evolved into the present terms: sine, cosine, tangent, cotangent, secant, and cosecant.

The exact origins of trigonometry are not known. There is, however, evidence that astronomy (requiring trigonometry) was studied by the ancient Babylonians and Chinese. Ancient Egyptians investigated the ratios of sides of a triangle as

Chord (bow string) | Arc (bow) | Spherical triangle | Plane triangle

recorded in the Ahmes papyrus (1550 B.C.). However, the first significant contributions to trigonometry were made by the Greeks. Motivated by their interest in astronomy, they systematically studied the relationship between arcs and chords of a circle. Hipparchus of Nicea (c. 140 B.C.), a mathematician and astronomer, wrote the first systematic study of trigonometry. He developed methods of studying spherical triangles, is given credit for dividing the circle into 360 degrees, and is considered the founder of trigonometry. Menelaus of Alexandria (c. 100 B.C.) contributed much to the study of spherical triangles as related to the study of astronomy. Claudius Ptolemy of Alexandria (A.D. 125), in his work *Syntaxis Mathematica*, now known as *Almagest* (the greatest), displayed a table of chords that is equivalent to a table of sines for angles from 0° to 90° at 15-minute intervals. The *Almagest* exerted a profound influence on astronomy and trigonometry for the next century.

During the Dark Ages in Europe from 400 to 1000, the development of trigonometry moved to the East. Hindu astronomers displayed their knowledge of trigonometry in the book entitled *Sûrya Siddhānta* (c. 400) and in the works of Varâhamihira (c. 505) and Āryabhata (c. 510). The Arabs took what the Hindus had done in trigonometry and built upon that. Al-Battânî (c. 920) and Abû'l-Wefâ (c. 980) used tangents and cotangents as well as the Laws of Sines and Cosines to solve spherical triangles, and computed tables of sines, cosines, tangents, and cotangents. Kûshyâr ibn Lebbân (c. 1000) wrote a book on astronomy and trigonometry and Nasîr ed-dîn al-Tûsî (1250) wrote the first work on plane and spherical trigonometry as a branch of mathematics separate from astronomy. The Arabs' work in trigonometry during the ninth and the tenth centuries is one of the reasons this period is called the golden age of Arabian mathematics.

As Europe emerged from the Dark Ages and moved into the Renaissance, contributions to the development of trigonometry again appeared. The major contributions are outlined below.

Leonardo Fibonacci (1220), in *Practica Geometriae*, summarized Greek trigonometry.

Johann Müller (1464), known as Regiomontanus, in his work *De triangulis omnimodis*, wrote Europe's first treatment of plane and spherical trigonometry in which trigonometry is treated separately from astronomy.

Reiner Gemma Frisius (1533) modernized surveying by introducing trigonometric techniques of triangulation.

Peter Apian (1534) published a table of sine values for every minute of arc.

Georg Joachim von Lauchen (1551), known as Rhaeticus, defined the trigonometric functions as ratios of sides of a right triangle in his work *Opus palatinum de triangulis.*

Francois Viète (1579–1591) constructed a trigonometry table for every second of arc and systematically applied algebra to trigonometry, obtaining algebraic forms for many identities.

Paul Wittich and Tycho Brahe (1580) introduced prosthaphaeresis, a method of calculating products and quotients by using trigonometric identities involving addition and subtraction.

Christopher Clavius (1593) used trigonometric identities to introduce new methods of computation.

Thomas Blundeville (1594) wrote England's first complete treatment of trigonometry.

Bartholomaus Pitiscus (1600), professor of mathematics in Heidelberg, wrote the first text to have the title *Trigonometry.*

By 1658, the names of the trigonometric functions had taken their present forms. The sine function was called *jyâ* or *jîva*, meaning chord, by the Hindu mathematician Āryabhata (c. 510). The Arabs phonetically created the meaningless Arabic word *jiba* for the Hindu word *jîva*. Later the Arabs rearranged the letters of *jiba* into an actual Arabian word, *jaib*, meaning bay. Although *jaib* had nothing to do with the mathematical concept of a chord of an arc, it was widely used by the Arabs.

Around 1150 Gherardo of Cremona, in making translations from Arabic to Latin, used the Latin word for bay, *sinus*, as a translation of the Arabic *jaib*. Thus, our present word ''sine'' has no relation to the mathematical concept it represents.

The present term ''cosine'' also originated with Āryabhata, who called it *kotijyâ* in 510. Over the centuries the term ''cosine'' was referred to by different names. In 1620, Edmund Gunter used the terminology *co.sinus*, which, after being modified by John Newton in 1658, became the standard term, *cosinus*. The present word ''tangent'' originated in a work by Danish mathematician Thomas Fincke (1583), when he used the term *tangens*. After the more renowned writer Bartholomaus Pitiscus also used *tangens* in his writing, the name became permanent. The terms ''cotangent,'' ''secant,'' and ''cosecant'' also have different origins. Edmund Gunter (1620) introduced the word *cotangens*, Thomas Fincke (1583) used the word *secant*, and Rhaeticus (1596) adopted the word *cosecant*.

By 1750, trigonometry had become more than merely a tool for the astronomer and the surveyor. It was used by mathematicians John Bernoulli, Abraham de Moivre, Leonhard Euler, Isaac Newton, and Gottfried Leibniz in analyzing mathematical concepts, studying complex numbers, modeling periodic phenomena, and studying mathematical physics. In the 20th century, trigonometric functions are still important. They are used in the study of electricity, light, sound, radio, television, and other areas where values occur repeatedly. They can also be utilized in finding distances that cannot be measured directly and, consequently, are used by surveyors, astronomers, navigators, engineers, architects, and others. In this chapter you will learn more about the trigonometric functions and see how they can actually be used to solve problems in some of the areas mentioned in this section.

CHECK YOUR READING

1. Interest in what area led to the development of trigonometry?
2. What is the difference between a spherical triangle and a plane triangle?
3. When a Chinese encyclopedia of 1000 volumes was being written in A.D. 980, what was Abû'l-Wefâ doing in India?
4. In 140 B.C., Hu Shin compiled a dictionary of 10,000 characters, and the statue of Venus of Milo was sculpted. At that time, what was Hipparchus of Nicea doing?
5. What is a major reason for the period from 400 to 1000 being called the golden age of Arabian mathematics?
6. Trace the development of the word *jîva* to the word *sinus* for the trigonometric function sine.
7. As the Babylonian King Hammurabi established the first legal system in 1550 B.C., what was being written on the Ahmes papyrus?
8. In the year 1533, Francisco Pizarro executed Inca Indians in Peru. During that year, what was Reiner Frisius doing?
9. While tomatoes were being introduced into England in 1596, what was Rhaeticus doing?
10. While Italian cuisine became the culinary rage in 1580 in Europe, what were Paul Wittich and Tycho Brahe working on?
11. Match each of the following names with the correct mathematical event, discovery, or concept.

    (a) Apian   Called the sine function *jîva*
    (b) Āryabhata   Coined word *tangens*
    (c) Blundeville   Wrote first text entitled *Trigonometry*
    (d) Fincke   Devised spherical trigonometry as related to astronomy
    (e) Gherardo   Devised table of sines for every minute of arc
    (f) Menelaus   Translated Arabic to Latin
    (g) Pitiscus   Wrote *Almagest*
    (h) Ptolemy   Wrote England's first complete treatment of trigonometry

---

RESEARCH QUESTIONS

In order to answer the following questions, you will need to refer to material not contained in the text. Possible sources of information are listed in the Bibliography at the end of the text.

1. Many of the mathematicians and astronomers mentioned in this short history of the development of trigonometry are also known for other mathematical endeavors or had other interests besides mathematics. Do some research on two of the mathematicians mentioned in this section. Tell something about their lives, their achievements, and their interests.
2. Explain how trigonometry is actually used in one of the areas mentioned in this section.
3. Discuss how and in what areas of study *sextants* and *transits* are used.
4. What were some of the contributions of the Arabs to mathematics during the golden age of Arabian mathematics, the ninth and tenth centuries?
5. Explain how trigonometry is actually used in astronomy. How did the ancients use trigonometry in their astronomical endeavors?
6. Discuss the development of trigonometry in the Far East.
7. What is a trig table? How is it used?

SECTION   5.0

REVIEW

Right Triangles

Before we start discussing trigonometry, we need to review some terms and concepts that we need in this section. A major point is that all discussions in this chapter refer to Euclidean space. None of the material in this chapter is related to the non-Euclidean geometries you may have studied in Chapter 3. A **right triangle** is a triangle with a 90° angle. The two other angles are acute angles (less than 90°). The sides of the right triangle that form the 90° angle are the **legs** of the right triangle, and the other side, the one opposite the 90° angle, is the **hypotenuse** of the right triangle. The hypotenuse is always the longest side of the right triangle. In △ABC,

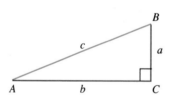

$\angle C$ = the right angle

$\angle A$ = an acute angle

$\angle B$ = an acute angle

c = hypotenuse

a = leg

b = leg

Example 1:

In the right triangles, determine which sides are legs and which side is the hypotenuse.

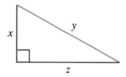
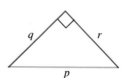
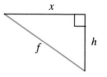

Solution:

First triangle:	y = hypotenuse, x = leg, z = leg	
Second triangle:	p = hypotenuse, q = leg, r = leg	
Third triangle:	f = hypotenuse, x = leg, h = leg	

In a right triangle, the hypotenuse is always opposite the 90° angle, but the legs of the triangle can be referred to by their orientation with respect to one of the acute angles of the triangle. The leg across the triangle from an acute angle is the opposite side, and the leg that forms the angle is the adjacent side for that acute angle. For example, in $\triangle ABC$, side c is the hypotenuse. With reference to $\angle A$, b = adjacent side, and a = opposite side. With reference to $\angle B$, a = adjacent side and b = opposite side.

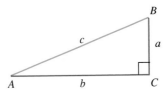

Example 2:

In the triangles, find sides opposite from and adjacent to $\angle K$.

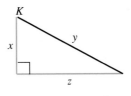 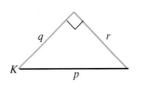 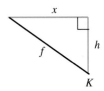

Solution: In reference to $\angle K$,

	Adjacent Side	Opposite Side
First triangle	x	z
Second triangle	q	r
Third triangle	h	x

The Pythagorean Theorem

The Greek mathematician Pythagoras (c. 582–c. 501 B.C.) is given credit for the basic theorem concerning the sides of a right triangle, the **Pythagorean Theorem**. Geometrically, it states that the sum of the squares on the legs of a right triangle is equal to the square on the hypotenuse. In algebraic terms, if the lengths of the legs of a right triangle are a and b and the length of the hypotenuse is c, then $a^2 + b^2 = c^2$.

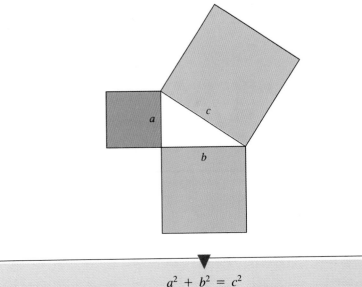

$$a^2 + b^2 = c^2$$

The Pythagorean Theorem is one of the most proved theorems in mathematics. In 1940, Elisha Scott Loomis compiled a book containing 370 proofs of the theorem. One of these proofs is credited to the 20th president of the United States, James A. Garfield. While a Congressman in 1876, he discovered what is now known as *Garfield's solution*. His proof is based on the formula for the area of a triangle, $A = 1/2 \times$ length of the base $\times$ the length of the height.

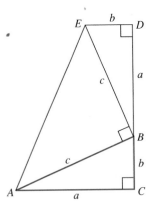

Starting with right $\triangle ABC$:

1. Extend side $\overline{CB}$ to D so that $BD = a$.

2. Draw $\overline{DE}$ so that $\angle D = 90°$ and $DE = b$.

3. Draw $\overline{BE}$ and $\overline{AE}$.

The area of *ACDE* can be determined by adding the areas of the right triangles $\triangle ABC$, $\triangle EDB$, and $\triangle ABE$.

$$\text{Area of } \triangle ABC = \frac{1}{2}ab$$

$$\text{Area of } \triangle EDB = \frac{1}{2}ab$$

$$\text{Area of } \triangle ABE = \frac{1}{2}c^2 \qquad \left[\text{Area} = \frac{1}{2}(\text{base})(\text{height}) = \frac{1}{2}c \cdot c \right]$$

$$\therefore \text{Area of } ACDE = ab + \frac{1}{2}c^2$$

The region *ACDE* can also be divided into two triangles by drawing $\overline{EC}$. The area of *ACDE* can be determined by adding the areas of $\triangle ACE$ and $\triangle EDC$. Noticing that the height in both triangles is $a + b$, we get

$$\text{Area of } \triangle ACE = \frac{1}{2}a(a + b) = \frac{1}{2}ab + \frac{1}{2}a^2$$

$$\text{Area of } \triangle EDC = \frac{1}{2}b(a + b) = \frac{1}{2}ab + \frac{1}{2}b^2$$

$$\therefore \text{Area of } ACDE = ab + \frac{1}{2}a^2 + \frac{1}{2}b^2$$

Since we have found the area of the region *ACDE* in two different ways, the two results must be equal.

$$ab + \frac{1}{2}a^2 + \frac{1}{2}b^2 = ab + \frac{1}{2}c^2$$

$$\frac{1}{2}a^2 + \frac{1}{2}b^2 = \frac{1}{2}c^2$$

$$\therefore a^2 + b^2 = c^2$$

Example 3:

If the legs of a right triangle are 5 inches and 12 inches, find the length of the hypotenuse.

Solution: According to the Pythagorean Theorem,

$$c^2 = a^2 + b^2$$
$$c^2 = 12^2 + 5^2$$
$$c^2 = 144 + 25$$
$$c^2 = 169$$
$$c = \pm\sqrt{169}$$
$$c = 13$$

The hypotenuse is 13 inches. (Note: The positive square root is taken since a distance cannot be negative.)

Example 4:

If the hypotenuse of a right triangle is 6.5 cm and one leg is 3.3 cm, find the length of the other leg.

Solution:

$$a^2 + b^2 = c^2$$
$$3.3^2 + b^2 = 6.5^2$$
$$10.89 + b^2 = 42.25$$
$$b^2 = 31.36$$
$$b = \pm\sqrt{31.36}$$
$$b = 5.6$$

The other leg is 5.6. cm.

Example 5:

The 13-ft pole of a TV antenna stands vertically on the flat roof of a building. A 15-ft support wire is attached to the top of the pole and is tied to the roof. If the wire is taut, how far from the bottom of the antenna should the wire be attached?

Solution:

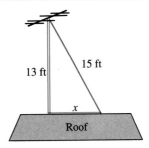

Let x = the distance from the bottom of the antenna pole to the point where the wire is attached to the roof. By the Pythagorean Theorem:

$$x^2 + 13^2 = 15^2$$

$$x^2 + 169 = 225$$

$$x^2 = 56$$

$$x = \pm\sqrt{56}$$

$$x \approx 7.5$$

The wire is attached approximately 7.5 ft from the bottom of the antenna.

Pythagorean Triples

Natural numbers that satisfy the Pythagorean Theorem are called **Pythagorean triples**. The first triple is 3, 4, and 5, since those numbers are the smallest natural numbers that satisfy the Pythagorean Theorem, $3^2 + 4^2 = 5^2$. Twenty-seven of these triples are listed below.

3	4	5	12	35	37	24	32	40
5	12	13	14	48	50	24	45	51
6	8	10	15	20	25	27	36	45
7	24	25	15	36	39	28	45	53
8	15	17	16	30	34	30	40	50
9	12	15	18	24	30	33	44	55
9	40	41	20	21	29	33	56	65
10	24	26	20	48	52	36	48	60
12	16	20	21	28	35	39	52	65

The Root Spiral

Right triangles with sides that are not natural numbers have also been of keen interest over the centuries. The study of these triangles enabled mathematicians to find approximations for the square roots of natural numbers that turn out to be irrational numbers, such as $\sqrt{2}$, $\sqrt{3}$, and $\sqrt{5}$. Today, to find $\sqrt{2}$ we simply press 2 and the square root button on a calculator and the answer 1.414213562 appears. But how could the ancients find $\sqrt{2}$? They did not have calculators. Further, can there really be a length $\sqrt{2}$ inches long? The answer to the question is yes. The Pythagorean Theorem allows us to find an approximation for the square roots of natural numbers and see lengths that are irrational numbers.

For example, to find $\sqrt{2}$, all we need to do is find the hypotenuse of a right triangle that has legs that are both one unit long. Using the Pythagorean Theorem, we get

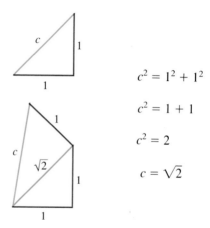

$$c^2 = 1^2 + 1^2$$

$$c^2 = 1 + 1$$

$$c^2 = 2$$

$$c = \sqrt{2}$$

Similarly, we can find $\sqrt{3}$ by finding the hypotenuse of a right triangle that has one leg with a length of $\sqrt{2}$ and the other leg with a length of 1.

$$c^2 = 1^2 + (\sqrt{2})^2$$

$$c^2 = 1 + 2$$

$$c^2 = 3$$

$$c = \sqrt{3}$$

Repeating this process gives us a root spiral. Such a spiral has simple geometric beauty and allows us to see that square roots of the natural numbers actually exist as lengths of hypotenuses of right triangles.

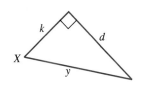

In the right triangles, determine which sides are legs and which side is the hypotenuse.

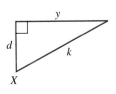

4. For each of the right triangles given in Problem 1, find the sides that are opposite from and adjacent to ∠X.

In the right triangle, find the length of the side that is not given.

5. $x = 7$, $n = 24$

6. $x = 10$, $n = 31$

7. $x = 4.3$, $n = 9.7$

8. $n = 9$, $t = 41$

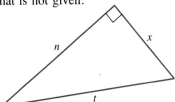

9. $n = 3.24$, $t = 67.24$

10. $n = 54.1$, $t = 76$

11. $x = 20$, $t = 25$

12. $x = 5$, $t = 8.4$

13. $x = 1.5$, $t = 1.7$

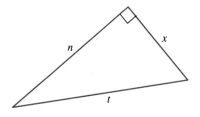

Determine if the following sets of numbers are Pythagorean triples.

14. 36, 48, 60

15. 18, 25, 33

16. 16, 63, 82

17. 55, 132, 143

18. 28, 96, 110

19. 21, 72, 75

20. 35, 120, 125

21. 24, 70, 74

22. A rectangular gate is 5 ft wide and 6 ft high. Find the length of the support wire running diagonally across the gate.

23. A standard baseball diamond is a square 90 ft on a side. Find the distance of a throw made from home plate to second base.

24. If a TV screen is a rectangle that has a 27-inch diagonal and a width of 21 inches, what is the height of the TV screen?

25. Continue the root spiral to find $\sqrt{19}$.

26. Explain why zero and negative integers cannot be used as the lengths of the sides of right triangles.

SECTION 5.1

▼

SINE, COSINE, TANGENT, AND RIGHT TRIANGLES

The right triangle and the Pythagorean Theorem reviewed in Section 5.0 are the basic building blocks of trigonometry. In order to simplify our excursion into the essentials of trigonometry, we begin by designating the vertices of the acute angles of a right triangle with the uppercase letters A and B and the sides opposite those angles with the lowercase letters a and b. The 90° angle of the right triangle will be designated by the uppercase letter C and the hypotenuse with the lowercase letter c. Later we use other uppercase letters for the angles at each vertex and the corresponding lowercase letter for the side opposite each vertex. The three fundamental trigonometric functions, **sine** (abbreviated **sin**), **cosine** (**cos**), and **tangent** (**tan**), are defined as ratios of the lengths of the sides of a right triangle. Whenever a side of a triangle is mentioned, we are referring to the *length* of that side.

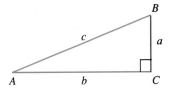

$$\frac{\text{side opposite } A}{\text{hypotenuse}} = \frac{a}{c} = \sin A \longleftarrow \boxed{\frac{\text{opp}}{\text{hyp}}} \longrightarrow \sin B = \frac{b}{c} = \frac{\text{side opposite } B}{\text{hypotenuse}}$$

$$\frac{\text{side adjacent } A}{\text{hypotenuse}} = \frac{b}{c} = \cos A \longleftarrow \boxed{\frac{\text{adj}}{\text{hyp}}} \longrightarrow \cos B = \frac{a}{c} = \frac{\text{side adjacent } B}{\text{hypotenuse}}$$

$$\frac{\text{side opposite } A}{\text{side adjacent } A} = \frac{a}{b} = \tan A \longleftarrow \boxed{\frac{\text{opp}}{\text{adj}}} \longrightarrow \tan B = \frac{b}{a} = \frac{\text{side opposite } B}{\text{side adjacent } B}$$

The three other trig functions, cosecant, secant, and cotangent, are the reciprocals of the sine, cosine, and tangent. In this essential coverage of trigonometry, we will not consider them.

Example 1:

In the right triangles, find sin A, cos A, tan A, sin B, cos B, and tan B.

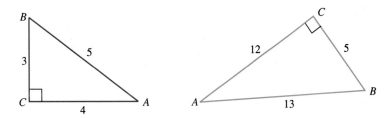

Solution:

First triangle:

$$\sin A = \left(\frac{\text{opp}}{\text{hyp}}\right) = \frac{3}{5} \qquad\qquad \sin B = \left(\frac{\text{opp}}{\text{hyp}}\right) = \frac{4}{5}$$

$$\cos A = \left(\frac{\text{adj}}{\text{hyp}}\right) = \frac{4}{5} \qquad\qquad \cos B = \left(\frac{\text{adj}}{\text{hyp}}\right) = \frac{3}{5}$$

$$\tan A = \left(\frac{\text{opp}}{\text{adj}}\right) = \frac{3}{4} \qquad\qquad \tan B = \left(\frac{\text{opp}}{\text{adj}}\right) = \frac{4}{3}$$

Second triangle:

$$\sin A = \left(\frac{\text{opp}}{\text{hyp}}\right) = \frac{5}{13} \qquad \sin B = \left(\frac{\text{opp}}{\text{hyp}}\right) = \frac{12}{13}$$

$$\cos A = \left(\frac{\text{adj}}{\text{hyp}}\right) = \frac{12}{13} \qquad \cos B = \left(\frac{\text{adj}}{\text{hyp}}\right) = \frac{5}{13}$$

$$\tan A = \left(\frac{\text{opp}}{\text{adj}}\right) = \frac{5}{12} \qquad \tan B = \left(\frac{\text{opp}}{\text{adj}}\right) = \frac{12}{5}$$

Using a Calculator to Find Trigonometric Functions

A scientific calculator can be used to find the ratio of sides for any given angle. First, you must put your calculator in degree mode. Check your calculator instruction booklet or ask your instructor if you do not know how to do this. Now, to find the value of a trig function, for example sin 30°, press the following keys:

Press	Display
3 0 sin	0.5

Thus, sin 30° = 0.5. This means that in a right triangle, the ratio of the side opposite a 30° angle to the hypotenuse of the triangle is 0.5 or 1/2. Each of the following right triangles has a 30° angle and its sine of 1/2.

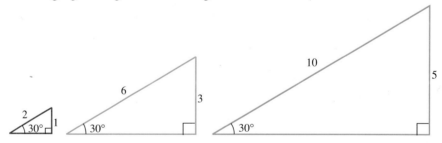

Example 2:

Use a calculator to find the following rounded off to four decimal places:

(a) sin 42°
(b) cos 67°
(c) tan 54.6°
(d) sin 5.79°
(e) tan 3.14°

Solution:

(a) 0.6691

Press	Display
4 2 sin	0.669130606

(b) 0.3907

Press	Display
6 7 cos	0.390731128

(c) 1.4071

Press	Display
5 4 . 6 tan	1.407136697

(d) 0.1009
(e) 0.0549

You must keep in mind that when you press the sin, cos, or tan key for a given angle, the calculator gives you a ratio of sides of a right triangle in decimal form. The calculator can also be used to determine an angle of a right triangle when the ratio of two sides is known. For example, if sin A = 0.6, the ratio of the length of opposite side to the length of the hypotenuse is 6/10. We can determine the measure of $\angle A$ by pressing the following keys on a calculator:

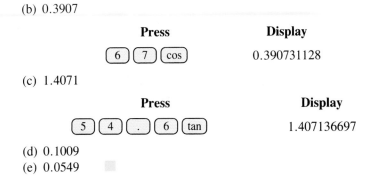

Press	Display
0 . 6 INV or 2nd sin	36.86989765 $\approx$ 36.9°

Your calculator may not do it in exactly the same manner. Check with the instruction booklet if this procedure does not work.

Example 3:

Find an angle that satisfies each of the following trig functions. Round off answers to the nearest tenth of a degree.

(a) cos B = 0.2588
(b) tan A = 3.29
(c) sin X = 2/9

Solution:
  (a) $B \approx 75.0°$

Press	Display
0 . 2 5 8 8 INV cos	75.00112969

  (b) $A \approx 73.1°$

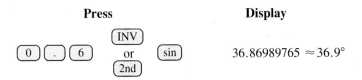

Press	Display
3 . 2 9 INV tan	73.09327892 ◂

(c) $X \approx 12.8°$

Press	Display
	12.83958839

Note:

When using a calculator to find the angle for a given trig function, you need to press the (INV) or (2nd) key before the trig function.

Solving Right Triangles

The trigonometric functions can be used to help **solve triangles**—that is, to find unknown angles and sides of the triangles. A triangle is solved when the lengths of all three sides and the measures of all three angles are known. Typically, some combination of three sides or angles will be given in the problem and we will find the values of the other three parts. To do this we use the three trig functions, the Pythagorean Theorem, the fact that the sum of the angles of a triangle equals 180°, and a calculator. In order to establish some uniformity in the answers we obtain in solving triangles, we use the following round-off rules in the rest of this chapter.

Round-Off Rules

The **final answers** to angles and sides of the triangles that have more than one decimal digit will be rounded off to the **nearest tenth**. The final answers will be computed using intermediate results that have been rounded off to four decimal places (to the right of the decimal point).

Example 4:

In the right triangle, find $\angle B$, a, and b.

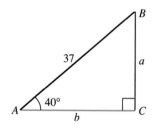

Solution:

$$\angle A + \angle B + \angle C = 180°$$

$$40° + \angle B + 90° = 180°$$

$$130° + \angle B = 180°$$

$$\angle B = 50°$$

To find side a, we use sin 40°, since a is the side opposite the 40° angle and we know the hypotenuse, 37.

$$\sin 40° = \frac{a}{37} \qquad \text{(using a trig ratio where only one}$$
$$\text{of the quantities is an unknown)}$$

$$0.6428 = \frac{a}{37}$$

$$37(0.6428) = a$$

$$23.8 = a$$

To find side b, we use cos 40°, since b is the side adjacent to the 40° angle and we know the hypotenuse, 37.

$$\cos 40° = \frac{b}{37}$$

$$0.7660 = \frac{b}{37}$$

$$37(0.7660) = b$$

$$28.3 = b$$

Example 5:

In the right triangle, find $\angle X$, $\angle Y$, and z.

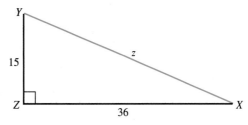

Solution: To find X, we can use the tangent function since we know the sides opposite and adjacent to angle X.

Press

$$\tan X = \frac{15}{36}$$

$$\tan X = 0.4167$$

$$X = 22.6°$$ $\left(\boxed{.}\ \boxed{4}\ \boxed{1}\ \boxed{6}\ \boxed{7}\ \boxed{\text{INV}}\ \boxed{\tan} \right)$

Since we know that the sum of the measures of the angles of a triangle is 180°, we can find the measure of angle Y.

$$\angle X + \angle Y + \angle Z = 180°$$

$$22.6° + \angle Y + 90° = 180$$

$$\angle Y = 67.4°$$

Finally, using the Pythagorean Theorem, we can find the value of z.

$$x^2 + y^2 = z^2$$

$$15^2 + 36^2 = z^2$$

$$225 + 1296 = z^2$$

$$1521 = z^2$$

$$39 = z$$

Example 6:

If an acute angle of a right triangle is 78° and the side adjacent to that angle is 48 cm, how long is the hypotenuse of the right triangle?

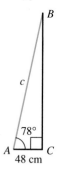

Solution: Let c = the length of the hypotenuse.

$$\cos 78° = \frac{48}{c}$$

$$0.2079 = \frac{48}{c}$$

$$0.2079c = 48 \qquad \text{(multiplying both sides by } c\text{)}$$

$$c = 230.9 \,\text{cm} \qquad \text{(dividing both sides by } 0.2079\text{)}$$

Example 7:

In the figure, find the length of side h.

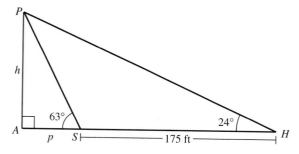

Solution: Since there is no right triangle with only one unknown side, we start by separating the figure into two right triangles, $\triangle SAP$ and $\triangle HAP$.

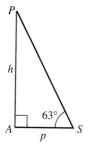 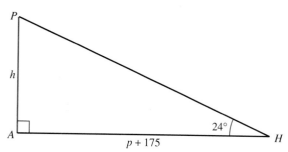

Using right $\triangle SAP$:

$$\tan 63° = \frac{h}{p}$$

$$1.9626 = \frac{h}{p}$$

$$1.9626p = h$$

$$p = \frac{h}{1.9626}$$

Using right $\triangle HAP$:

$$\tan 24° = \frac{h}{p + 175}$$

$$0.4452 = \frac{h}{p + 175}$$

$$0.4452(p + 175) = h$$

$$0.4452p + 77.9150 = h$$

$$0.4452p = h - 77.9150$$

$$p = \frac{h - 77.9150}{0.4452}$$

Since we have two expressions for p, we can set them equal to each other and solve for h.

$$\frac{h}{1.9626} = \frac{h - 77.9150}{0.4452}$$

$$0.4452h = 1.9626(h - 77.9150)$$

$$0.4452h = 1.9626h - 152.9160$$

$$-1.5174h = -152.9160$$

$$h = 100.8$$

This gives the height of the figure as 100.8 feet.

SECTION 5.1

PROBLEMS

In the right triangles, find sin A, cos A, tan A, sin B, cos B, and tan B.

1.

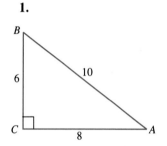

2.

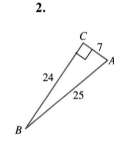

3.

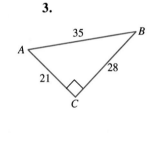

Use a calculator to find the following:

4. sin 59°

5. sin 12.6°

6. sin 8.25°

7. cos 82°

8. cos 5.9°

9. cos 43.88°

10. tan 33°

11. tan 76.3°

12. tan 17.95°

13. cos 0.59°

Use a calculator to find the angle for each trigonometric function:

14. sin A = 0.8974

15. cos Y = 0.123

16. tan B = 6.548

17. $\sin G = 0.67$

18. $\cos W = 0.5555$

19. $\tan D = 19.035$

20. $\sin F = 5/12$

21. $\cos K = 4/11$

22. $\tan J = 24/7$

Find the parts of each triangle that are not given.

23.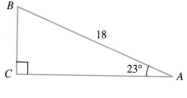

24.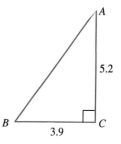

25.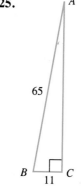

26.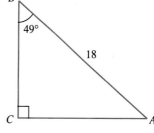

27.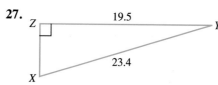

28.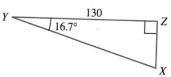

29.

30.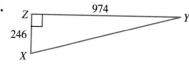

Find the angles of the right triangles whose sides are the Pythagorean triples listed.

31. 8, 15, 17

32. 9, 40, 41

33. 18, 24, 30

34. 27, 36, 45

35. 33, 44, 55

36. 102, 2600, 2602

Determine the value of h in the following diagrams.

37.
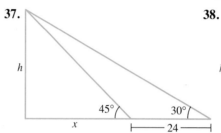

38.
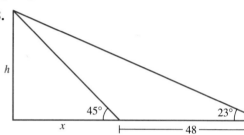

39.
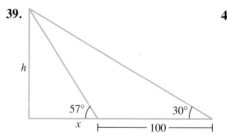

40.
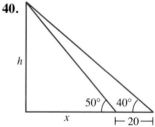

Eight Bells by Winslow Homer shows one of the devices used by navigators in determining angles. (National Gallery of Art)

SECTION 5.2

▼

RIGHT TRIANGLE APPLICATIONS

The trigonometric functions studied in the previous section can be used to solve many different kinds of practical problems. In solving these problems, you will find it helpful to do the following:

1. Sketch the situation and the right triangle involved.
2. Write the known angles or sides on the triangle.
3. Use letters to represent the unknown angles or sides.
4. Use trig functions to solve the triangle, remembering to have only one unknown quantity in a trigonometric equation.

Example 1:

The instruction booklet for a 50-ft ladder states that, for safety reasons, when the ladder is leaning against a vertical surface, the angle the ladder makes with the horizontal ground must be from 60° to 75°. Under those constraints, what are the minimum and maximum distances that the ladder will reach on the wall?

Solution: The minimum angle and maximum angle are shown in the right triangles. If we let h = the height the ladder reaches up the wall, using the sine function, we can solve for h in each case.

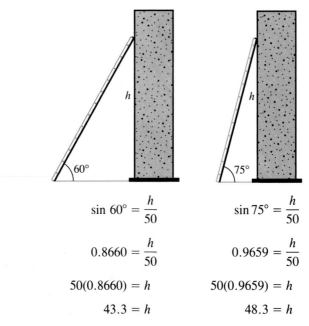

$$\sin 60° = \frac{h}{50} \qquad\qquad \sin 75° = \frac{h}{50}$$

$$0.8660 = \frac{h}{50} \qquad\qquad 0.9659 = \frac{h}{50}$$

$$50(0.8660) = h \qquad\qquad 50(0.9659) = h$$

$$43.3 = h \qquad\qquad\qquad 48.3 = h$$

Thus, the ladder will safely reach heights between 43.3 and 48.3 feet on the wall.

Example 2:

A small airplane takes off from an airport at an angle of 32.3° with level ground. Three-fourths of a mile (3960 ft) from the airport is a 1500 ft peak in the flight path of the plane. If the plane continues that angle of ascent, find (a) its altitude when it reaches the peak and (b) how far it will be above the peak.

Solution:

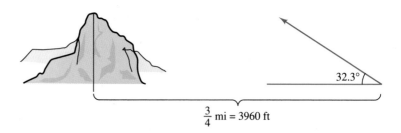

$$\frac{3}{4}\text{ mi} = 3960\text{ ft}$$

Let a = the altitude of the plane

$$\tan 32.3° = \frac{a}{3960}$$

$$0.6322 = \frac{a}{3960}$$

$$3960(0.6322) = a$$

$$2503.5 = a$$

Thus, (a) the altitude of the plane is 2503.5 ft and (b) it is 2503.5 ft − 1500 ft = 1003.5 ft above the peak.

Example 3:

The swimming area at Shadow Cliffs Lake is roped off with floating markers as shown in the figure. If the beach area is 350 yd long and the ropes make a 90° angle at the platform, how long is the swim from one corner of the beach along the floating markers to the middle of the stationary platform and then to the other corner of the beach?

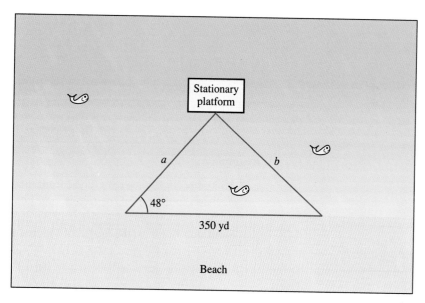

Solution: Let a and b = the legs of the right triangle. We need to find $a + b$.

$$\cos 48° = \frac{a}{350} \qquad\qquad \sin 48° = \frac{b}{350}$$

$$0.6691 = \frac{a}{350} \qquad\qquad 0.7431 = \frac{b}{350}$$

$$350(0.6691) = a \qquad\qquad 350(0.7431) = b$$

$$234.2 = a \qquad\qquad 260.1 = b$$

Thus, the total distance is $234.2 + 260.1 = 494.3$ yd.

Angles of Elevation and Depression

Many problems with right triangles involve the angle made with an imaginary horizontal line. An angle between such a horizontal line and the line of sight to an object that is above the horizontal is called the **angle of elevation**, and the angle made between such a horizontal line and the line of sight to an object that is below the horizontal is called the **angle of depression**. Instruments such as transits and sextants can be used to measure such angles.

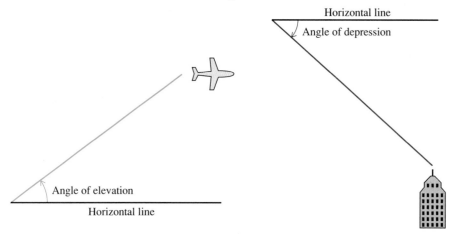

Example 4:

At a point 75 ft on level ground from the base of a tree the angle of elevation to the top of the tree is 70°. Find the height of the tree.

Solution: Let h = the height of the tree in feet.

$$\tan 70° = \frac{h}{75}$$

$$2.7475 = \frac{h}{75}$$

$$75(2.7475) = h$$

$$206.1 = h$$

The height of the tree is 206.1 ft.

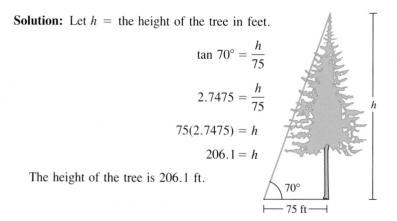

Example 5:

A point on the edge of the Grand Canyon in Arizona is 4600 ft above the Colorado River. At this point the angle of depression from the edge of the canyon to the middle of the canyon floor is 16°. Find, to the nearest mile, the distance across the Grand Canyon at that point.

Solution: Let x = the horizontal distance to the middle of the Grand Canyon floor.

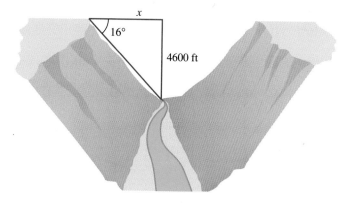

$$\tan 16° = \frac{4600}{x}$$

$$0.2867 = \frac{4600}{x}$$

$$0.2867x = 4600$$

$$x = \frac{4600}{0.2867}$$

$$x = 16{,}044.6 \text{ ft}$$

$$2x = 32{,}089.2 \text{ ft}$$

$$32{,}089.2 \text{ ft} \approx 6.1 \text{ mi}$$

Thus, at this point, the distance across the Grand Canyon is approximately 6.1 miles.

Example 6:

The sign on the side of a straight uphill stretch of highway reads, "9% GRADE NEXT 5 MI."

(a) Find the angle of elevation of the highway.
(b) Determine the change in altitude in feet after driving the 5 miles.

Solution: A 9% grade indicates that the slope of the road is 9/100, which means the highway rises 9 ft vertically for every 100-ft change in the horizontal direction.

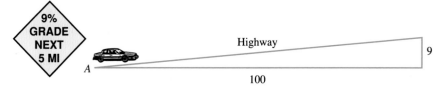

(a) To find the angle of elevation, we need to find $\angle A$.

$$\tan A = \frac{9}{100} = 0.09$$

$$A = 5.1°$$

(b) Using the result from part (a), we get

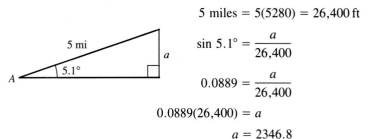

$$5 \text{ miles} = 5(5280) = 26,400 \text{ ft}$$

$$\sin 5.1° = \frac{a}{26,400}$$

$$0.0889 = \frac{a}{26,400}$$

$$0.0889(26,400) = a$$

$$a = 2346.8$$

Thus, the angle of elevation of the highway is 5.1°, and after 5 miles of driving there is a change in altitude of 2346.8 ft.

Example 7:

To find the height of Mission Peak near the Ohlone College campus, a student went to the football field with a transit and found that the angle of elevation to the top of the peak was 9.8°. At 100 yd (300 ft) from that point and in line with the first measurement, the angle of elevation was 9.6°. How far above the football field is the top of Mission Peak?

Solution: The following figure shows Mission Peak along with the two measurements of the angles of elevation. We need to find the value of a to find the height of Mission Peak above the football field. Both right triangles, $\triangle BCA$ and $\triangle BCD$, will be used in solving for a.

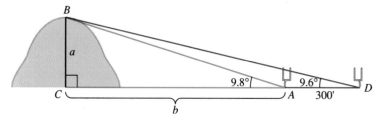

In $\triangle BCA$,	In $\triangle BCD$,

$$\tan 9.8° = \frac{a}{b} \qquad\qquad \tan 9.6° = \frac{a}{b + 300}$$

$$0.1727 = \frac{a}{b} \qquad\qquad 0.1691 = \frac{a}{b + 300}$$

$$0.1727b = a \qquad\qquad 0.1691(b + 300) = a$$

$$\qquad\qquad\qquad\qquad 0.1691b + 50.73 = a$$

$$b = \frac{a}{0.1727} \qquad\qquad 0.1691b = a - 50.73$$

$$\qquad\qquad\qquad\qquad b = \frac{a - 50.73}{0.1691}$$

Since we have found two different expressions for b, we can set them equal to each other and solve for a:

$$\frac{a}{0.1727} = \frac{a - 50.73}{0.1691}$$

$$0.1691a = 0.1727(a - 50.73)$$

$$0.1691a = 0.1727a - 8.7611$$

$$-0.0036a = -8.7611$$

$$a = 2433.6$$

Therefore, Mission Peak is approximately 2433.6 ft above the football field.

<table>
<tr><td>

S E C T I O N   5.2

P R O B L E M S

</td><td>

1. An Eagle Scout taking trigonometry finds the distance across a river by doing the following:

(a) He stands on the bank of the river and chooses a boulder directly across the river as a marker.

(b) He paces off 25 yd along the bank.

(c) From that point he approximates that the angle back to the rock is 60°.

(d) Being well prepared, he takes out his calculator, uses trig, and determines that the river is 43.3 yd wide.

</td></tr>
</table>

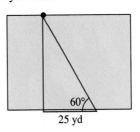

Show that the Eagle Scout was correct in his approximation.

2. A sign on a straight stretch of freeway reads, "10% GRADE altitude 3000 ft." If the next altitude sign you see states that the altitude is 4350 ft, how many miles have you driven since seeing the 10% grade sign?

3. A guy-wire, which supports a vertical circus tent pole, makes a 76.5° angle with level ground. If the guy wire is secured to the ground 12 ft away from the bottom of the pole, how tall is the pole and how long is the guy wire?

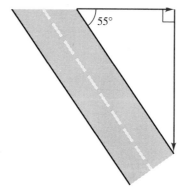

4. Due to road construction a 36-mile section of a highway is closed. The detour makes a 55° angle with the highway as shown. How many additional miles does one travel using the detour?

5. The pitch of a roof is 5/12. That means the roof rises 5 ft for each 12-ft change in the horizontal direction. What is the angle of elevation of the roof? If the actual length of the roof is 32 ft, how much does the roof rise in that distance?

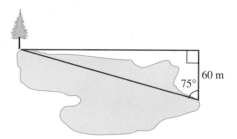

6. To find the distance across a lake, a tree on the opposite side of the lake was taken as a marker and 60 m was walked off, as shown in the figure. If the angle to the tree was measured at 75°, how far is it across the lake?

7. How far up a vertical wall will a 32-ft ladder reach if it makes a 67° angle with the level ground?

8. Radar indicates that the distance to an approaching airplane is 8.6 miles and the angle of elevation to the plane is 26°. At what altitude is the plane flying?

9. From a point at eye level (5 ft off the ground) the angle of elevation to the top of a radio transmitting tower is 70°. If the person measuring this angle is 40 ft from the tower, what is the height of the tower?

10. The angle of depression from the roof of a 310-ft office building to the bottom of a statue in the Civic Center is 8.2°. If the ground between the building and the statue is level, find the distance from the building to the statue.

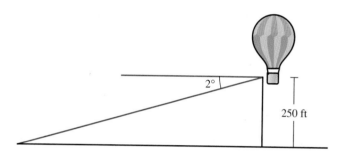

11. After lifting off from its launch site, a hot-air balloon floats along over an open field with the top of its basket 250 ft above ground level. If the angle of depression to its take-off point is 2°, how far is the balloon from its take-off point?

12. The angle of depression from the top of a 504-ft building to the bottom of a nearby 300-ft building measures 12.7°. How far apart are the two buildings?

13. A sea-to-air guided missile shot from a submarine leaves the water at an angle of elevation of 18.6° traveling at 480 ft/s. If the missile maintains a constant angle of ascent and the same speed, how far above sea level will it be after 30 seconds?

14. In Problem 13, how long will it take the missile to reach an altitude of 10,000 ft?

15. A ship at sea measures the angle of elevation to the top of a cliff on shore to be 14.8°. After traveling a half mile closer to the cliff, the angle of elevation is now 26.5°. How many feet is the top of the cliff above sea level?

16. A tennis player hits an overhead smash 35 ft from the net. If the ball is hit 10.5 ft off the ground and just clears the net at height of 3 ft, how far from the net and at what angle will the ball strike the ground?

SECTION   5.3

▼

THE LAWS OF SINES AND COSINES

The three trigonometric functions studied in the previous sections were defined and used in reference to right triangles. The next two laws of trigonometry, the Law of Sines and the Law of Cosines, will give us the means to solve triangles that are not right triangles. A triangle with each angle measuring less than 90° is called an **acute triangle**, and a triangle with one angle greater than 90° is called an **obtuse triangle**. The Laws of Sines and Cosines can be used to solve acute and obtuse triangles. However, in this survey of the essentials of trigonometry we apply them only to acute triangles that have a unique solution, and we will not cover situations where there is more than one possible triangle for the information given.

The Law of Sines

The **Law of Sines** gives a relationship between the sides and angles of a triangle. It states that the ratio of the length of the side of any triangle to the sine of the angle opposite that side is the same for all three sides of the triangle. That is, for any $\triangle ABC$:

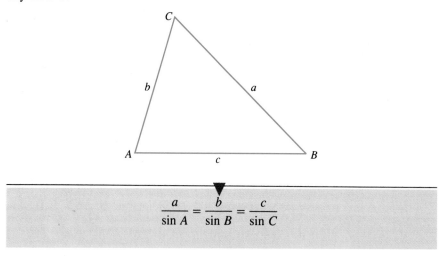

$$\frac{a}{\sin A} = \frac{b}{\sin B} = \frac{c}{\sin C}$$

Derivation of the Law of Sines

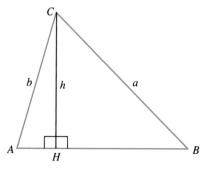

Let h be the length of a segment from C forming right angles with $\overline{AB}$ at H.

In △ACH,

$$\sin A = \frac{h}{b}$$

$$b \sin A = h$$

In △CHB,

$$\sin B = \frac{h}{a}$$

$$a \sin B = h$$

Since we have found two expressions for h, they must be the same. Setting them equal to each other, we get

$$a \sin B = b \sin A$$

$$\frac{a \sin B}{(\sin A)(\sin B)} = \frac{b \sin A}{(\sin A)(\sin B)} \qquad \text{(dividing both sides by } (\sin A)(\sin B))$$

$$\frac{a}{\sin A} = \frac{b}{\sin B}$$

If we use the same process with a segment from B making right angles with $\overline{AC}$, we can show that the third ratio, $c/(\sin C)$, is equal to the two ratios given above.

The Law of Sines can be used to solve any triangle in which two angles and one side are known. In each example, you will notice that the ratio of the sine of a known angle and its opposite side will be set equal to a ratio that has either an unknown angle or an unknown side.

Example 1:

In △ABC, $\angle A = 40°$, $\angle B = 60°$, and $b = 9$. Find the measure of $\angle C$ and the lengths of a and c.

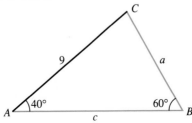

Solution: $\angle C = 80°$, since the sum of the angles of a triangle is $180°$ and $180° - 40° - 60° = 80°$.

To find sides a and c, we use the Law of Sines.

$$\frac{a}{\sin A} = \frac{b}{\sin B} \qquad\qquad \frac{c}{\sin C} = \frac{b}{\sin B}$$

$$\frac{a}{\sin 40°} = \frac{9}{\sin 60°} \qquad\qquad \frac{c}{\sin 80°} = \frac{9}{\sin 60°}$$

$$\frac{a}{0.6428} = \frac{9}{0.8660} \qquad\qquad \frac{c}{0.9848} = \frac{9}{0.8660}$$

$$0.8660a = 9(0.6428) \qquad\qquad 0.8660c = 9(0.9848)$$

$$0.8660a = 5.7852 \qquad\qquad 0.8660c = 8.8632$$

$$a = 6.7 \qquad\qquad c = 10.2$$

Note

The Law of Sines should be used to solve any triangle in which two angles and one side are known. This situation is referred to as angle-angle-side (AAS) or angle-side-angle (ASA). The Law of Sines can also be used when two sides and an angle opposite one of the sides is known (SSA). Since this case may lead to more than one solution, it will not be discussed in this survey of trigonometry.

Example 2:

In $\triangle XYZ$, $\angle Y = 86.2°$, $\angle Z = 21.5°$, and $y = 110$. Find the measure of $\angle X$ and the lengths of sides x and z.

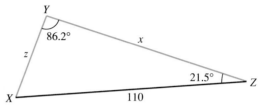

Solution: $\angle X = 180° - 86.2° - 21.5° = 72.3°$.
To find sides x and z, we use the Law of Sines.

$$\frac{x}{\sin X} = \frac{y}{\sin Y} \qquad\qquad \frac{z}{\sin Z} = \frac{y}{\sin Y}$$

$$\frac{x}{\sin 72.3°} = \frac{110}{\sin 86.2°} \qquad\qquad \frac{z}{\sin 21.5°} = \frac{110}{\sin 86.2°}$$

$$\frac{x}{0.9527} = \frac{110}{0.9978} \qquad\qquad \frac{z}{0.3665} = \frac{110}{0.9978}$$

$$0.9978x = 110(0.9527) \qquad\qquad 0.9978z = 110(0.3665)$$

$$0.9978x = 104.797 \qquad\qquad 0.9978z = 40.315$$

$$x = 105.0 \qquad\qquad z = 40.4$$

Law of Cosines

As seen in the previous examples, the Law of Sines gives a very efficient means for solving acute triangles in which two angles and one side are known. However, it is not possible to use the Law of Sines to solve a triangle in which the three sides (SSS) or one angle and the two sides that form the angle (SAS) are known. The law of trigonometry that enables us to solve triangles with those conditions is called the **Law of Cosines**. This law gives us a different relationship involving the sides and an angle of a triangle than does the Law of Sines. It states that for any $\triangle ABC$,

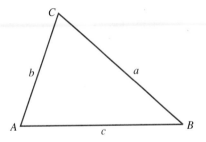

$$a^2 = b^2 + c^2 - 2bc \cos A$$
$$b^2 = a^2 + c^2 - 2ac \cos B$$
$$c^2 = a^2 + b^2 - 2ab \cos C$$

Derivation of the Law of Cosines

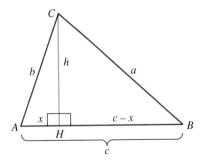

Let h be the length of a segment from C forming right angles with $\overline{AB}$ at H. Using the Pythagorean Theorem in $\triangle CHB$ and $\triangle CHA$, we get in right $\triangle CHB$,

$$a^2 = (c - x)^2 + h^2$$

$$a^2 = c^2 - 2cx + x^2 + h^2$$

But in right $\triangle CHA$, we have $\quad b^2 = x^2 + h^2$, so

$$a^2 = c^2 - 2cx + b^2$$

$$a^2 = b^2 + c^2 - 2cx$$

Also in $\triangle CHA$, $\cos A = \dfrac{x}{b}$ so $b \cos A = x$.

$$\therefore a^2 = b^2 + c^2 - 2cb \cos A$$

$$a^2 = b^2 + c^2 - 2bc \cos A$$

If we use the same process, drawing segments from A or B that make right angles with the sides opposite those angles, we can derive the other forms of the Law of Cosines.

Notice that the variable of the triangle used on the left of the equal sign corresponds to the angle opposite that side on the right of the equals sign. That is, in $a^2 = b^2 + c^2 - 2bc \cos A$, a^2 on the left corresponds to $\cos A$ on the right side of the equation. Recognizing that this is true for all three forms of the Law of Cosines makes the task of remembering the Law of Cosines a little easier.

Example 3:

In $\triangle ABC$, $\angle A = 64°$, $b = 18$, and $c = 39$. Use the Law of Cosines to find (a) side a and (b) $\angle B$.

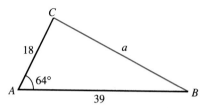

Solution:

(a) Since two sides and the included angle are known (SAS), this triangle can be solved by the Law of Cosines.

$$a^2 = b^2 + c^2 - 2bc \cos A$$

$$a^2 = 18^2 + 39^2 - 2(18)(39) \cos 64°$$

$$a^2 = 324 + 1521 - 1404(0.4384)$$

$$a^2 = 1229.4864$$

$$a = \sqrt{1229.4864} = 35.1$$

(b) Since we now know a, b, and c, we can find $\angle B$ from the Law of Cosines, where B is the only unknown quantity.

$$b^2 = a^2 + c^2 - 2ac \cos B$$

$$18^2 = 35.1^2 + 39^2 - 2(35.1)(39) \cos B$$

$$324 = 1232.01 + 1521 - 2737.8 \cos B$$

$$-2429.01 = -2737.8 \cos B$$

$$0.8872 = \cos B$$

$$27.5° = B$$

Note

The Law of Cosines can be used to solve any triangle in which a side, an angle, and a side (**SAS**) or three sides (**SSS**) are known.

Example 4:

In $\triangle USA$, $u = 38$, $s = 42$, and $a = 29$. Find the measures of $\angle U$, $\angle S$, and $\angle A$.

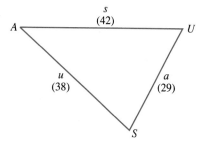

Solution: Since the three sides if the triangle are known, we first find $\angle U$ by writing the Law of Cosines, using u, s, a, and U.

$$u^2 = s^2 + a^2 - 2sa \cos U$$

$$38^2 = 42^2 + 29^2 - 2(42)(29) \cos U$$

$$1444 = 1764 + 841 - 2436 \cos U$$

$$-1161 = -2436 \cos U$$

$$0.4766 = \cos U$$

$$61.5° = U$$

We can now find $\angle S$ by using the Law of Cosines again. However, it would be easier to use the Law of Sines with u and $\sin U$ forming the known ratio and S being the only unknown quantity.

$$\frac{u}{\sin U} = \frac{s}{\sin S}$$

$$\frac{38}{\sin 61.5°} = \frac{42}{\sin S}$$

$$\frac{38}{0.8788} = \frac{42}{\sin S}$$

$$38 \sin S = 42(0.8788)$$

$$\sin S = 0.9713$$

$$S = 76.2°$$

Since we now know two of the angles of $\triangle USA$, we can find $\angle A$ by using the fact that the sum of the angles of a triangle equals $180°$.

$$\angle A = 180° - 61.5° - 76.2° = 42.3°$$

SECTION 5.3

PROBLEMS

Use the Law of Sines to find the designated side in $\triangle SUN$.

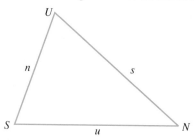

1. $\angle S = 36°$, $\angle U = 70°$, $s = 7$; find u.

2. $\angle S = 56.5°$, $\angle U = 62.9°$, $s = 25$; find n.

3. $\angle S = 9°$, $\angle U = 87°$, $n = 34.6$; find s.

4. $\angle S = 47°$, $\angle U = 60°$, $n = 450$; find u

5. $\angle S = 28.7°$, $\angle N = 71.5°$, $u = 56$; find n.

6. $\angle S = 66.6°$, $\angle N = 55.5°$, $s = 44.4$; find u.

7. $\angle S = 57°$, $\angle N = 57°$, $n = 7.5$; find s.

8. $\angle N = 12.5°$, $\angle U = 80.25°$, $u = 1240$; find n.

9. $\angle N = 75°$, $\angle U = 30°$, $s = 1.23$; find u.

Use the Law of Cosines to find the designated angle or side in $\triangle DOG$.

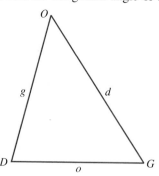

10. $\angle D = 73°$, $o = 12$, $g = 34$; find d.

11. $\angle O = 40.6°$, $g = 23$, $d = 45.5$; find o.

12. $\angle G = 37.25°$, $d = 5.5$, $o = 6.75$; find g.

13. $d = 15$, $o = 16$, $g = 17$; find $\angle D$.

14. $d = 9.4$, $o = 8.3$, $g = 5.8$; find $\angle O$.

15. $d = 189$, $o = 213$, $g = 220$; find $\angle G$.

16. Solve $\triangle CAT$ if $\angle A = 56.7°$, $\angle T = 44.7°$, and $c = 32.1$.

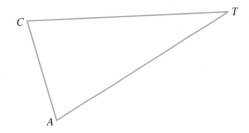

17. Solve $\triangle KEY$ if $\angle Y = 55°$, $\angle E = 55°$, and $k = 100$.

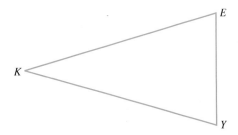

18. Solve $\triangle CUP$ if $c = 19.8$, $p = 20.6$, and $u = 14.4$.

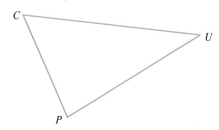

19. Solve $\triangle CAR$ if $c = 106$, $a = 155$, and $r = 127$.

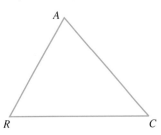

*20. Determine why it is impossible to have a triangle with sides $a = 10$, $b = 12$, and $c = 23$.

Surveyors make extensive use of trigonometry. (Courtesy of Kurt Viegelmann)

SECTION 5.4

▼

ACUTE TRIANGLE APPLICATIONS

In Section 5.2, we saw how the trigonometry of right triangles can be applied to many different kinds of problems. In Example 7 of that section, we showed a method for solving an acute triangle that involved using two right triangles and a great deal of algebra. In this section, we will see how the Laws of Sines and Cosines can simplify some of these problems.

Example 1:

Two fire-lookout stations are 15 miles apart, with station B directly east of station A. Both stations spot a fire on a mountain to the north. The line of sight to the fire from station A makes a 37.3° angle with a line running between the two stations (the east-west line), and the line of sight to the fire from station B makes a 54.2° angle with the east-west line. How far is the fire from station A?

Solution: The figure shows the information given in the problem. Since $A = 37.3°$ and $B = 54.2°$, $F = 180° - 37.3° - 54.2° = 88.5°$. Since we now know $\angle F$ and the side opposite that angle, we can apply the Law of Sines to find side b.

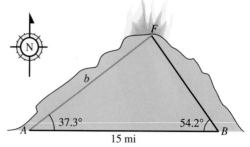

Let b = distance to the fire from A.

$$\frac{f}{\sin F} = \frac{b}{\sin B}$$

$$\frac{15}{\sin 88.5°} = \frac{b}{\sin 54.2°}$$

$$\frac{15}{0.9997} = \frac{b}{0.8111}$$

$$0.9997b = 15(0.8111)$$

$$b = 12.2$$

The distance to the fire from station A is approximately 12.2 mi.

Example 2:

The bottom of a hot-air balloon is tethered at the top of a small hill with 200 ft of rope. Due to the wind blowing from the west, the angle of elevation to the balloon is 67.2°. At a point 56 ft down the hill, the balloon is directly overhead. If the hill makes an angle of 9° with the horizontal and the rope to the balloon is taut, how far above the ground is the bottom of the hot-air balloon?

Solution:

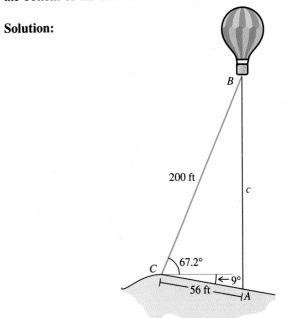

The hot-air balloon along with the given information is shown in the figure. The angle at C is 76.2° (67.2° + 9°). Now in $\triangle BCA$, a side, an angle, and a side are known (SAS). This allows us to use the Law of

Cosines to find the height of the balloon above the ground. Let c represent the height of the bottom of the balloon above the ground.

$$c^2 = a^2 + b^2 - 2ab \cos 76.2°$$

$$c^2 = 200^2 + 56^2 - 2(200)(56)(0.2385)$$

$$c^2 = 40,000 + 3136 - 5342.4$$

$$c^2 = 37,793.6$$

$$c = 194.4 \text{ ft}$$

Example 3:

A mining company digs a 750-yd horizontal mine shaft into a hill with an incline of 17°. How far up the hill should an air shaft, making an 87° angle with the hill, be drilled so that it will meet the end of the mine shaft? How long is the air shaft?

Solution: The angle where the air shaft meets the mine shaft is 76° (180° − 87° − 17°). Since two angles and a side are known (AAS), the Law of Sines can be used to find the distance up the hill where the air shaft is to be drilled and the length of the air shaft.

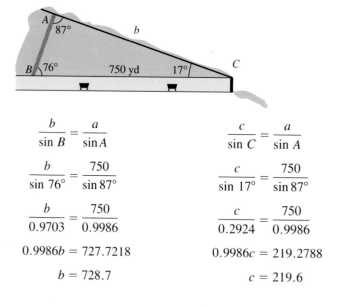

$$\frac{b}{\sin B} = \frac{a}{\sin A} \qquad\qquad \frac{c}{\sin C} = \frac{a}{\sin A}$$

$$\frac{b}{\sin 76°} = \frac{750}{\sin 87°} \qquad\qquad \frac{c}{\sin 17°} = \frac{750}{\sin 87°}$$

$$\frac{b}{0.9703} = \frac{750}{0.9986} \qquad\qquad \frac{c}{0.2924} = \frac{750}{0.9986}$$

$$0.9986b = 727.7218 \qquad\qquad 0.9986c = 219.2788$$

$$b = 728.7 \qquad\qquad c = 219.6$$

Therefore, the shaft should be drilled 728.7 yards up the hill and should be 219.6 yards long.

Navigation Problems

In navigation problems, one of the common ways to give the course of a plane or ship is in terms of a **bearing**. A bearing is an acute angle measured from a north-south line toward either the east or the west. In this system either N (north) or S (south) is written, followed by an acute angle, then E (east) or W (west). The following examples show how this system is used to give a direction.

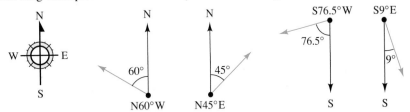

Example 4:

An airplane leaves an airport and flies directly north at 450 mph while a second airplane leaves the airport at the same time flying at 360 mph on a bearing of N70°E. How far apart are the airplanes after 2.5 hours?

Solution: Traveling at 450 mph after 2.5 hours, the plane flying directly north would have traveled 1125 miles (2.5 × 450) and the plane flying N70°E at 360 mph would travel 900 miles (2.5 × 360). Placing that information on the diagram shows that we have the SAS situation, so we will use the Law of Cosines.

Let a = the distance between the planes after 2.5 hours.

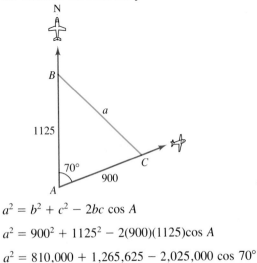

$$a^2 = b^2 + c^2 - 2bc \cos A$$

$$a^2 = 900^2 + 1125^2 - 2(900)(1125)\cos A$$

$$a^2 = 810,000 + 1,265,625 - 2,025,000 \cos 70°$$

$$a^2 = 2{,}075{,}625 - 692{,}590.8$$

$$a^2 = 1{,}383{,}034.2$$

$$a = 1176.0$$

Therefore, the planes are 1176 miles apart after 2.5 hours.

Example 5:

A sport-fishing boat leaves Bob's Pier heading directly east. After traveling for 50 miles, the captain hears a fishing report on the radio, which causes him to turn the boat and proceed on a bearing of S42°W for 27 miles. How far is the boat from Bob's Pier, and what bearing should the boat have originally taken to arrive at the fishing spot?

Solution: The figure shows the course taken by the fishing boat (starting at point B). Since a line going east forms a 90° angle with one going south, $\angle BAC = 90° - 42° = 48°$, and since we have an SAS situation, we can use the Law of Cosines to find the distance a from Bob's Pier.

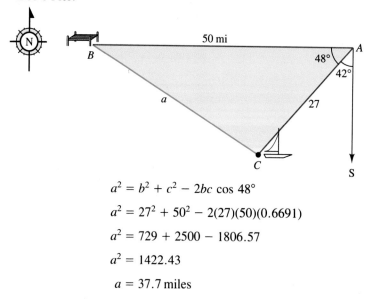

$$a^2 = b^2 + c^2 - 2bc \cos 48°$$

$$a^2 = 27^2 + 50^2 - 2(27)(50)(0.6691)$$

$$a^2 = 729 + 2500 - 1806.57$$

$$a^2 = 1422.43$$

$$a = 37.7 \text{ miles}$$

Since we know the three sides of the triangle (SSS), we will use the Law of Cosines to find the bearing from Bob's Pier to point C.

$$b^2 = a^2 + c^2 - 2ac \cos B$$

$$27^2 = 37.7^2 + 50^2 - 2(37.7)(50) \cos B$$

$$729 = 1421.29 + 2500 - 3770 \cos B$$

$$0.8468 = \cos B$$

$$32.1° = B$$

Since bearing is measured from the north-south line, we need to subtract 32.1° from 90° to find the angle made by the line from Bob's Pier to the fishing spot. Thus, the bearing angle is 90° − 32.1° = 57.9°, and the actual bearing is S57.9°W.

In solving acute triangles, you will find it helpful to:

1. Sketch the situation and the triangle involved.
2. Write the known angles and sides on the triangle.
3. Use letters to represent the unknown angles and sides.
4. If two angles are known, find the unknown angle by subtracting the sum of the two angles from 180°.
5. For triangles in which two angles and a side are known (AAS), use the Law of Sines.
6. For triangles in which a side, an angle, and a side (SAS) or three sides (SSS) are known, use the Law of Cosines.

The trigonometric methods shown in this chapter give you powerful tools for solving problems that contain triangles. The problems that follow will show you more applications that involve both right and oblique triangles.

SECTION 5.4

PROBLEMS

1. A tall fir tree growing on the side of a hill makes a 70° angle with the hill. From a point 60 ft up the hill, the angle of elevation to the top of the tree is 65° and the angle of depression to the bottom of the tree is 20°. How tall is the fir tree?

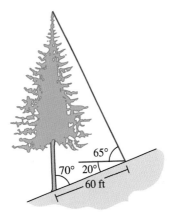

2. A large helium balloon advertising a sale at a local auto dealer is tethered by a rope at the west end of a level car lot. A wind blowing from the west causes the balloon to have an angle of elevation of 73°. If, from the other end of the car lot, 500 ft away, the angle of elevation to the balloon is 52°, how far above the car lot is the balloon?

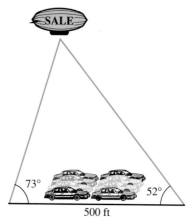

3. To find the distance between a fire-lookout station and a cabin on the other side of a canyon, the ranger uses a transit to measure angles at two different points as shown in the figure. Using the information shown, determine the distance from the fire-lookout station to the cabin.

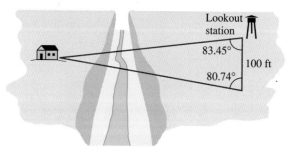

4. The walls of a trench form a 65° angle. To get out of the trench, highway workers place the bottom of a 25-ft plank on one side of the trench and lean the top of the plank on the other side. If the bottom of the plank makes an 80° angle with the wall of the trench, how far up the other side does the top of the plank reach?

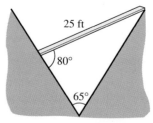

5. A pilot planned to fly a small plane from Kodiak, Alaska, to Tikchik Lakes, a distance of 300 miles. After flying for 2 hours at 150 mph, the pilot realized that she had been flying on a course that was off by 2°. How far from Tikchik Lakes was the airplane at this point? At what angle from the present course must the pilot turn to arrive at Tikchik Lakes?

6. Two cross-country skiers are at the bottom of a ravine. The sides of the ravine form a 72° angle. The first skier goes straight up one side of the ravine while the second one goes straight up the other side. After 20 minutes the first skier is 1600 m up one side of the ravine while the second skier is only 1000 m up the other side. How far apart are the two skiers at that point?

7. A ship leaves port and cruises 74 miles on a bearing of S60°E. Another ship leaves the port at the same time and sails for 56 miles on a bearing of S20°E. How far apart are the two ships at this point?

8. An airplane leaves an airport at 1:00 P.M. on a bearing of N20°E flying at 280 mph. At 1:30 P.M. a second airplane leaves the airport on a bearing of N15°W flying at 375 mph. If the two airplanes continue flying on those courses, how far apart will they be at 3:30 P.M.?

9. To find the distance across Mallard Cove at Bass Lake, a Girl Scout troop made the measurements in the diagram. What is the distance across Mallard Cove?

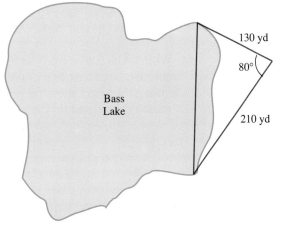

10. An A-frame mountain cabin is 30 ft wide. If the roof of the cabin makes a 63° angle with the base of the cabin, what is the length of the roof from ground level to the peak of the roof?

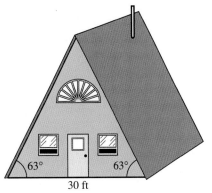

11. The pitch of a roof can be determined by taking the tangent function of the angle of elevation of the roof. Find the pitch of both sides of the roof in the figure, and determine the distance between the ground and the peak of the roof.

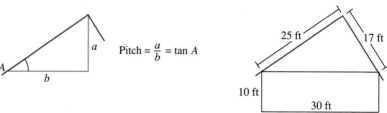

Pitch $= \dfrac{a}{b} = \tan A$

12. A triangular-shaped piece of property has sides that are 136 ft, 125 ft, and 178 ft. What are each of the angles formed by the property lines of this triangular lot?

13. A parallelogram-shaped lot has sides that are 120 m and 232 m. If the angle between the two sides is 58°, how long is the diagonal of the parallelogram that is opposite that angle?

14. When a kite is flying high in the sky, you will notice that the kite string does not make a straight line to the kite. Realizing this, find a method for determining the height above the ground for a kite that is flying in the air if (a) the ground is level and (b) the ground is not level.

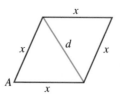

15. A rhombus is a parallelogram with equal sides, as shown. If $\angle A$ is an acute angle, find a formula for the length of the diagonal of the rhombus that is opposite $\angle A$. That is, if $d =$ the length of the diagonal, represent d in terms of x and A.

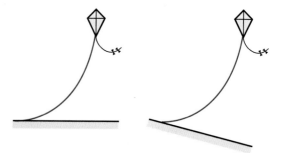

16. A hot-air balloon is hovering over a lake. From one side of the lake the angle of elevation to the bottom of the balloon is 54°, and from the other side of the lake, 1660 ft away, the angle of elevation is 69°. How far is the bottom of the hot-air balloon above the lake?

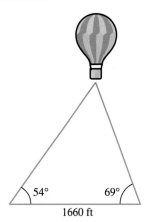

54°   69°

1660 ft

*17. Explain how a person in a ship that is traveling parallel to the coast could use a lighthouse, the speed of the ship, a device for measuring angles, and a knowledge of trigonometry to determine the distance from the ship to the lighthouse.

C H A P T E R	5	**SUMMARY**

KEY TERMS, CONCEPTS, AND FORMULAS

The important terms in this chapter are:

Acute triangle: A triangle with each angle measuring less than 90°.   p. 282

Angle of depression: An angle made between a horizontal line and a line to an object that is below the horizontal line.   p. 276

Angle of elevation: An angle made between a horizontal line and a line to an object that is above the horizontal line.   p. 276

Bearing: A measure of direction relative to a north-south line.   p. 293

Cosine: The ratio of the side adjacent to an angle to the hypotenuse of a right triangle.   p. 262

Hypotenuse: The side opposite the 90° angle in a right triangle.   p. 254

Law of Cosines: The relationship between the sides and angles of a triangle, which states, for any $\triangle ABC$,

$$a^2 = b^2 + c^2 - 2bc \cos A$$

$$b^2 = a^2 + c^2 - 2ac \cos B$$ p. 285

$$c^2 = a^2 + b^2 - 2ab \cos C$$

Law of Sines: The relationship among the sides and angles of a triangle, which states, for any $\triangle ABC$,

$$\frac{a}{\sin A} = \frac{b}{\sin B} = \frac{c}{\sin C}$$

p. 282

Legs: The sides of a right triangle that form the 90° angle.   p. 254

Obtuse triangle: A triangle with one angle measuring greater than 90°.   p. 282

Pythagorean Theorem: The relationship of the sides of a right triangle, which states that, if a and b are the legs and c is the hypotenuse,

$$a^2 + b^2 = c^2$$

p. 255

Pythagorean triple: A trio of natural numbers that satisfy the Pythagorean Theorem.   p. 259

Right triangle: A triangle with a 90° angle   p. 254

Sine: The ratio of the side opposite an angle to the hypotenuse of a right triangle.   p. 262

Solving triangles: The process of finding unknown angles and sides of a triangle.   p. 266

Tangent: The ratio of the side opposite an angle to the side adjacent to an angle of a right triangle.   p. 262

After completing this chapter, you should be able to:

1. Define the sine, cosine, and tangent trigonometric functions in reference to right triangles.   p. 263

2. Solve right triangles using the sine, cosine, and tangent functions.   p. 266

3. Use trigonometric functions to solve various application problems involving right triangles.   p. 273

4. Use the Law of Sines and the Law of Cosines to solve acute triangles.   p. 290

5. Use the Law of Sines and Law of Cosines to solve various application problems involving acute triangles.   p. 290

SUMMARY

PROBLEMS

Solve each of the triangles shown.

1.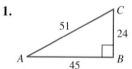

2.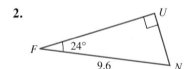

3.

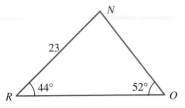

4.

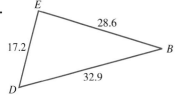

5.

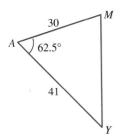

6.

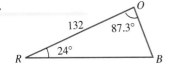

7. What angle does a 30-ft plank make with level ground if it is placed so that it reaches 20 ft up a vertical wall?

8. From a point 50 m from the bottom of a radio tower along level ground, the angle of elevation to the top of the tower is 67°. Find the height of the tower.

9. To determine the altitude of an approaching airplane, Debra and Charles measured the angle of elevation to the plane at the same time from locations that were 2000 ft apart, as shown in the figure. What is the altitude of the airplane?

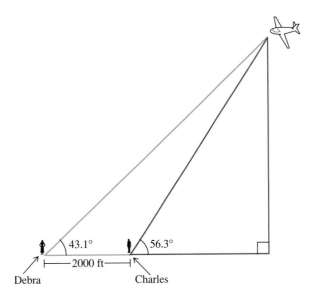

10. The Leaning Tower of Pisa in Italy is 177 ft tall and leans at an angle of about 84.5°.

(a) If a ball is dropped from the edge of the tower and strikes the ground at a 90° angle, how far from the base of the tower does the ball hit the ground and how far does the ball fall?

84.5°

(b) If, because of the wind, a ball dropped from the tower takes a straight path to the ground and strikes the ground at an 80° angle of elevation to the top of the tower, how far from the base of the tower does it hit the ground and how far did the ball fall?

11. With the use of modern electronic equipment, the distance for various field events in a track meet can be measured without the use of measuring tapes. For example, in the discus throw, after a competitor has made a fair throw from the discus ring to point *D*, an electronic transmitter placed at *D* sends a signal to a device in the official's booth above the track. The device then determines the angles at *D* and at *B*. Since the distance from the booth to the center of the discus ring is a known distance, the length of the throw can be found from trigonometry.

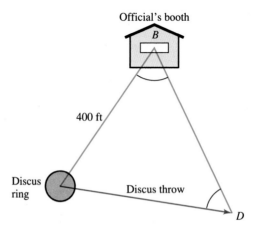

Official's booth

B

400 ft

Discus
ring

Discus throw

D

At an invitational track meet, the distance from the official's booth to the center of the discus ring is 400 ft, and the radius of the discus ring is 4 ft. If the angle at *D* is 50.1° and the angle at *B* is 24.6°, determine the length of a discus throw. Since a discus throw is measured from the outer edge of the discus ring, to get a final answer, be sure to subtract 4 ft from the distance you get from *D* to the center of the ring.

12. Two lookout stations, which are 25 miles apart along the coast on a north-south line, spot an approaching yacht. One lookout station measures the direction to the yacht at N33°E, and the other station measures the direction to the yacht at S62°E, How far is the yacht from each lookout station? How far is the yacht from the coast?

13. Two airplanes leave an airport at 8:00 A.M. on different runways. One flies on a bearing of N64.5°W at 315 mph and the other plane on a bearing of S27°W at 295 mph. How far apart will the airplanes be at 10:00 A.M.?

14. In order to chart the movement of a polar bear, scientists attached a radio transmitter to its neck. Two tracking stations are monitoring the radio signals from the bear. Station B is 10 miles directly east of station A. On Monday, station A measured the direction to the bear at N43°E, and station B at N30°W. Three days later the directions to the bear from the two tracking stations were N24°E and N30°W, respectively. How much further from station B was the polar bear after those three days?

15. Three islands are located in the South Pacific. Island A is located 252 miles directly west of island B. Island C is located to the north of island A and island B. If the distance from island A to island C is 195 miles and the distance from island B to island C is 287 miles, on what bearing should one navigate to go from island A to island C and from island B to island C?

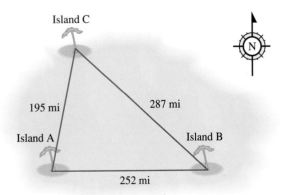

16. To determine the distance to an oil platform in the Pacific Ocean from both ends of a beach, a surveyor measures the angle to the platform from each end of the beach. The angle made with the shoreline from one end of the beach is 83°, from the other end 78.6°. If the beach is 950 yd long, what are the distances to the oil platform from both ends of the beach?

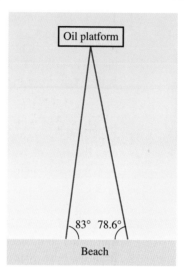

MATH OF FINANCE

The Interior of the Pantheon by Giovanni Paolo Pannini illustrates the classic architectural style that we associate with financial institutions. (National Gallery of Art)

A SHORT HISTORY OF INTEREST AND BANKING

Interest

Interest has been charged for the use of money since Babylonian times (2000–500 B.C.). Ancient cuneiform tablets show that the Sumerians used both simple and compound interest. A 1700 B.C. tablet contains a problem concerning how long would it take an amount of money to double if interest was compounded annually at a certain rate. In addition, interest rates have varied greatly throughout history. Babylonian interest rates were 20%, and rates in Cicero's Rome (c. 60–43 B.C.) reached 48%. By the time of Justinian (483–565), rates were limited by law to 6%, but the Indian mathematician Bhāskara (c. 1150) mentions interest rates as high as 60%. In 1304, interest rates in Nuremberg were an astounding 220%!

Historically, lending money for a fee has been opposed. The Greek philosophers

Plato and Aristotle wrote against the taking of interest. In fact, Aristotle believed that money is, by nature, "barren," that the birth of money from money was "unnatural," and therefore condemned the taking of interest.

Men such as Martin Luther and Thomas Aquinas argued that the Scriptures specifically forbade the taking of interest. The Roman Catholic Church was officially against **usury**, the charging of interest, until the 1830s, and penalties for disobeying Church law included being denied a Christian burial. Public feeling toward usury was so strong that in the Middle Ages it was believed that a prolonged rainstorm was caused by the burial of an Italian money lender in consecrated ground. In an attempt to stop the downpour, the body was disinterred from the grave and thrown into the Po River. In spite of the strong feelings against charging interest, lending still occurred. Powerful banks were founded in Venice in the late 1100s and in Genoa and Barcelona in the early 1400s. The success of these areas in commerce and the arts can be partially attributed to the availability of money from interest-charging banks.

Banks were also started by Jewish families. Since Jews were not associated with the Catholic Church, there was no risk in charging interest. However, the stereotype that Jews charged unreasonably high interest rates during this time is not necessarily correct. Christian bankers operated under a much higher risk in the lending of money because of possible censure by the Church. Due to the risk involved, they often charged higher rates.

One method of avoiding the conflict with the Church over charging of interest was by calling it something else. A lender would agree to lend a sum of money at no charge if the money was returned within a specified time. If not, the borrower paid the lender an additional fee. The fee was computed by the lender (hence being as high as he chose) and was the difference between the lender's current financial standing and what his standing would have been had the money been repaid on time. The word "interest" comes from the Latin *Id quod interest* or "that which is between."

Since the availability of money is necessary for the economy, negative attitudes toward interest have diminished. However, if the interest rate is extremely high, it is still called usury and is still viewed with disfavor.

Banking

The original bankers were the money changers. As long ago as the Roman Empire, there was a need to exchange the coins of one country for another. The money changers would sit in the plaza or in front of their shops, counting coins on a bench. It is from the Italian word for bench, *banco*, that we get the current word "bank."

As the Dark Ages ended and the amount of commercial activity in Europe increased, it became increasingly difficult to carry on all transactions in cash. The currency of the time was almost always coin. Bulky when carried in large amounts and very heavy, gold and silver coin were accepted by all merchants but were very impractical for the demands of the growing economy. Coupled with the necessity for increased amounts of cash, this situation created the need for an institution that would handle long-distance transactions and supply ready cash.

The powerful banks in Venice, Genoa, and Barcelona had branches in the major trading spots throughout Europe. These banks were able to complete transactions without the transfer of coin. All that was needed was a letter of credit that could be honored by any of the bank's branches. These powerful banks also were willing to defy the Church and lend money in return for the payment of interest.

Another activity of these banks was to act as a clearing house where money from different countries could be exchanged. As is true today, the rates of exchange fluctuated. The banks would exchange coins for their customers immediately, but would hold the foreign currency until a more favorable rate of exchange materialized. By this process of speculation in the currency markets, the banks were able to accumulate profits. The Church considered this activity a legitimate way of accumulating profits because a risk was involved.

Much of the modern system of banking is based on the arrangement started in England during the late 1600s. King Charles II of England was a profligate spender. In 1694, when Parliament refused to give him the money he needed to support his army, the king raided the Royal Mint. The merchants, whose money he stole, were outraged. To prevent a recurrence, the merchants decided to deposit their money in the vaults of the local goldsmiths. In return, the goldsmiths would issue a note saying that the merchant had a certain amount of gold or silver. Instead of handling all transactions in coin, merchants could now purchase goods by giving the seller a note. In time, a note attesting that John Doe had 20 ounces of gold coin kept with a certain goldsmith might pass through the hands of several people. None of these people ever saw the gold because the note was accepted by most everyone as money, and the possession of the note was far more convenient than keeping the actual coin.

When the goldsmiths realized that these notes of deposits were being used like real money, major changes ensued. First, the notes they issued to their depositors were no longer issued to the individual. Instead, the notes indicated that the person who possessed the note was the owner of the gold. This eliminated the difficulty of redeeming a note in someone else's name. The second major change was that the goldsmiths realized that only rarely did they need to redeem large numbers of these notes for the precious metals they represented. Usually, the daily deposits of coin were sufficient to supply the gold requested by customers that same day. Betting that they would never need to redeem all the outstanding notes, the goldsmiths started to print more notes. These additional notes were not backed by actual assets, but, if they were never redeemed, it didn't matter. The goldsmiths then used these notes to provide the public with loans. The person taking out the loan received the notes and promised to pay the goldsmith interest on the loan. The interest could be paid either with notes or with real money—gold and silver. If the loan was repaid in real money, the goldsmith could print more notes and issue more loans.

This was a sure method for the goldsmith to become wealthy as long as the public maintained confidence in him. As long as the noteholders believed the paper was worth real gold, they appreciated the convenience of not lugging around heavy sacks of coins. If public confidence in the goldsmith did falter, trouble ensued. Lack of confidence could cause all the noteholders to demand the gold that their certificates represented. Because there were more notes than actual coin, not all the customers would receive their money. A similar situation can be seen in modern times when a majority of the customers of a bank decide to withdraw their deposits. Called a "run on the bank," this was a problem in the United States during the 1930s and the 1980s.

The goldsmiths' system developed into the Bank of England and the modern system of banking used today. As safeguards for both the depositors and the stockholders in the bank, regulations regarding the required amounts of reserves and the number of loans are strictly enforced.

Banking in the United States

The First Bank of the United States was established in 1791 in Philadelphia, Pennsylvania, and had eight branches throughout the new country. This bank issued currency, and provided loans to and accepted deposits from the federal government, business, and the public. Although the bank was considered a success, in 1811 Congress did not renew its charter due to pressure from the smaller, state-chartered banks.

To fill the void left by the demise of the Bank of the United States, 120 state-chartered banks were created within a year. Like the goldsmiths, many of the bankers saw a path to great wealth. Unfortunately, in 1812, the United States was at war with Great Britain and borrowed extensively from the state banks. By 1814, many of these banks stopped specie payments, and public confidence dropped. Many believed this would not have occurred if a national bank had been in existence. Thus, in 1816, the Second Bank of the United States was created.

During its short life, the bank had a turbulent history. Run by Nicholas Biddle, a Philadelphia banker, the bank was opposed by the seventh president of the United States, Andrew Jackson (1829–1837). Biddle claimed that Jackson wanted to use a spoils system to appoint the directors of the bank. In return, Jackson claimed that Biddle was using the bank for private purposes and was opposed to government interests. Jackson won the battle. Instead of waiting for the charter to expire in 1836, Jackson ordered the Secretary of the Treasury to withdraw all federal funds from the bank in 1833. The funds were deposited in the state banks that Jackson favored. After 1836, the Bank tried to remain in business as a state-chartered bank but failed.

The next 30-year period is considered a disaster in U.S. banking history. Large numbers of state-chartered banks were quickly established only to fail due to mismanagement, greed, or insufficient reserves. These smaller banks issued their own currency and did not coordinate policy with either the government or other banks. Public distrust in this system led to the establishment of national banks in 1863 and the National Bank Act of 1864.

Having twice failed in attempts to create a national branch banking system, the government did not intend the new national banks to operate as a branch system.

Instead, they were similar to the state-chartered banks but had a uniform currency and were chartered by the federal government. The advantages of this system were that

1. The currency was widely recognized and, in the event of bank failure, backed by the federal government. Although this did not protect depositors, people holding cash were protected.
2. The number of bank failures were reduced due to the more conservative practices of the national banks.

The disadvantages of this system were that

1. Due to lack of centralization, the clearing of checks and other interbank transfers were costly and time-consuming.
2. Cash reserves were inadequate in times of a crisis, such as a run on the bank.
3. The total cash available did not fluctuate to meet the changes in demand that occur at times such as the Christmas shopping season.
4. Because federal funds were deposited in these banks, the banks were easily upset when the federal government made large deposits or withdrawals.

To help correct the drawbacks of the national banks, the Federal Reserve Act of 1913 set up the current system of banking in the United States. In addition to alleviating the problems of the national banks, the act created the Federal Reserve Bank. Further regulations regarding the Federal Reserve were passed in 1962. The actions of the Federal Reserve Bank appear frequently in the daily news and affect both business and the individual citizen.

CHECK YOUR READING

1. What was the general feeling about interest throughout history?
2. What is a ''run on the bank''?
3. The late 1100s saw the arrival of tea in Japan from China while the Mayans of Central America were in the second stage of the development of their civilization. What event was occurring in banking history at this time?
4. While banks were being formed in Barcelona and Genoa, the Great Temple of the Dragon was being erected in Peking, China. During what time period did this happen?
5. Give a brief history of a national bank in the United States.
6. What role did goldsmiths play in the history of banking?
7. The period 46–44 B.C. saw Brutus and Cassius assassinate Julius Caesar and the Roman legions make Africa a Roman province. What were interest rates in Rome during this time?
8. In the early 1300s, Edward I of England was standardizing the units of measurement *yards* and *acres*. However, interest rates were far from being standardized. In what city did interest rates reach the amazing level of 220%?

9. Mozart's famous composition, *The Magic Flute*, had its first performance in 1791. What U.S. financial institution was being established during this same year?

10. When R. T. Laënnec invented the stethoscope and Nikolai Karamzin was writing *History of the Russian Empire*, the Second Bank of the United States was established. In what year did all three of these events occur?

11. In 1913, the U.S. Congress instituted the first federal income tax. What federal legislation was passed concerning banking during the same year, and what institution did it create?

12. When the first U.S. salmon cannery was being established in 1864, what piece of federal legislation was being passed?

13. Match each of the following names with the associated event or action.

(a) Aquinas	Argued that the Scriptures forbade interest
(b) Aristotle	Condemned taking interest
(c) Bhāskara	Favored the Roman Catholic Church's policy against the taking of interest
(d) Biddle	Mentioned interest rates of 60% in India
(e) Charles II	Interest rates in his Rome reached 48%
(f) Cicero	Opposed deposits in the Bank of the United States
(g) Jackson	Raided the Royal Mint
(h) Luther	Ran the Second Bank of the United States

RESEARCH QUESTIONS

In order to answer the following questions, you will need to refer to material not contained in the text. Possible sources of information are listed in the bibliography at the end of this book.

1. In modern television shows, the word "shylock" is used in reference to gangsters who charge exorbitant amounts of interest and enforce the penalties with violence. Determine the origin of the word "shylock." What was the interest charged on a loan by the original Shylock?

2. What interest rates were common in the 1960s? in the early 1970s? in the late 1970s? Compare these rates with those charged in Rome in 40 B.C. or in Germany in the 1300s. Discuss whether you consider the interest rates in the late 1970s to be high or low.

3. Find common interest rates for the United States in each decade of the 20th century. Plot the information on a graph. Does there appear to be a trend?

4. Repeat Question 3 for three other countries.

5. Find some common interest rates for Europe in A.D. 1400. Be sure to cite your references.

6. What connection did banking and interest rates play in the historic European rivalries between Christians and Jews?

7. What is the difference between usury and interest in modern times?

8. In reference to money and banking, what is meant by ''specie''?
9. What is meant by ''unit banking''? What countries use this method? What is meant by ''branch banking''? What countries use this method?
10. What is a federal reserve note?
11. What is a silver certificate?
12. What are the main points of the Federal Reserve Act of 1913?
13. What is the Federal Reserve Bank? Who are its customers? What does the Bank do? Where are the Federal Reserve Banks located? Who is the current chairman of the Federal Reserve?
14. What do the initials F.D.I.C. stand for? When was the organization started? What is the purpose of the organization?

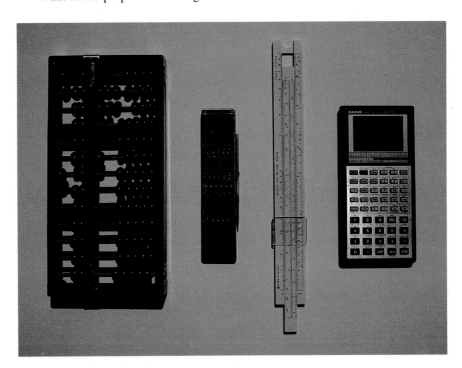

Through the centuries, the abacus, mechanical accumulator, slide rule, and hand-held calculator have been used to help in computation. (Courtesy of Kurt Viegelmann)

SECTION 6.0

▼

REVIEW

In this section, we want to review some of the ideas from algebra that will be needed to solve problems in the mathematics of finance. We will discuss the use of a calculator, logarithms, and equations containing exponents.

Using Your Calculator

You should be familiar with some of the keys on your calculator. This section will discuss three keys needed in financial math. For a preliminary review of using a calculator, see Appendix I.

Note

In order to understand this material, it is very important for you to have a calculator available when reading this section. As we do each example, you should try the example on your own calculator. We will demonstrate one method in the text. However, because of the differences between calculators, this method may not work with your calculator.

For further help, read your calculator instruction manual or ask your instructor.

When we want to indicate that a particular key is being used, the symbol is enclosed in a box. For example, for $3 \times 4 = 12$, we use the following format:

Press   **Display**

   12

Since we pushed the keys for 3, 4, $\times$, and =, these characters are in boxes. The answer, 12, is not in a box since we did not push those keys.

The first key we discuss is the exponent key. Depending on your calculator, it looks like

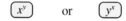   or

Example 1:

Use a calculator to find the value of 1.065^{-58}.

Solution: The sequence of buttons pressed is

Press   **Display**

   0.025925

Because the exponent is negative, we needed to use the $\pm$ symbol *after* entering 58. Entering this symbol before 58 may result in an incorrect answer. If you do not have a $\pm$ key, look for one labeled CHS (change sign).

The next key we will be using is the reciprocal key. This key is discussed in Appendix I. It looks like

$\boxed{x^{-1}}$ or $\boxed{1/x}$

This key provides a shortcut for the division problem $1 \div x$.

From algebra, you may remember that fractional exponents are the same as roots. For example,

$$\sqrt{x} = \sqrt[2]{x} = x^{1/2} \quad \text{and} \quad \sqrt[5]{x} = x^{1/5}$$

Although most calculators have a key to calculate square roots, calculators do not have a fifth-root key. As a result, to compute most roots, it is necesary to use fractional exponents. To do this on a calculator, we use the reciprocal key.

In the next example, we want to combine the use of the reciprocal and exponent keys to perform calculations involving fractional exponents.

Example 2:

Calculate $85^{1/25}$.

Solution: Using the reciprocal key and exponent keys on the calculator gives

Press	**Display**
$\boxed{8}\ \boxed{5}\ \boxed{x^y}\ \boxed{2}\ \boxed{5}\ \boxed{1/x}\ \boxed{=}$	1.194474

Throughout the chapter, we use six places after the decimal point unless we are talking about money. For greater accuracy, we could use more places, but this will usually not be necessary.

Equations with Exponents

There are two types of equations involving exponents. The first type has a constant in the exponent. The second type has a variable in the exponent. The remainder of this section is a review on how to solve both types of equations.

To solve equations that have constants in the exponent, we need to recall one of the rules of exponents.

$$(x^m)^n = x^{m \times n}$$

For example, $(x^4)^3 = x^{4 \times 3} = x^{12}$. We will use this rule to solve equations that have a constant in the exponent. Beginning with a problem with a known answer will allow us to verify that our method is correct.

Example 3:

Solve the problem $x^3 = 8$.

Solution: To solve this, we need to eliminate the exponent from the variable. We do this by raising both sides to the one-third power.

$$x^3 = 8$$

$$(x^3)^{1/3} = 8^{1/3} \qquad \text{Now apply the rule of exponents.}$$

$$x^{3 \times 1/3} = 8^{1/3}$$

$$x^1 = 8^{1/3}$$

$$x = 8^{1/3}$$

Using the following keys on a calculator gives the answer

Press	Display
⑧ x^y ③ $1/x$ =	2

Example 4:

Solve the problem $x^{14} = 75$.

Solution: To solve this, we need to eliminate the exponent from the variable. We do this by raising both sides to the 1/14 power.

$$x^{14} = 75$$

$$(x^{14})^{1/14} = 75^{1/14}$$

$$x^{14 \times 1/14} = 75^{1/14}$$

$$x = 75^{1/14}$$

Using a calculator, we have

Press	Display
⑦ ⑤ x^y ① ④ $1/x$ =	1.361234

We can check this result by raising 1.361234 to the 14th power.

$$1.361234^{14} = 74.999615 \approx 75$$

The value was not exactly 75 because 1.361234 is an approximate value. For increased accuracy, use more decimal places.

The other type of equation we need to discuss is one in which the exponent is a variable. For example,

$$5^x = 25 \qquad \text{or} \qquad 2^x = 20$$

We know that the first equation is solved when $x = 2$ because $5^2 = 25$. The second equation is more difficult. Since $2^4 = 16$ and $2^5 = 32$, the answer must be between 4 and 5, but there is no simple method of solving this. To find the solution, we use logarithms.

Note

When solving equations in which the variable is in the exponent, use logarithms.

As you may remember, logarithms can be written with different bases. Throughout the chapter, we use natural logarithms. On a calculator, the key is

$$\boxed{\ln x}$$

To calculate ln 5, press the following keys. Notice that we do *not* need to press the equals button.

Press	**Display**
$\boxed{5}\ \boxed{\ln x}$	1.609438

For the problems we will be solving, we need the following rule logarithms:

$$\ln x^n = n \ln x$$

For example, $\ln 5^3 = 3 \ln 5$. To find this value on a calculator, we press the following keys:

Press	**Display**
$\boxed{5}\ \boxed{\ln x}\ \boxed{\times}\ \boxed{3}\ \boxed{=}$	4.828314

We will use logarithms to solve problems in which the variable is in the exponent. The first example is a problem with an answer that is known.

Example 5:

Solve $5^x = 25$.

Solution: Since the variable is in the exponent, we will use logarithms to solve the equation.

$$5^x = 25$$ First, take the natural log of both sides.

$$\ln (5^x) = \ln 25$$ Now, use the rule of logarithms.

$$x \ln 5 = \ln 25$$ Finally, divide both sides by ln 5.

$$x = \frac{\ln 25}{\ln 5}$$

Using the ⎡ln x⎤ key on a calculator gives

Press	**Display**
⎡2⎤ ⎡5⎤ ⎡ln x⎤ ⎡÷⎤ ⎡5⎤ ⎡ln x⎤ ⎡=⎤	2

Note that this gives the expected answer.

Confident that the method of Example 5 will work, we can now attempt a problem whose answer is not as easily guessed.

Example 6:

Solve $2^x = 20$.

Solution: Since the variable is in the exponent, we will again use logarithms.

$$2^x = 20$$

$$\ln (2^x) = \ln 20$$

$$x \ln 2 = \ln 20$$

$$x = \frac{\ln 20}{\ln 2} \approx 4.321928$$

Example 7:

$$\text{Solve} \frac{(1.07)^x - 1}{0.07} = 3.29.$$

Solution: The equation contains a variable in the exponent, so we will use logarithms to solve the problem. First, however, we must isolate the term containing the exponent. To do this, multiply both sides of the equation by 0.07. This gives

$$(1.07)^x - 1 = 3.29(0.07) = 0.2303$$

Next, add 1 to both sides of the equation.

$$(1.07)^x = 1.2303$$

At this point, we can solve the problem as we did in Example 6.

$$x = \frac{\ln 1.2303}{\ln 1.07} \approx 3.063290$$

In summary, this section demonstrated the use of three keys on the calculator and recalled two formulas from algebra. It is important to master this material before attempting the rest of the chapter.

The Keys	The Formulas

$\boxed{x^y}$ is the exponent key. $(x^m)^n = x^{m \times n}$

$\boxed{1/x}$ is the reciprocal key. $\ln (x^n) = n \ln x$

$\boxed{\ln x}$ is the natural logarithm key.

SECTION 6.0
PROBLEMS

Solve Problems 1–8 with your calculator. Round off your answers to six places after the decimal point.

1. $3^{2.3}$

2. $3^{-2.3}$

3. $6^{-0.53}$

4. $5^{-4.5}$

5. $81^{1/81}$

6. $17^{-1/17}$

7. $17^{1/17}$

8. $81^{-1/81}$

Solve for x in Problems 9–24. Round off your answers to six places after the decimal point.

9. $x^{10} = 108$

10. $x^7 = 18$

11. $x^{-7} = 18$

12. $x^{-10} = 108$

13. $10^x = 108$

14. $7^x = 108$

15. $4^{3x} = 108$

16. $5^{-12x} = 108$

17. $4 + 5^x = 27$

18. $5 + 8^x = 53$

19. $17 + 8^{3x} = 81$

20. $4 + 8^{-x} = 36$

21. $(1 + x)^5 = 27$

22. $(1 + x)^7 = 39$

23. $\dfrac{(1.06)^x - 1}{0.06} = 2.56$

24. $\dfrac{(1.03)^x - 1}{0.03} = 4.29$

SECTION   6.1

▼

SIMPLE INTEREST

Interest is the fee charged for the use of money. If we deposit money in a bank, the bank may use the money to provide loans for other customers. In return for the use of the money, the bank pays a certain percentage of the amount invested. In a similar manner, if we borrow money from a bank, we are required to pay interest to the bank in return for the privilege of using the money.

One way to calculate interest is to use **simple interest**. Simple interest is used when money is deposited in a bank and all the interest is paid only at the end of a specified time and is earned only on the principal. The formula used to calculate simple interest is

Simple Interest

▼

$$I = Prt \qquad \text{where} \begin{cases} I = \text{interest} \\ P = \text{principal or amount deposited} \\ r = \text{interest rate} \\ t = \text{time} \end{cases}$$

Example 1:

If we deposit \$1500 in a bank for three years at an annual rate of 9%, find the amount of simple interest we will earn.

Solution: Since $I = Prt$,

$$I = (1500)(0.09)(3) = \$405$$

Example 2:

If we plan to deposit \$1500 in the bank for three years and the bank is paying simple interest of 1.5% each month, find the amount of interest earned.

Solution: Because the time and the interest rate are not given in the same units of time, we cannot merely substitute the numbers into the formula as we did in Example 1. We should first change the time, three years, into months by multiplying by 12. This gives $t = 3 \times 12 = 36$ months. We now have the interest rate per month and the time in months so we can substitute $P = \$1500$, $r = 0.015$, and $t = 36$ months into $I = Prt$.

$$I = (1500)(0.015)(36) = \$810.00$$

Example 3:

If Mr. Jackson earned $500 on a $12,000 investment that earned simple interest for 18 months, what was the annual interest rate?

Solution: Since we want to find the annual interest rate, convert time into years. This gives

$$t = 18 \div 12 = 1.5 \, \text{years}$$

Now substituting $P = \$12,000$, $I = \$500$, and $t = 1.5$ into the formula $I = Prt$ gives

$$500 = (12,000)(1.5)r$$

$$500 = 18,000r$$

$$r = \frac{500}{18,000} = 0.0278 = 2.78\%$$

If interest is left in the bank account along with the principal, the amount in the account is given by

$$A = P + I$$

$$A = P + Prt \qquad \text{Substituting } I = Prt$$

$$A = P(1 + rt) \qquad \text{Factoring a } P \text{ out of the right side}$$

Amount in a Simple Interest Account

$$A = P(1 + rt) \qquad \text{where} \begin{cases} A = \text{amount in the account} \\ \quad\;\; \text{(including interest)} \\ P = \text{principal} \\ r = \text{interest rate} \\ t = \text{time} \end{cases}$$

Example 4:

If Ms. Wilson deposited $1500 in a bank for three years and the bank pays her 9% simple interest per year, find the amount in the account after the interest has been added to the account.

Solution: Subsituting $P = \$1500$, $r = 0.09$, and $t = 3$ into $A = P(1 + rt)$ gives

$$A = 1500[1 + 0.09(3)] = 1500(1.27) = \$1905$$

Example 5:

Suppose a bank pays Bill 6% simple interest each year on the amount in the account at the beginning of each year. He deposits $1000 on January 1. If Bill lets the interest accumulate in the account, how much is in the account after one year? If the simple interest for the second year is based on the amount in the account after the first year's interest is added to the account, how much is in the account two years? Repeat this process to determine the amount in the account after three years.

Solution: Using the formula $A = P(1 + rt)$, with $P = \$1000$, $r = 0.06$, and $t = 1$ year, we have

$$A = 1000(1 + 0.06) = \$1060.00$$

Thus, during the second year, $1060 is the principal in the account, so the amount at the end of the second year is

$$A = 1060(1 + 0.06) = \$1123.60$$

Similarly, during the third year, $1123.60 is the principal in the account, so the amount at the end of the third year is

$$A = 1123.60(1 + 0.06) = \$1191.02$$

As you can see, calculating the amount in the account after 30 years by this method would be a very tedious process. The amount in the account during each intermediate year must be calculated before you arrive at the final amount.

SECTION 6.1

PROBLEMS

In Problems 1–22, use the simple interest formula $I = Prt$ and $A = P(1 + rt)$ and the given information to find the indicated value.

1. $P = \$2000$　　$r = 5\%$ annually　　$t = 4$ years　　Find I

2. $P = \$3000$　　$r = 4\%$ annually　　$t = 6$ years　　Find I

3. $P = \$25,000$　$r = 5\%$ annually　　$t = 3$ months　　Find I

4. $P = \$35,000$　$r = 4\%$ annually　　$t = 4$ months　　Find I

5. $P = \$2500$　　$r = 0.75\%$ monthly　$t = 3$ months　　Find I

6. $P = \$3500$　　$r = 0.5\%$ monthly　$t = 6$ months　　Find I

7. $P = \$1000$　　$r = 0.0329\%$ daily　$t = 1$ year　　Find I

8. $P = \$1000$　　$r = 0.0247\%$ daily　$t = 1$ year　　Find I

9. $P = \$3000$　　$r = 4\%$ annually　　$t = 6$ years　　Find A

10. $P = \$2000$　　$r = 5\%$ annually　　$t = 4$ years　　Find A

11. $P = \$35,000$ $r = 4\%$ annually $t = 4$ months   Find A

12. $P = \$25,000$ $r = 5\%$ annually $t = 3$ months   Find A

13. $P = \$3500$ $r = 0.5\%$ monthly $t = 6$ months   Find A

14. $P = \$2500$ $r = 0.75\%$ monthly $t = 3$ months   Find A

15. $P = \$1000$ $r = 0.0247\%$ daily $t = 1$ year   Find A

16. $P = \$1000$ $r = 0.0329\%$ daily $t = 1$ year   Find A

17. $A = \$3100$ $r = 4\%$ annually $t = 6$ years   Find P

18. $A = \$6000$ $r = 5\%$ annually $t = 4$ years   Find P

19. $P = \$3000$ $r = 4\%$ annually $A = \$3300$ Find t

20. $P = \$2000$ $r = 5\%$ annually $A = \$2350$ Find t

21. $P = \$2000$ $A = \$3000$ $t = 2$ years   Find r (annually)

22. $P = \$2500$ $A = \$2600$ $t = 3$ months   Find r (monthly)

23. Nina deposits $3400 into a savings account earning simple interest at 9.3% annually. She intends to leave the money in the bank for eight months. How much money, including both principal and interest, can be withdrawn at the end of this time?

24. Diane deposits $4700 into a savings account earning simple interest at 8.6% annually. She intends to leave the money in the bank for six months. How much money, including both principal and interest, can be withdrawn at the end of this time?

25. You win $4700 in a charity drawing and decide to deposit it into a savings account earning simple interest at 8.51% annually. You intend to leave the money in the bank until the account is worth $5000. How long must you wait?

26. You earn $6350 for completing a special project at work and decide to deposit it into a savings account. What annual simple interest rate must be earned if you want to withdraw $7000 in one year?

27. The Radoviches need $20,000 as the down payment for a house. If they currently have $18,500 in a bank account, what annual simple interest rate must the bank pay the Radoviches so that the account will have the total down payment after one year?

28. Suppose you have a savings account that earns 5% interest annually, and you let the interest accumulate in your account at the end of each year. If the account initially has a balance of $10,000, use the method of Example 5 to find how much is in the account at the end of each of the next three years.

29. Suppose you have a savings account that earns 10% interest annually, and you let the interest accumulate in your account at the end of each year. If the account initially has a balance of $1000, use the method of Example 5 to find how much is in the account at the end of each of the next three years.

SECTION 6.2

COMPOUND INTEREST

In the last example of Section 6.1, we discussed what would happen when the interest was added to the account at the end of each year. Each successive year's earnings included interest on the interest left in the account the year before. This method of calculation is called **compound interest**.

The problem turned out to be difficult because the amount in the account had to be computed for each year in order to get the final result. If the interest were to be added at the end of each month, more than 100 calculations would be necessary for a nine-year period. As you may have guessed, there is a better way to do this.

Let us examine what is done when the amount in the account is computed. We use the formula $A = P(1 + rt)$ with $t = 1$, giving $A = P(1 + r)$. The amount in the account at the beginning of the year is multiplied by $1 + r$ to give the amount in the account at the end of the year. This final amount is used as the principal for the next year. Continuing that process, we have the following table:

Year Number	Amount at the Beginning of the Year	Amount at the End of the Year
1	P	$P(1 + r)$
2	$P(1 + r)$	$[P(1 + r)](1 + r) = P(1 + r)^2$
3	$P(1 + r)^2$	$[P(1 + r)^2](1 + r) = P(1 + r)^3$
4	$P(1 + r)^3$	$[P(1 + r)^3](1 + r) = P(1 + r)^4$
5	$P(1 + r)^4$	$[P(1 + r)^4](1 + r) = P(1 + r)^5$

The important thing to notice is that the exponent is the same as the year number. This pattern gives a formula to obtain the amount in the account at the end of any year:

$$A = P(1 + r)^t \qquad \text{where} \begin{cases} r = \text{annual interest rate} \\ t = \text{time in years} \end{cases}$$

Now try Example 5 of Section 6.1 again.

Example 1:

Suppose a bank pays Ron 6% interest, compounded annually. He deposits $1000 on January 1. If he lets the interest accumulate in the account, how much does he have after one year? after two years? after three years?

Solution: By the formula $A = P(1 + r)^t$, after one year Ron has

$$A = 1000(1 + 0.06) = \$1060.00$$

For the second year:

$$A = 1000(1 + 0.06)^2 = 1000(1.12360) = \$1123.60$$

For the third year:

$$A = 1000(1 + 0.06)^3 = 1000(1.19102) = \$1191.02$$

Note that the results of the calculations are the same as in Example 5 of Section 6.1. More importantly, we can immediately calculate the results for any year.

Example 2:

Carol is depositing $1500 into an account earning 9%, compounded annually. How much money will be in the account after 25 years?

Solution: Using the formula $A = P(1 + r)^t$, with $P = \$1500$, $r = 0.09$, and $t = 25$, gives

$$A = 1500(1 + 0.09)^{25}$$

$$= 1500(8.623081) = \$12,934.62$$

Now suppose that the interest were added to the account at the end of every month rather than at the end of the year. If the annual interest rate were 6%, the monthly interest rate would be 6% ÷ 12 = 0.06 ÷ 12 = 0.005. Over the course of one year, interest would be compounded (added to the account) 12 times. Thus, the expression for the amount in the account at the end of the year would be

$$A = P\left(1 + \frac{0.06}{12}\right)^{12(1)} = P(1.005)^{12}$$

Using this as an example gives us the compound interest formula for any rate of compounding:

Compounded Interest Formula

$A = P(1 + r)^n$ where $\begin{cases} A = \text{amount in the account after } n \text{ time periods} \\ P = \text{present value of the account (the amount} \\ \quad \text{deposited)} \\ r = \text{annual interest rate} \div \text{number of periods} \\ \quad \text{per year (periodic interest rate)} \\ n = \text{number of times time periods (number of years} \\ \quad \times \text{number of periods per year)} \end{cases}$

The word **period** means the number of times per year that interest is compounded. For example, if interest is compounded monthly, the number of periods per year is 12. If the interest is compounded daily, the number of periods per year is 365.

Example 3:

Carol is depositing $1500 into a savings account with an annual rate of 9%, compounded monthly. How much money will be in the account after 25 years?

Solution: Using the formula $A = P(1 + r)^n$, with $P = \$1500$, $r = 0.09 \div 12 = 0.0075$, and $n = 25 \times 12 = 300$, gives

$$A = 1500(1 + 0.0075)^{300}$$

$$= 1500(9.408415) = \$14,112.62$$

Compare this result with Example 2. Notice that by compounding more frequently, the amount of interest earned has increased. What do you think will happen if the interest is compounded daily?

Example 4:

If $1500 is deposited into an account earning 9%, compounded daily, how much money will be in the account after 25 years?

Solution: Using $r = 0.09 \div 365 = 0.0002466$ and $n = 25 \times 365 = 9125$, we have

$$A = 1500(1 + 0.0002466)^{9125} = 1500(9.4872386) = \$14{,}230.86$$

(Note: If values are not rounded off, $A = \$14{,}227.61$.)

Starting the compound interest formula, we can solve for the amount in the account (A), the present value (P), the rate per period (r), or the number of times the account is compounded (n). The next problem involves solving for P, the present value of the account.

Example 5:

How much money must be deposited into an account that earns 6%, compounded monthly, so that $20,000 can be withdrawn in seven years?

Solution: Using $r = 0.06 \div 12 = 0.005$ and $n = 7 \times 12 = 84$, we have

$$20{,}000 = P(1 + 0.005)^{84}$$

$$20{,}000 = P(1.520370)$$

$$P = 20{,}000 \div 1.520370 = \$13{,}154.69$$

Most people don't have $13,154.69 available to deposit into an account. Suppose we have only half this amount, $6577.35. If this money is deposited into the account used in Example 5, will it take twice the time, 14 years, to reach the desired $20,000?

Example 6:

If $6577.35 is deposited into an account that earns 6%, compounded monthly, how long must we wait for the account to be worth $20,000?

Solution: Using $r = 0.06 \div 12 = 0.005$, $P = \$6577.35$, and $A = \$20{,}000$, we have

$$20{,}000 = 6577.35(1 + 0.005)^{n}$$

$$\frac{20{,}000}{6577.35} = 1.005^{n}$$

$$3,040738 = 1.005^n$$

$$\ln(3.040738) = \ln(1.005^n)$$

$$\ln(3.040738) = n\ln(1.005)$$

$$n = \frac{\ln 3.040738}{\ln 1.005} = 223$$

Now we need to either think or worry. If $n = 223$ is measured in years, we will never live to see this money. The good news is that since the interest in the account was compounded monthly, n is measured in months. Therefore, we will have the $20,000 in 223 months, or $223 \div 12 = 18.58$ years, or 18 years, 7 months. The important thing to notice here is that you made one-half the original investment, but it required more than double the time to achieve the same account balance.

If we really wanted to have the $20,000 in seven years, but we have only $6577.35, we can meet our financial needs by securing a higher interest rate.

Example 7:

If $6577.35 is deposited into an account, what annual rate, compounded monthly, is necessary to accumulate $20,000 in the account after seven years?

Solution: Using $t = 7 \times 12 = 84$, $P = \$6577.35$, and $A = \$20,000$ gives

$$20,000 = 6577.35(1 + r)^{84}$$

$$\frac{20,000}{6577.35} = (1 + r)^{84}$$

$$3.040738 = (1 + r)^{84}$$

$$3.040738^{1/84} = [(1 + r)^{84}]^{1/84}$$

$$1.013327 = 1 + r$$

$$r = 0.0133$$

As in the previous example, this is a problem in which interest is compounded monthly. Thus, the annual interest rate is $0.0133 \times 12 = 0.1596$, or 15.96%.

Interest Before Calculators

If you noticed that we relied heavily on a calculator while doing the problems, you may question how students of the 1960s, as well as the bankers of the 1600s, solved these problems. They did it through the extensive use of tables. Students and other users looked up the interest rate and number of periods in the table to find the appropriate value. Where did the tables come from? They were the result of long years of computations done by hand. To appreciate the magnitude of this effort, try computing 1.0075^5 without the use of a calculator.

When people in the Middle Ages did computations, they did not merely use multiplication. The methods were very clever and involved algebra as well as arithmetic.

Example 8

Compute the value of 1.04^5 using the methods available in the Middle Ages.

Solution: First compute the value of the algebra expression

$$(1 + r)^2 = (1 + r)(1 + r) = (1 + 2r + r^2)$$

Multiplying this result by itself gives

$$(1 + r)^4 = (1 + 2r + r^2)(1 + 2r + r^2) = 1 + 4r + 6r^2 + 4r^3 + r^4$$

Multiply this result by $1 + r$. This gives

$$(1 + r)^5 = (1 + 4r + 6r^2 + 4r^3 + r^4)(1 + r)$$
$$= 1 + 5r + 10r^2 + 10r^3 + 5r^4 + r^5$$

If we let $r = 0.04$ and calculate each term separately, we notice that several of the terms are very small.

$$(1 + 0.04)^5 = 1 + 5(0.04) + 10(0.04)^2 + 20(0.04)^3$$
$$+ 5(0.04)^4 + (0.04)^5$$

$$= 1 + 0.20 + 0.016 + 0.00064$$
$$+ 0.0000128 + 0.0000001024$$

$$= 1.2166529024$$

Notice that a good approximation to this value can be found by adding only $1 + 5r^2 + 10r^2$. In general, to estimate $(1 + r)^n$, you can use the formula

$$(1 + r)^n \approx 1 + nr + \frac{n(n - 1)r^2}{2}$$

Using this formula gives

$$(1 + 0.04)^5 \approx 1 + 5(0.04) + \frac{5(4)(0.04)^2}{2}$$

$$(1.04)^5 \approx 1 + 0.2 + 0.016$$

$$(1.04)^5 \approx 1.216$$

Notice that this is very close to the exact answer of 1.2166529024.

SECTION 6.2
PROBLEMS

Use the compound interest formula $A = P(1 + r)^n$ and the given information to solve the following problems. In all cases, the interest rates are given as annual rates.

1. $P = \$2000$ $r = 6\%$ compounded monthly $t = 4$ years Find A

2. $P = \$3000$ $r = 9\%$ compounded monthly $t = 6$ years Find A

3. $P = \$6000$ $r = 5\%$ compounded daily $t = 3$ years Find A

4. $P = \$5000$ $r = 10\%$ compounded daily $t = 4$ years Find A

5. $P = \$6000$ $r = 5\%$ compounded daily $t = 3$ months Find A

6. $P = \$5000$ $r = 10\%$ compounded daily $t = 4$ months Find A

7. $A = \$6000$ $r = 6\%$ compounded monthly $t = 2$ years Find P

8. $A = \$5000$ $r = 12\%$ compounded monthly $t = 3$ years Find P

9. $A = \$5000$ $r = 9\%$ compounded monthly $P = \$3500$ Find t

10. $A = \$6000$ $r = 6\%$ compounded monthly $P = \$2000$ Find t

11. $A = \$5000$ $t = 2$ years $P = \$3500$ Find r compounded monthly

12. $A = \$6000$ $t = 9$ years $P = \$2000$ Find r compounded monthly

13. Which is the better investment for a gift of $1000, an 8% account compounded annually or a 7.8% account compounded daily? Each investment is for one year.

14. Which is the better investment for a gift of $3000, an 8.5% account compounded annually or an 8.3% account compounded daily? Each investment is for one year.

15. Suppose you invest $2500 in an account that earns 9% compounded monthly. After eight years you withdraw the entire amount and deposit it into an account that earns 10% compounded quarterly for six years. How much money have you accumulated at the end of those 14 years?

16. An inheritance from your great aunt in Des Moines of $7000 is deposited into an account that earns 7.5% compounded monthly. After eight years you withdraw the entire amount and deposit it into an account that earns 10% compounded quarterly. This second account requires you to keep the money in the account for seven years. How much money have you accumulated at the end of those seven years?

17. Uncle Bill and Aunt Marilyn plan on buying a vacation home in the future. They have $20,000 to invest and want to make a down payment of $40,000 on the home. If the best investment currently available is a 12% account compounded daily, how long do they have to wait until they have enough money to make the down payment?

18. You, being the wise parent, decide to invest $10,000 for your newborn child's college education. Setting your sights high, you aim for an education at Vine Covered University (VCU). Estimating the future costs at VCU, you arrive at a figure of $150,000. If you can get a 15% annual rate, compounded monthly, how old will your child be when you have the funds to send her to VCU?

19. After extensive negotiations, the Indians of Manhattan Island agree with the bankers of Amsterdam to invest $24 at 5% interest, compounded daily. After keeping this investment for 400 years, the Indians decide to cash in the account. What is the account balance?

*20. Determine the value of a $100 deposit at the end of one year if the account earns 12% interest, compounded (a) monthly, (b) weekly, (c) daily, (d) every second. Compare these values to the value of $A = 100e^{0.12t}$, where $t = 1$ year.

In problems 21–27, use the Middle Ages formula

$$(1 + r)^n \approx 1 + nr + \frac{n(n - 1)r^2}{2}$$

21. Compute the value of 1.0075^{12}.

22. Compute the value of 1.005^{10}.

23. Compute the value of 1.01^{24}.

24. Compute the value of a $200 account earning 8.1%, compounded monthly, for two years.

25. Compute the value of a $300 account earning 9.6%, compounded monthly, for three years.

26. Compute the value of a $200 account earning 8.1%, compounded daily, for two years.

27. Compute the value of a $300 account earning 9.6%, compounded daily, for three years.

SECTION 6.3

▼

ANNUITIES

As you were working the problems in Section 6.2, the situations may have seemed a little beyond your current financial status. For many, the idea of depositing $10,000 is not realistic. Most people are more likely to save a little money every month or every week rather than make one large deposit. An account in which money is deposited at the end of each period is called an **ordinary annuity**.*

Suppose you deposit $100 into an account at the end of every month for four months. Interest is to be compounded monthly at 12%. How much is in the account at the end of four months? To solve this problem, consider the compound interest earned by each deposit, using the formula $A = P(1 + r)^n$.

The first deposit is in the bank for three months, so its value is $100(1 + 0.01)^3$.

The value of the second deposit is $100(1 + 0.01)^2$.

The value of the third deposit is $100(1 + 0.01)^1$.

The value of the fourth deposit is $100 (since it has not earned any interest).

Adding these four terms gives

$$100 + 100(1.01)^1 + 100(1.01)^2 + 100(1.01)^3 = \$406.04$$

This method certainly solved the problem, but suppose these monthly deposits continued for 30 years. Since this would mean 360 deposits, this process would soon become very tiresome. Instead, if you look at the calculations, you may recognize that this is the sum of the terms of a geometric series. Using the formula for the sum of a geometric series, we can find the formula for the sum of all the payments in an annuity. The derivation of the formula is not the intent of this book, but we will be using the formula for all the remaining problems. It will allow us to easily determine the sum of an annuity without repetitive calculations.

Annuity Formula

▼

$$S = \text{PMT}\left[\frac{(1 + r)^n - 1}{r}\right] \quad \text{where} \begin{cases} S = \text{amount in the annuity} \\ \text{PMT} = \text{amount of each deposit} \\ r = \text{periodic interest rate} \\ n = \text{number of payments} \end{cases}$$

We use PMT (which stands for payment) as a reminder that an annuity is different from an account with one deposit. You will need to make payments into the account every period.

---

*An annuity that has payments made at the beginning of the period is called an annuity due. Only ordinary annuities will be discussed here.

Example 1:

Suppose Mildred deposits $100 every month for 20 years into an account earning 6%, compounded monthly.

(a) What is the value of the account after 20 years?
(b) How much of the total value of the account was paid through the deposits?
(c) How much interest was earned?

Solution:

(a) The amount of the annuity is to be found. Using PMT $= 100$, $r = 0.06 \div 12 = 0.05$, and $n = 20 \times 12 = 240$ gives

$$S = 100 \left(\frac{(1 + 0.005)^{240} - 1}{0.005} \right) = 100 \left(\frac{3.310204 - 1}{0.005} \right) = \$46{,}204.09$$

(b) The total deposits were 240 payments of $100 each, which gives $24,000.00.
(c) The amount of interest earned is the difference between the amount in the annuity and the amount deposited. Therefore the interest earned is

$$\$46{,}204.09 - \$24{,}000 = \$22{,}204.09$$

Example 2:

Suppose we deposit $100 every month into an account earning 6%, compounded monthly. How long will we need to continue making the deposits so that the account is worth $100,000?

Solution: The number of payments, n, is to be determined. Using PMT $= 100$, $r = 0.06 \div 12 = 0.005$, and $S = 100{,}000$, we have

$$100{,}000 = 100 \left(\frac{(1 + 0.005)^n - 1}{0.005} \right)$$

Dividing both sides by 100 gives

$$1000 = \left(\frac{(1 + 0.005)^n - 1}{0.005} \right)$$

Multiplying both sides by 0.005 gives

$$5 = 1.005^n - 1$$
$$6 = 1.005^n$$
$$\ln 6 = \ln(1.005^n)$$
$$\ln 6 = n \ln 1.005$$
$$n = \frac{\ln 6}{\ln 1.005} = 359.2 \approx 360 \text{ months or } 30 \text{ years}$$

There are two interesting things to notice here. The first is that even though the calculation for n is 359.2, the answer is 360 months, not 359 months. The reason is that if we only made 359 deposits, the account would be slightly less than $100,000. By making 360 payments, the account is slightly over $100,000. The second important thing to notice is that while it took 20 years to accumulate the first $46,000, the account reached $100,000 in only ten additional years. The reason is that during the last ten years of the account, the first $46,000 was earning a large amount of interest.

SECTION 6.3
PROBLEMS

$$S = \text{PMT} \left[\frac{(1 + r)^n - 1}{r} \right] \quad \text{where} \begin{cases} S = \text{amount in the annuity} \\ \text{PMT} = \text{amount of each deposit} \\ r = \text{periodic interest rate} \\ n = \text{number of payments} \end{cases}$$

Use the annuity formula and the given information to solve the following problems. In all cases, interest rates are given as annual rates.

1. PMT = $200 r = 6% compounded monthly t = 5 years   Find S

2. PMT = $100 r = 4% compounded quarterly t = 2 years   Find S

3. S = $20,000 r = 4% compounded quarterly t = 10 years   Find PMT

4. S = $35,000 r = 12% compounded monthly t = 15 years   Find PMT

5. S = $20,000 r = 9% compounded monthly   PMT = $100   Find t, in years

6. S = $80,000 r = 6% compounded quarterly   PMT = $250   Find t, in years

7. George listened when his banker told him to start saving money in an IRA account. Beginning when he was 22, George deposited $100 every month into an account earning 9% compounded monthly.

   (a) How much will be in the account when George retires at age 70?
   (b) How much of this money did George deposit?
   (c) How much of this money is interest?

   George's brother Skippy decided to spend the first ten years buying himself toys. He reasoned that he could accumulate more money than George if he deposited $200 every month starting at age 32. Skippy also plans to retire at age 70 and to use the same 9% account as George.

    (d) How much money will be in Skippy's account?

    (e) How much of this money did Skippy deposit?

8. After hearing all the advertisements about becoming wealthy when you retire, you decide to contribute to a mutual fund that averages 13% per year.

    (a) If you contribute $2500 each year for the next 25 years, how much will be in the account?

    (b) How much of this money did you deposit?

    (c) How much of this money is interest?

9. When Jill was first hired by SemiTechCorp as a design engineer, she had sufficient income to deposit $400 each month into an IRA paying 9% interest, compounded monthly. The monthly deposits lasted for ten years.

    (a) How much was in the account at the end of ten years?

    (b) Due to family responsibilities and investments in real estate, she was not able to continue with these IRA contributions. Instead, she deposited the entire IRA account into a 25-year certificate of deposit earning 11% compounded quarterly. What was the value of the account when it matured?

10. When Lisa was first hired by the Environmental Protection Agency as a research scientist, she had sufficient income to deposit $600 each quarter into an IRA paying 10% interest, compounded quarterly. The quarterly deposits lasted for 12 years.

    (a) How much was in the account at the end of 12 years?

    (b) Because of costs of maintaining her parents in a nursing home, she was not able to continue these deposits. Instead, she deposited the entire IRA account into a 30-year certificate of deposit earning 12% compounded monthly. What was the value of the account when it matured?

11. In the hopes of driving a luxurious Belchfire 8088, Bert has been setting aside $150 every month into an account earning 9%, compounded monthly. How long will it take to accumulate the necessary $42,000 purchase price of the car?

12. Grandpa has decided to set up a college fund for his newborn grandson. How much should he deposit every month into an account paying 7.5% interest compounded monthly so that the account will be worth $30,000 by the time his grandson is 18?

13. You are the owner of a printing company and know that you will need to buy $35,000 in new equipment seven years from now. To finance this purchase, you decide to deposit a fixed amount every month into an annuity. If the annuity pays 8.4% compounded monthly, how much should your deposits be?

14. Anticipating the need for $150,000 as a college fund for the children, the Cleavers deposit $300 every month into an account earning 7.8% compounded monthly. How long will it take to accumulate the tentative college fund?

For Sale by Jeff Peterson.
(Courtesy of the artist)

SECTION   6.4

▼

LOANS

In Section 6.3, we discussed the idea of making repeated deposits into an account. The bank added interest, and the amount in the account accumulated rapidly. Banks acquire the money they pay out as interest from loans and other investments. In this section, we will discuss what happens when a loan is created and eventually paid off. Although we will not show the derivation, the formula can be derived by using the concepts of geometric series. The formula that gives loan payments is

Loan Formula

$$L = \text{PMT}\left[\frac{1 - (1 + r)^{-n}}{r}\right] \quad \text{where} \begin{cases} L = \text{the amount of the loan} \\ \text{PMT} = \text{the amount of each} \\ \quad\quad\quad \text{payment} \\ r = \text{periodic interest rate} \\ n = \text{the number of payments} \end{cases}$$

Example 1:

Suppose Bill receives a loan from his bank for $9000. He must make monthly payments for four years. The annual interest rate is 6%, compounded monthly. What are his monthly payments?

Solution: We are trying to find the payments PMT. Using $L = 9000$, $r = 0.06 \div 12 = 0.005$, and $n = 4 \times 12 = 48$, we have

$$9000 = \text{PMT}\left[\frac{1 - (1 + 0.005)^{-48}}{0.005}\right]$$

$$9000 = \text{PMT}\left[\frac{1 - 0.787098}{0.005}\right]$$

$$9000 = \text{PMT}\,[42.580318]$$

$$\text{PMT} = \$211.37 \text{ is the monthly payment}$$

Example 2:

When buying a $180,000 home in Milpitas, Theresa made a down payment of $40,000 and took out a loan for the remaining $140,000. The loan has a 30-year term with monthly payments and an annual rate of 10.8%.

(a) What is the monthly payment?
(b) What is the total of the payments over the 30 years?
(c) How much interest will be paid on the loan?

Solution:

(a) Using $L = 140,000$, $r = 0.108 \div 12 = 0.009$, and
$n = 30 \times 12 = 360$, we have

$$140,000 = \text{PMT}\left[\frac{1 - (1 + 0.009)^{-360}}{0.009}\right]$$

$$140,000 = \text{PMT}\left[\frac{1 - 0.039736}{0.009}\right]$$

$$140,000 = \text{PMT}\,[106.696041]$$

$$\text{PMT} = \$1312.14 \text{ are the monthly payments}$$

(b) 360 payments of $1312.14 give $360 \times 1312.14 = \$472,370.40$.
(c) Since the interest is the difference between the total payments and the value of the loan, the total interest is

$$472,370.40 - 140,000 = \$332,370.40$$

Since the bank collects this interest, you can see how it manages to pay interest to its customers at a 7% rate.

As we saw in Example 2, interest payments can exceed $300,000. Often when paying off a loan, people decide to **accelerate** the payments to lower the amount of interest paid. In the next example, we look at the effects of accelerating the payments on the mortgage of Example 2.

Example 3:

Theresa took out a loan for $140,000. The loan had a 30-year term with monthly payments and an annual rate of 10.8%. The loan payments were $1312.14. Instead, Theresa decided to pay $1500 each month.

(a) How long did it take to pay off the loan?
(b) What is the total amount paid on the loan?
(c) What is the total interest paid?

Solution:

(a) The question asks us to determine n. Using PMT $= 1500$, $L = 140{,}000$, and $r = 0.009$, we have

$$140{,}000 = 1500 \left[\frac{1 - 1.009^{-n}}{0.009} \right]$$

Dividing by 1500 gives

$$93.3333 = \left[\frac{1 - 1.009^{-n}}{0.009} \right]$$

Multiplying by 0.009 gives

$$0.84 = 1 - 1.009^{-n}$$

$$1.009^{-n} = 1 - 0.84$$

$$1.009^{-n} = 0.16$$

$$\ln (1.009^{-n}) = \ln 0.16$$

$$-n \ln 1.009 = \ln 0.16$$

$$n = \frac{\ln 0.16}{- \ln 1.009} = 204.53$$

so Theresa has to make 205 monthly payments (17 years and 1 month). Notice that this cuts almost 13 years off the duration of the loan!

(b) The total amount paid on the loan is given by 205 payments of $1500 each:

$$205 \times 1500 = \$307{,}500$$

(c) The total interest paid is the difference between the value of the loan and the total payments. So the total interest paid is

$$307{,}500 - 140{,}000 = \$167{,}500$$

This looks very nice. By paying roughly $200 a month more than is required, total interest paid is reduced from $332,370.40 to $167,500. This is a savings of $164,870.40!

In summary, loan payments can be calculated quickly by using the formula presented in this section. Familiarity with the formula and the necessary algebra enables anyone to feel comfortable with the ideas behind borrowing money for a car or any other purchase. In addition, the actual costs of borrowing money can be computed. This will help you make intelligent choices when it comes time for major purchases.

SECTION 6.4
PROBLEMS

$$L = \text{PMT} \left[\frac{1 - (1 + r)^{-n}}{r} \right] \quad \text{where} \begin{cases} L = \text{amount of the loan} \\ \text{PMT} = \text{amount of each payment} \\ r = \text{periodic interest rate} \\ n = \text{number of payments} \end{cases}$$

Use the loan payment formula and the given information to find the indicated value. In all cases, interest rates are given as annual rates.

1. PMT = $200 r = 6% compounded monthly t = 5 years   Find L

2. PMT = $100 r = 4% compounded quarterly t = 2 years   Find L

3. L = $20,000 r = 4% compounded quarterly t = 10 years   Find PMT

4. L = $35,000 r = 12% compounded monthly t = 15 years   Find PMT

5. L = $20,000 r = 9% compounded monthly   PMT = $200   Find t, in years

6. L = $80,000 r = 6% compounded quarterly   PMT = $2000   Find t, in years

7. Bill and Judy are buying a seaside cottage in Bolinas. The mortgage will be $109,000, to be repaid monthly within 15 years. Find the monthly payments if the interest rate is 10.5%, compounded monthly.

8. The Hopkins family is purchasing a Wave Cruiser yacht costing $75,000. If the down payment is $60,000 and the loan is $15,000, find the monthly payments on their five-year, 15% loan (compounded monthly).

9. You have decided to purchase a new Toyota, using your savings and an $8000 loan. If the loan is at 13.2%, compounded monthly, and has monthly payments for four years, find the (a) monthly payment, (b) total paid over four years, and (c) total interest paid.

10. Olivia's MasterDebt Card has a balance of $4250.00. You plan on paying it off in three years, using equal monthly payments. The interest rate is 20.4%,

compounded monthly. Assuming no additional charges are made to the account, find the (a) monthly payment, (b) total paid over three years, and (c) total interest paid.

11. Lisa plans to accelerate the payments on her $5000 car loan. The original loan had an interest rate of 13.5% compounded monthly for four years and Lisa plans on paying $250 per month.

   (a) How much were the original loan payments?
   (b) How long will it take Lisa to pay off the loan with her $250 payments?
   (c) How much will the accelerated payments save Lisa over the life of the loan?

12. Ron and Michelle plan to accelerate the payments on their $200,000 home loan. The original loan had an interest rate of 10.5% compounded monthly for 30 years.

   (a) How much were the original loan payments?
   (b) How long will it take to pay off the loan if they pay $100.00 extra each month?
   (c) How much will the accelerated payments save over the life of the loan?

| C H A P T E R   6 | **SUMMARY** |

KEY TERMS, CONCEPTS, AND FORMULAS

The important terms in this chapter are:

Accelerated payments: When the actual loan payments are greater than is required by the terms of the loan, the payments are said to be accelerated; accelerated payments allow the loan to be repaid earlier than is required.   p. 334

Annuity: A type of account into which money is deposited on a regular basis.   p. 329

Compound interest: The interest paid on both the principal and the accumulated interest.   p. 322

Deposit: The amount of money put into an account for the purpose of earning interest.   p. 318

Interest: The fee charged for the use of money.   p. 318

Loan: An amount of money that is borrowed.   p. 333

Period: The interval of time between successive additions of interest to an account   p. 323

Present value: See **Principal.**   p. 323

Principal: The beginning value in an account; the amount deposited.   p. 318

1-10

Simple interest: When interest is added or charged to the account only once. p. 318

Usury: A practice of charging extremely high interest rates. p. 306

After completing this chapter, you should be able to:

1. Use the formulas

Simple interest $I = Prt, A = P(1 + rt)$ p. 318

Compounded interest $A = P(1 + r)^n$ p. 322

Annuities $S = \text{PMT} \left[\dfrac{(1 + r)^n - 1}{r} \right]$ p. 329

Loans $L = \text{PMT} \left[\dfrac{1 - (1 + r)^{-n}}{r} \right]$ p. 333

to calculate interest, interest rates, annuities, and loan payments.

2. Decide what type of situation (**simple interest, compound interest, annuity, or loan**) is being described in a problem and apply the appropriate formula(s).

SUMMARY
PROBLEMS

1. Alice invests $10,000 in an account that earns 8% simple interest. What is the value of the account after three years?

2. A certain investment has earned simple interest for five years. The initial investment was $10,804.85. The account is now worth $14,700. What is the annual interest rate?

3. Suppose $1000 is deposited in an account earning 10% interest. Find the value of the account at the end of one year if the interest is compounded (a) annually, (b) quarterly, (c) monthly, (d) daily.

4. Grandma wants to create an account for her newborn grandchild's college fund. She wants the account to be worth $25,000 in 18 years. If the account earns 8.1%, compounded monthly for the next 18 years, how much must be deposited?

5. A $20,000 certificate of deposit will be worth $26,500 in two years. If interest is compounded quarterly, what is the annual interest rate?

6. Joe wants to create an annuity that will ensure a comfortable retirement. He estimates that he will need $500,000 to meet his retirement plans. How much must Joe deposit each month for 32 years into an account earning 7.65% to meet his goal?

7. After depositing $400 per quarter for ten years into an account earning 8% compounded quarterly, Amanda is forced to stop making deposits.

(a) How much is in the account at the end of the ten years?

(b) How much interest has the account earned?

(c) If the account continues to earn the same interest rate for another 25 years and all interest is accumulated in the account, how much will the account be worth 35 years from when Amanda made her initial deposit?

8. A $65,000 annuity was created by depositing $100 every month into an account earning 6% interest compounded monthly. How many deposits were needed to create this annuity?

9. The purchase of a $15,000 automobile is to be accomplished with a 20% down payment. The remainder will be financed at 11.4%, compounded monthly, for three years.

(a) What are the monthly payments?

(b) What is the total amount paid for the car?

10. A $130,000 mortgage at 10.2%, compounded monthly, is to be paid with equal monthly payments of $1600. How long will it take to pay off the loan?

PROBABILITY

The Card Players by Lucas van Leyden shows an activity in which probability theory has relevant application. (National Gallery of Art)

A SHORT HISTORY OF PROBABILITY

Probability is the science of determining the likelihood, or chance, that an event will occur. Combinatorics is the mathematical tool used to find the number of ways in which an event can occur. The histories of these two topics are interwoven, developing with people's interest in games and, later, science.

Originally, interest in probability arose from the study of games similar to dice and other modern pastimes. Evidence of this has been found in archaeological digs of Assyrian and Sumerian sites. Scorecards from games, tomb engravings, and dice-like implements called *tali* clearly demonstrate that the ancient Egyptians had an interest in games and gambling. A *talus*, or *astralagus*, is the heel bone of a running animal. Polished and engraved, tali were used by the Egyptians the way dice are used today. When thrown, a talus could land on any of four different sides. Since it was not uniformly shaped, each side had a different probability of landing face up.

Although many civilizations, such as the Greeks and the Chinese, developed advanced mathematics, modern probability theory did not begin to develop until the late 1500s. Since (as we shall see) probability depends heavily on arithmetic, it is believed that the development of probability was hampered by cumbersome systems of numeration. Little research has been conducted on the history of probability in India; however, an Indian text from A.D. 400 seems to indicate that the Indians possessed a greater knowledge of probability than did Westerners. It is believed that their arithmetic system, one which far surpassed other systems in ease of use, allowed for these advances in probability.

Early work on combinatorics has been contributed by writers from several civilizations. In China in 1100 B.C., permutations were mentioned in *I-Ching* [Book of Changes] concerning the possible number of trigrams. The Latin writer Boethius (c. 510) gave a rule for selecting items two at a time from a large set. The Hindu mathematician Bhāskara gave rules for calculating permutations and combinations, and discussed them as they related to such varied topics as medicine, music, and architecture. Although the Hebrew writer Rabbi ben Ezra did not provide a formula, he used combinations to discuss possible arrangements of Saturn and the other planets. Hérigone (1634) was the first to give the general formula for combinations (see Section 7.0) and Leonhard Euler used the notation

$$\left[\frac{p}{q} \right]$$

for combinations, a form close to the modern

$$\binom{p}{q}$$

Although probability was mentioned as early as 1477 in a commentary on Dante's *Divine Comedy*, it is said to have its origins in an unfinished dice game. Two gamblers were unable to complete a game of chance. They agreed to divide the stakes according to their respective chances of winning the game but could not decide what these chances were. The mathematician Blaise Pascal received a letter from his friend Chevalier de Méré requesting a solution to the problem (c. 1654). Pascal sent the problem to another French mathematician, Pierre de Fermat. Working together, they are credited with developing modern probability theory.

As is always true in science, probability did not spring forth as a completely developed theory. There have been many who have made substantial contributions to the topics we will study. The Spanish alchemist Raymond Lulle (1234—1315) is credited as being the father of combinatorics. He wanted to find the symbols for all the chemical elements and then to write down all possible arrangements of these symbols. By doing so, he believed he would be able to construct every possible thing.

It was during the 16th and 17th centuries that European mathematicians developed combination theory and applied it to games of chance. In 1663, *Liber de ludo aleane* [The book on games of chance] was published. Written by the Italian Girolamo Cardano (1501–1576) nearly a century earlier, it was published after the works of Pascal and Fermat.

The Dutch astronomer Christiaan Huygens (1629–1695) wrote an introduction to dice games in *De ratiociniis in ludo aleane* [On reasoning in games of dice] in 1657. This treatise included the concept of mathematical expectation (see Section 7.3). Huygens was also one of the first to study probability from what is now considered the classical viewpoint. Whereas the investigations of Fermat and Pascal started with games, Huygens considered probability as the ratio of the number of successful outcomes of an event to the total number of possible outcomes.

The first substantial book on probability was published in 1713. Entitled *Ars conjectandi* [Art of conjecture], it was a posthumous work of the Swiss mathematician Jakob Bernoulli (1654–1705). Bernoulli developed the theory of probability, discussed the Law of Large Numbers (see Section 7.2), and provided a general theory of permutations and combinations. The work of Abraham De Moivre (1667–1754) played an important role in the development of actuarial mathematics and the theory of probability. The classical use of probability theory and combinatorics in the study of games of chance continued to develop throughout the 18th and 19th centuries. In the 1700s, probability was also used in courts of law to determine the validity of evidence and in the insurance industry to help calculate the proper rates to charge for an annuity. However, since the theory of probability was not yet firmly grounded in theory, its applications were limited to the social sciences.

In 1812, Pierre Simon de Laplace published *Théorie analytique des probabilités*. This gave the first complete theory of probability. Two years later, Laplace published *Essai philosophique sur les probabilités*, which was a compilation of the conceptual principles involved in probability. The arrival of these two works allowed probability, now firmly based in mathematical theory, to be used in the physical sciences. It quickly became one of the major mathematical tools of the 19th and 20th centuries.

In the 160 years since Laplace, probability theory has played a major role in science. From 1866 to 1887, Ludwig Boltzmann used probability to develop the kinetic theory of gases. In 1905, Albert Einstein used probability in developing the theory of Brownian motion. In 1907, A. A. Markov began the development of Markov chains. This method was soon applied to epidemiology, sociology, and population studies in emigration and immigration. In the 1940s, combinatorics and probability were used in a new area—game theory. This new area of study included the games of Fermat and Pascal, but it is also used in the study of economics, military strategy, politics, and psychology.

Today, probability is applied to many different fields. It is no longer merely a study of how the heel bone of a sheep will land.

CHECK YOUR READING

1. What role did gamblers play in the development of probability theory?
2. What role did the study of alchemy play in the study of combinatorics?

3. Pigtails were introduced in the Prussian army during the same year that Jakob Bernoulli developed the theory of probability. What year was this?

4. In 1100 B.C., the Sun Pyramid was built in Mexico and silk fabrics were made available in China. What event was occurring in the history of probability?

5. In 1634, Jean Nicolet explored Wisconsin while Anne Hutchinson arrived in Massachusetts. What was Hérigone doing this same year?

6. One eventful year saw all four of the following events: The drinking of chocolate was introduced to England; Velázquez painted *Las Hilanderas* (The Spinners); Parisian manufacturers produced fountain pens; Christiaan Huygens wrote an introduction to dice games. In what year did all these events occur?

7. In 1654, the Portuguese drove the Dutch out of Brazil, and Rembrandt painted *Portrait of Jan Six*. What work was being done on gambling during this year?

8. When Louisiana became a state and Beethoven wrote his seventh and eighth symphonies during 1812, what was Pierre Simon de Laplace doing?

9. Probability was mentioned in Dante's *Divine Comedy* during the same year that Chaucer's *Canterbury Tales* were published. What year was this?

10. In what year did neon lights appear, did work progress on the Panama Canal, and did Albert Einstein use probability theory to develop Brownian motion?

11. Match each of the following names with the correct event, idea, or occurrence.

    (a) Bernoulli   Development of modern probability theory
    (b) Bhāskara   Father of combinatorics
    (c) Boethius   First complete discourse on theory of probability
    (d) Hérigone   First substantial book on probability
    (e) Huygens   General formula for combinations
    (f) Laplace   Reasoning in games of dice
    (g) Lulle   Rules for calculating permutations and combinations
    (h) Pascal/Fermat   Rule for selecting items two at a time

RESEARCH QUESTIONS

In order to answer the following questions, you will need to refer to materials not contained in this book. Possible sources of information are listed in the Bibliography at the end of this book.

1. Investigate five areas that use probability. Write a paragraph or two about each area and how it uses probability. Possible topics are meteorology, sports, biology, genetics, insurance, psychology, advertising, and education.

2. Throughout history, people studying various topics have found the need to understand probability. Though only remotely connected to probability, these topics are of interest in themselves. Write a paragraph or two on the following topics.

    (a) What is *I-Ching*? Who wrote it? What does it discuss?
    (b) What are trigrams? What is their use and significance?
    (c) What is an alchemist?

(d) What is the kinetic theory of gases?

(e) What is Brownian motion?

3. Discuss the Bernoulli family. What areas besides probability did they investigate?

4. Who was Georges Buffon and what is the Needle Problem?

5. Look up the word "probability" in a dictionary. After reading the definition, try to define probability in your own words.

6. Do some research on two of the mathematicians mentioned in the text. Write two or three paragraphs about each.

SECTION 7.0

REVIEW

Before discussing probability, we need to review a few algebraic concepts, namely factorials, permutations, and combinations.

Factorials

The expression $n!$ is a special shorthand in mathematics. It is read a **n factorial**. When a number is written with an exclamation point, such as 5!, it means to do the following calculation:

$$5! = 5 \times 4 \times 3 \times 2 \times 1 = 120$$

In general,

$$n! = n \times (n - 1) \times (n - 2) \times \cdots \times 3 \times 2 \times 1$$

where n is any natural number.

Note

In the formula for $n!$, the "$\cdots$" indicates that there are factors not being written. For example, instead of writing

$$8! = 8 \times 7 \times 6 \times 5 \times 4 \times 3 \times 2 \times 1,$$

we could write

$$8! = 8 \times 7 \times \cdots \times 2 \times 1.$$

Even though the numbers 3 through 6 are not written, they are still used in the calculation. Called an **ellipsis**, "$\cdots$" is used to abbreviate a long, repetitive mathematical expression.

The reason for this notation is that factorials can be very large numbers even though n is relatively small. For example, 12 is not a very large number but 12! is

$$12! = 12 \times 11 \times 10 \times \cdots \times 3 \times 2 \times 1 = 479{,}001{,}600$$

It is much easier to write equations using 12! rather than 479,001,600.

We now need to discuss some rules used with factorials. The first is multiplication of factorials.

Example 1:

Multiply $4! \times 3!$.

Solution:

$$4! \times 3! = (4 \times 3 \times 2 \times 1) \times (3 \times 2 \times 1)$$
$$= 24 \times 6 = 144.$$

Note

Although it may be tempting, factorials **cannot** be multiplied by the following method.

$$4! \times 3! \neq 12! = 12 \times 11 \times 10 \times \cdots \times 2 \times 1 = 479{,}001{,}600$$

This method gives an incorrect answer.

As seen in Example 1, there is no shortcut for multiplying factorials. However; Example 2 will show how **division of factorials** can be done without calculating the value of each factorial separately.

Example 2:

Divide $4! \div 3!$.

Solution:

$$\frac{4!}{3!} = \frac{4 \times 3 \times 2 \times 1}{3 \times 2 \times 1} = \frac{4}{1} = 4$$

When dividing factorials, some factors in the numerator will cancel with factors in the denominator.

Example 3:

Divide $148! \div 146!$.

Solution: Calculating 148! and 146! is a difficult task, even with a calculator. However, the division can be accomplished by using the methods of Example 2.

$$\frac{148!}{146!} = \frac{148 \times 147 \times 146 \times 145 \times \cdots \times 2 \times 1}{146 \times 145 \times \cdots \times 2 \times 1} = 148 \times 147 = 21{,}756$$

Thus, by canceling, we are able to perform the division without actually calculating either of the factorials.

We conclude the review of factorials by discussing the following sequence:

$$4! = 24$$
$$\Big) \div 4$$
$$3! = 6$$
$$\Big) \div 3$$
$$2! = 2$$
$$\Big) \div 2$$
$$1! = 1$$
$$\Big) \div 1$$
$$0! = ?$$

In this sequence, we see that as we decrease from 4! to 3!, we are actually dividing by 4. This process continues until we reach 0!. Two inferences can be drawn from this table. First, 0! is $1! \div 1 = 1$. Thus we define

$$0! = 1$$

The second inference is that it is not possible to discuss the factorial of a negative number. Since the pattern developed at the right indicates that $(-1)!$ must come from $0! \div 0$ and division by zero is not possible, $(-1)!$ is not allowed.

Permutations

A **permutation** is one of the different arrangements of a group of items. For example, three objects ▌ ◆ ❋ can be arranged in the following orders:

▌	◆	❋
▌	❋	◆
◆	❋	▌
◆	▌	❋
❋	▌	◆
❋	◆	▌

Note

Different arrangements of the same symbols count as different permutations.

These are the six possible permutations of the three objects. All six arrangements are different, and it is not possible to find any other arrangement.

Instead of listing all the arrangements, often we will be concerned only with the number of permutations. This will be true particularly when we deal with large numbers of objects. Thus, we want to develop a formula that will determine the number of permutations. To do this, reexamine the situation in Example 3. There are three choices for the first symbol. This leaves only two choices for the second symbol, which, in turn, leaves only one choice for the third symbol. If we compute $3 \times 2 \times 1 = 6$, we arrive at the number of permutations listed.

Example 4:

Calculate the number of ways to arrange two objects selected from the following group of four.

Solution: We expect that since there are four choices for the first object and three choices for the second object, there will be $4 \times 3 = 12$ possibilities. Listing the possibilities verifies this result.

1. ☐ ◆
2. ☐ ✸
3. ☐ ▲
4. ◆ ☐
5. ◆ ✸
6. ◆ ▲
7. ✸ ☐
8. ✸ ◆
9. ✸ ▲
10. ▲ ☐
11. ▲ ◆
12. ▲ ✸

We can now use these examples to help generate a formula. If we have a set of ten objects and we want to find the number of ways to arrange a set of three, there are ten ways to pick the first item, nine ways to pick the second, and eight ways to pick the third. Multiplying gives $10 \times 9 \times 8 = 720$ ways. If we rewrite $10 \times 9 \times 8$ in the following way, we can make a connection between permutations and factorials:

$$10 \times 9 \times 8 = \frac{10 \times 9 \times 8 \times 7 \times 6 \times 5 \times 4 \times 3 \times 2 \times 1}{7 \times 6 \times 5 \times 4 \times 3 \times 2 \times 1} = \frac{10!}{7!} = \frac{10!}{(10 - 3)!}$$

Thus, if we have a group of ten objects from which we want to arrange a set of three, there are $10!/(10 - 3)!$ ways in which this can be done.

In general, the number of permutations of n objects taken r at a time is

$$P_{n,r} = \frac{n!}{(n - r)!}$$

Note

The symbol $P_{n,r}$ is not the only symbol used for permutations. Other books may use $_nP_r$ or P_r^n.

$P_{n,r}$ is read as "the number of permutations of n objects taken r at a time."

Example 5:

Find $P_{4,4}$.

Solution: Using the permutation formula with $n = 4$ and $r = 4$ gives

$$P_{4,4} = \frac{4!}{(4 - 4)!} = \frac{4!}{0!} = \frac{24}{1} = 24$$

We can see that the number of permutations of four objects taken four at a time is given by 4! Similarly, the number of permutations of r objects taken r at a time is given by $r!$ We can also see that it is important that $0! = 1$. If $0! = 0$, we would not be able to use the formula to calculate $P_{4,4}$.

Example 6:

Find $P_{48,3}$.

Solution: Using the formula above with $n = 48$ and $r = 3$ gives

$$P_{48,3} = \frac{48!}{(48-3)!} = \frac{48!}{45!}$$

$$\frac{48!}{45!} = \frac{48 \times 47 \times 46 \times 45 \times 44 \times \cdots \times 2 \times 1}{45 \times 44 \times \cdots \times 2 \times 1}$$

$$= 48 \times 47 \times 46 = 103{,}776$$

Thus, by canceling, we are able to perform the division without actually calculating either of the factorials.

Since permutations are the number of different arrangements of objects, **the order of the objects makes a difference**. For example, (1) ▌ ◆ ✱ and (2) ▌ ✱ ◆ are considered two different permutations (arrangements) of the same three objects because the order of the objects is different.

Combinations

Combinations are similar to permutations except that the **order of the objects does not make a difference**. In other words, although (1) ▌ ◆ ✱ and (2) ▌ ✱ ◆ are considered different permutations, they are the same combination of items. With combinations, we want to pick items from a set, but not arrange them.

Example 7:

Calculate the number of combinations of two objects selected from the following group of four.

Solution: We will do the problem by listing the possibilities.

1. ▢ ◆
2. ▢ ✿
3. ▢ ▲
4. ◆ ✿
5. ◆ ▲
6. ✿ ▲

As long as order is not important, we have listed all the possibilities. Thus, there are six combinations when selecting two items from a group of four. If we compare this to Example 4, we find that there are fewer combinations than there are permutations.

Example 8:

Calculate the number of combinations of four objects selected from the following group of four.

Solution: Since order is not important, there is only one choice.

Thus, there is only one combination of four items selected from a group of four.

As we saw in Example 5, the number of arrangements of a group of r objects is $r!$. Therefore, any set of r objects can be arranged in $r!$ different ways. Since combinations do not depend on the order of the objects, dividing the number of permutations by $r!$ eliminates the repeated combinations. Thus, the number of combinations of n objects taken r at a time equals $P_{n,r} \div r!$. From this, we find that the formula for combinations is

$$C_{n,r} = \frac{n!}{r!(n-r)!}$$

Note

The symbol $C_{n,r}$ is not the only symbol used for combinations. Other books may use $\binom{n}{r}$ or $_nC_r$ or C_r^n.

$C_{n,r}$ is read as "the number of combinations of n objects taken r at a time."

Example 9:

Given the objects

(a) Find the number of combinations when two items are selected.
(b) List the combinations.
(c) Find the number of permutations when two items are selected.
(d) List the permutations.

Solution:

(a) For $n = 4$ and $r = 2$, the number of combinations is

$$C_{4,2} = \frac{4!}{2!(4-2)!} = \frac{4!}{2! \times 2!} = \frac{24}{2 \times 2} = 6$$

(b) The six combinations are

1. □ ▼
2. □ ▌
3. □ ◆
4. ▼ ▌
5. ▼ ◆
6. ▌ ◆

(c) For $n = 4$ and $r = 2$, the number of permutations is

$$P_{4,2} = \frac{4!}{(4-2)!} = \frac{4!}{2!} = \frac{24}{2} = 12$$

(d) The 12 permutations are

1. □ ▼
2. □ ▌
3. □ ◆
4. ▼ □
5. ▌ □
6. ◆ □
7. ▼ ▌
8. ▼ ◆
9. ▌ ◆
10. ▌ ▼
11. ◆ ▼
12. ◆ ▌

Example 10:

Compute the values of $P_{10,0}$ and $C_{10,0}$.

Solution: Applying the appropriate formulas to these problems gives

$$P_{10,0} = \frac{10!}{(10-0)!} = \frac{10!}{10!} \qquad C_{10,0} = \frac{10!}{0!(10-0)!} = \frac{10!}{0!\,10!}$$

$$= \frac{1}{1} = 1 \qquad\qquad = \frac{1}{0!} = \frac{1}{1} = 1$$

Notice that whether we are determining permutations or combinations, when choosing groups containing zero items the result is 1. Intuitively, this makes sense. There is only one way to pick a group of zero items, and that is not to pick any of the items. ■

Example 11:

Find $C_{48,3}$.

Solution: Using the formula with $n = 48$ and $r = 3$ gives

$$C_{48,3} = \frac{48!}{3!\,(48-3)!} = \frac{48!}{3!\,45!}$$

$$\frac{48!}{3!\,45!} = \frac{48 \times 47 \times 46 \times 45 \times 44 \times \cdots \times 2 \times 1}{3 \times 2 \times 1 \times 45 \times 44 \times \cdots \times 2 \times 1}$$

$$= \frac{48 \times 47 \times 46}{3 \times 2 \times 1} = \frac{103,776}{6} = 17,296 \quad ■$$

In summary, this section has discussed the following topics:

Factorials $n! = n \times (n-1) \times (n-2) \times \cdots \times 3 \times 2 \times 1$

Permutations $P_{n,r} = \dfrac{n!}{(n-r)!}$

Combinations $C_{n,r} = \dfrac{n!}{r!\,(n-r)!}$

Permutations are used when order is essential.

Combinations are used when order is *not* important.

Pascal's Triangle

Pascal's triangle is an arrangement of numbers that has an interesting property. All the values in the triangle are combinations. The first nine rows are

								1									0th row
							1		1								1st row
						1		2		1							2nd row
					1		3		3		1						3rd row
				1		*4*		*6*		*4*		*1*					4th row
			1		5		10		10		5		1				5th row
		1		6		15		20		15		6		1			6th row
	1		7		21		35		35		21		7		1		7th row
1		8		28		56		70		56		28		8		1	8th row

Suppose we look at the fourth row of the triangle. The values in this row are the same as the possible combinations of 4. In other words,

$$C_{4,0} = 1 \qquad C_{4,1} = 4 \qquad C_{4,2} = 6 \qquad C_{4,3} = 4 \qquad C_{4,4} = 1$$

While it seems easy enough to write down a triangle full of combinations, the amazing aspect of Pascal's triangle is the pattern that can be used to construct the triangle. To find the terms in the triangle, add two consecutive terms in a row to get the term that is between these terms on the following row. The first and last terms in a row will always be 1. For example, let's look at the fourth and fifth rows:

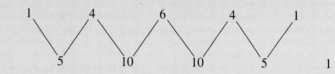

Writing the terms of Pascal's triangle in this way allows us to compute many combinations quickly. For example, to find $C_{8,3}$, we need to write the eighth row of the triangle. The combinations, beginning with $C_{8,0}$, will start at the left. Thus, $C_{8,3}$ will be the fourth term from the left, so $C_{8,3}$ equals 56.

Example 12:

Find $C_{9,5}$ from Pascal's triangle.

Solution: The ninth row of Pascal's triangle is

$$1 \quad 9 \quad 36 \quad 84 \quad 126 \quad 126 \quad 84 \quad 36 \quad 9 \quad 1$$

Thus, $C_{9,5}$, the sixth term in the row, is 126.

SECTION 7.0

PROBLEMS

In Problems 1–24, calculate the value of each expression.

1. $7!$

2. $9!$

3. $13!$

4. $12!$

5. $C_{7,3}$

6. $C_{8,3}$

7. $C_{71,3}$

8. $C_{68,3}$

9. $C_{7,7}$

10. $C_{8,8}$

11. $C_{71,0}$

12. $C_{68,0}$

13. $P_{7,3}$

14. $P_{8,3}$

15. $P_{71,3}$

16. $P_{68,3}$

17. $P_{7,7}$

18. $P_{8,8}$

19. $P_{7,0}$

20. $P_{6,0}$

21. $C_{7,3} \div C_{9,4}$

22. $C_{8,3} \div C_{10,5}$

23. $C_{7,3} \times C_{9,2}$

24. $C_{8,3} \times C_{10,2}$

25. Given the set of objects ☆ ✕ :

   (a) How many combinations of zero objects are there?
   (b) How many combinations of one object are there? List all of the combinations.

(c) How many combinations of two objects are there? List all of the combinations.

(d) How many total combinations are there?

26. Given the set of objects ♥ → ✚ :
    (a) How many combinations of zero objects are there?
    (b) How many combinations of one object are there? List all of the combinations.
    (c) How many combinations of two objects are there? List all of the combinations.
    (d) How many combinations of three objects are there? List all of the combinations.
    (e) How many total combinations are there?

27. Given the set objects ☆ ✕ :
    (a) How many permutations of zero objects are there?
    (b) How many permutations of one object are there? List all of the permutations.
    (c) How many permutations of two objects are there? List all of the permutations.
    (d) How many total permutations are there?

28. Given the set of objects ♥ → ✚ :
    (a) How many permutations of zero objects are there?
    (b) How many permutations of one object are there? List all of the permutations.
    (c) How many permutations of two objects are there? List all of the permutations.
    (d) How many permutations of three objects are there? List all of the permutations.
    (e) How many total permutations are there?

29. Given the set of objects ✕ ▢ ▼ ▮ ◈ , how many permutations of two objects are there? List all of the permutations.

30. Given the set of objects ✕ ▢ ▼ ▮ ◈ , how many combinations of two objects are there? List all of the combinations.

*31. How many zeros are at the end of the expansion of 100!? For example, 5! = 120 has one zero on the end, and 13! = 6,227,020,800 has two zeros on the end.

*32. Arrange Pascal's triangle as shown on the next page.

$$
\begin{array}{ccccccc}
1 \\
1 & 1 \\
1 & 2 & 1 \\
1 & 3 & 3 & 1 \\
1 & 4 & 6 & 4 & 1 \\
1 & 5 & 10 & 10 & 5 & 1 \\
1 & 6 & 15 & 20 & 15 & \cdots
\end{array}
$$

Show how the Fibonacci numbers can be found by a systematic process of adding terms in the triangle.

SECTION 7.1

▼ INTRODUCTION TO COUNTING

Every day people use the process of counting in many activities. Most of the time, the counting is fairly simple: ''How many people are coming to dinner?'' or ''How many shopping days are left until Christmas?'' When a more difficult problem arises, simple methods either fail or are overpowered by the problem. For example, in how many different ways can the spark plug wires be connected to the distributor cap of your car? Although only one arrangement is correct, there are 720 ways for a six-cylinder car. This section will show how permutations and combinations can make counting an easier task.

With or Without Replacement?

The first topic we need to discuss is **replacement**. Counting is done **with replacement** if the same object can be used more than once. For example, suppose a person is buying a candy bar from a well-stocked candy machine. If the machine is working correctly and is well stocked, choosing a particular brand of candy bar does not prohibit the next person using the machine from choosing the same brand of candy. The candy bar chosen by the first person was replaced by another bar of the same brand. If the machine had only one bar of each brand, the candy would be chosen **without replacement**.

Another example occurs in many card games. Suppose a player is to draw two cards, and the queen of hearts is drawn on the first card. If the card is chosen without replacement (that is, not returned to the deck) by the player, it is not possible to draw another queen of hearts. On the other hand, suppose the cards are chosen with replacement. Since the queen has been replaced, it is possible to draw the queen of hearts a second time.

Does Order Matter?

The second factor we need to consider when doing a counting problem is to decide whether the order of the items makes a difference. In many circumstances, the order of the items can make a great difference. For example, it is common to dress by putting on socks followed by shoes. Most people would be surprised to see that someone had put on his shoes followed by his socks. On the other hand, it does not matter which foot gets a shoe first. As mentioned in Section 7.0, permutations will be used if the order of the items is essential. Combinations will be used if order does not make a difference.

Basic Counting Law

The first rule of counting problems is called the **Basic Counting Law**. The Basic Counting Law says that if there are n choices for the first item and m choices for the second item, there are $n \times m$ ways in which to pick a set consisting of two items.

Example 1:

At the Produce Market Restaurant, the light lunch special consists of a choice of one of the four salads and one of the six types of fruit. How many different lunches are available?

Solution: Since there are four choices of salad and six choices of fruit, the Basic Counting Law says that there are $4 \times 6 = 24$ different light lunch specials.

Example 2:

A group of three people decides to have the special at the Produce Market Restaurant. In how many different ways can the group of three order lunches?

Solution: Assuming that there are enough supplies at the restaurant to accommodate many orders of the same item, this is a situation involving replacement. This means that all the people can order the same item. Using the results of Example 1, each person has 24 different choices for lunch. Thus, by the Basic Counting Law, there are $24 \times 24 \times 24 = 13,824$ different orders.

Example 3:

For those whose appetites are not satisfied by the lunch special, the restaurant has a dessert cart. There are ten different desserts on the cart, but only one of each type. In how many ways can our group of three each order a dessert?

Solution: In this case, it is not possible for the same dessert to be chosen by more than one person. The first person will have ten choices for dessert, but the second person will have only nine choices and the third person only eight choices. Thus, by the Basic Counting Law, there are $10 \times 9 \times 8 = 720$ different possibilities. ▨

In Examples 1–3 the Basic Counting Law was used. In Examples 1 and 2, the selections were made with replacement. In Example 3, the selections were made without replacement. Notice that Example 3 is similar to the permutations that were discussed in Section 7.0. If we reword Example 3, the similarities will become apparent.

Example 4:

In how many ways can three items, selected one at a time, be chosen from a dessert tray containing ten different desserts?

Solution: Since we are choosing without replacement and are concerned about the number of different orders, we can use permutations. Using $n = 10$ and $r = 3$, the number of permutations of ten items, choosing three at a time, is

$$P_{10,3} = \frac{10!}{(10-3)!} = \frac{10!}{7!} = \frac{10 \times 9 \times 8 \times 7 \times \cdots \times 2 \times 1}{7 \times \cdots \times 2 \times 1}$$

$$= 10 \times 9 \times 8 = 720 \quad ▨$$

Example 5:

The lock on a safe is a combination lock with 50 numbers on the dial. Four numbers are needed to unlock the safe.

(a) How many four-number sequences are possible if a number can be used only once?
(b) How many four-number sequences are possible if a number can be used more than once?

Solution:

(a) If the numbers can only be used once, the selection of numbers is done without replacement. Since the order of the numbers is essential in a combination lock, permutations should be used. Thus, the number of four-number sequences is

$$P_{50,4} = \frac{50!}{(50-4)!} = \frac{50!}{46!} = \frac{50 \times 49 \times 48 \times 47 \times 46 \times \cdots 2 \times 1}{46 \times \cdots 2 \times 1}$$

$$= 50 \times 49 \times 48 \times 47 = 5,527,200$$

(b) If the numbers can be used more than once, the numbers are chosen with replacement. There are 50 choices for each of the four numbers in the combination. Therefore, using the Basic Counting Law, the number of possible four-number sequences is

$$50 \times 50 \times 50 \times 50 = 6,250,000 \quad ▨$$

Example 6:

A researcher has determined that a certain characteristic of rabbits is determined by three genes. She has also determined that these three genes must be selected from a group of five. How many different sets of three must be tested to see if they are the genes in question?

Solution: Since we need to select three genes from a set of five, the selection is done without replacement. Since there is no mention that the order of the genes selected is important, we will use combinations with $n = 5$ and $r = 3$.

$$C_{5,3} = \frac{5!}{3!\,(5-3)!} = \frac{5!}{3!\,2!} = \frac{5 \times 4 \times 3 \times 2 \times 1}{3 \times 2 \times 1 \times 2 \times 1} = \frac{5 \times 4}{2 \times 1} = 10$$

Example 7:

In the game of lotto, each contestant picks some numbers in the hope of matching the winning numbers. For example, in a state lotto game, seven different numbers between 1 and 49 are chosen. How many different sets of seven are possible?

Solution: Because the problem states that seven different numbers are drawn, we cannot use the same number twice. Therefore, the sampling is done without replacement. Since we are concerned only about a set of numbers and not the order in which they are drawn, we want to use combinations. Thus, the number of combinations of 49 numbers, taken 7 at a time, is

$$C_{49,7} = \frac{49!}{7!\,(49-7)!} = \frac{49!}{7!\,42!} = \frac{49 \times 48 \times 47 \times 46 \times 45 \times 44 \times 43}{7 \times 6 \times 5 \times 4 \times 3 \times 2 \times 1}$$

Dividing 7 into 49; 6, 4, and 2 into 48; and 5 and 3 into 45 gives

$$C_{49,7} = 7 \times 1 \times 47 \times 46 \times 3 \times 44 \times 43 = 85{,}900{,}584$$

Example 8:

A jar contains 75 balls, numbered 1 through 75. If balls are selected without replacement and the order of selection does not matter, are there more ways to select groups of 2 balls from the jar, or groups of 73 balls?

Solution: If we compute the number of combinations in both cases, we find

$$C_{75,2} = \frac{75!}{2!\,(75-2)!} = \frac{75!}{2!\,73!} = 2775$$

$$C_{75,73} = \frac{75!}{73!\,(75-73)!} = \frac{75!}{73!\,2!} = 2775$$

The results are the same! After arriving at this answer, it is not hard to see why it is true. Imagine being told to select 73 items from a jar containing 75 items. Not wanting to go through the tedious chore of selecting 73 items, it would be simpler to select and discard 2 items while keeping the remaining 73 items. This means that there are as many groups of 2 as groups of 73 that can be chosen from this set of 75 items.

In general, this gives the formula

$$C_{n,r} = C_{n,n-r}$$

We have now done a simple example of each of the three types of problems we will be considering:

1. Counting with replacement using the Basic Counting Law.
2. Counting without replacement where the order of the objects is essential. This type of problem requires the use of permutations.
3. Counting without replacement where the order of the objects is not important. This type of problem requires the use of combinations.

Now that we have the basic counting rules, the remainder of this section is devoted to several examples of a more complex nature.

Example 9:

A standard deck has 52 cards arranged in four suits of 13 cards each. In five-card poker, three cards of one rank and two cards of another rank are called a full house. How many ways are there to deal a five-card hand consisting of three 8's and two 7's?

Solution: Since the order of selection does not matter and the cards are being drawn without replacement, we use combinations. Since we want to select three of the four 8's in the deck, the number of ways to draw three 8's is

$$C_{4,3} = \frac{4!}{3!\,(4-3)!} = 4$$

Similarly, the number of ways to draw two 7's is

$$C_{4,2} = \frac{4!}{2!\,(4-2)!} = 6$$

Now, by the Basic Counting Law, the number of ways to deal three 8's and two 7's is

$$C_{4,3} \times C_{4,2} = 4 \times 6 = 24$$

Example 10:

How many ways are there to deal a full house of any type?

Solution: This problem is like Example 9 except that there are fewer conditions. Instead of having three 8's, we now need three cards of any rank. Since there are 13 different ranks, there are 13 ways to have the set of three of a kind. Similarly, there will be 12 ranks from which to receive the pair. Therefore, the number of ways to deal a full house is

$$13 \times C_{4,3} \times 12 \times C_{4,2} = 13 \times 4 \times 12 \times 6 = 3744$$

Example 11:

(a) How many different five-card hands include four aces?
(b) How many different five-card hands include four cards of the same rank?

Solution:

(a) It seems that it is necessary only to compute $C_{4,4}$, but it is not that simple. Because we have a five-card hand, it is necessary to include the number of ways to select the fifth card. Since there are 48 cards in the deck that are not aces, the number of ways to select the fifth card is given by $C_{48,1}$. Thus, the Basic Counting Law gives

$$C_{4,4} \times C_{48,1} = 1 \times 48 = 48$$

(b) To find the number of hands with four cards of the same rank, we need to realize that this is the same problem as part (a) except that we now have 13 choices for the rank (aces through kings). Therefore, the number of possible hands with four cards of the same rank is

$$13 \times C_{4,4} \times C_{48,1} = 13 \times 1 \times 48 = 624$$

Example 12:

In the game Blackjack (also called Twenty-One or Vingt-et-Un), a player can win the hand by receiving a blackjack: an ace and a ten-point card in the first two cards. A ten-point card is a king, queen, jack, or ten. Find the number of ways a player can draw a blackjack from a standard deck of 52 cards.

Solution: Since we want to draw 1 of the 4 aces and 1 of the 16 ten-point cards, the number of ways to draw a blackjack is

$$C_{4,1} \times C_{16,1} = 4 \times 16 = 64$$

Example 13:

In the commercial casinos, found in Nevada or Atlantic City, it is common that Blackjack be played with several decks of cards. Find the number of ways a player can draw a blackjack from three standard decks of 52 cards.

Solution: Since there are three decks of cards, each containing four aces, the number of ways to draw one ace is given by $C_{12,1}$. Similarly, since there are a total of 48 ten-point cards in the three decks, the number of ways to draw a ten-point card is $C_{48,1}$. Thus, the number of ways to draw a blackjack is

$$C_{12,1} \times C_{48,1} = 12 \times 48 = 576$$

It seems odd that a casino would want to increase the number of winning hands. In the next section, we investigate why the casino would want to increase the number of winning hands.

Example 14:

In the game of Keno, 80 numbers are displayed on a board. Twenty of these numbers are chosen to be the winning numbers. Suppose a person has selected 16 numbers on his or her playing card. In how many ways can the person select ten numbers correctly?

Solution: This problem is similar to the card problems. We are playing a game with 80 possibilities, 20 of which are considered the winning values. Since we want to select 10 correct numbers from these 20, there are $C_{20,10}$ ways to pick the correct numbers. Since we are picking a total of 16 numbers, we need to also account for the 6 numbers we pick incorrectly. Since there are $80 - 20 = 60$ losing values, the 6 incorrect numbers can be chosen in $C_{60,6}$ ways.

Therefore, when playing a Keno card with 16 numbers, the number of ways to pick 10 of the 20 winning numbers is

$$C_{20,10} \times C_{60,6} = 184,756 \times 50,063,860 = 9,249,598,518,160$$

SECTION 7.1

PROBLEMS

1. A slot machine consists of three wheels with 12 different objects on a wheel. How many different outcomes are possible?

2. A computer chip consists of four different switches. Each switch can be in either the off position or the on position. Find the total number of arrangements of the chip's switches.

3. My Mastercard™ has 16 digits on it. How many different accounts does this allow?

4. Social Security numbers have nine digits. How many different people can have distinct social security numbers?

5. How many 7-digit phone numbers are possible within an area code? (Assume 0 and 1 cannot be used as the first or second digit of the number.)

6. A young couple has decided they will have three children. How many different orderings of the children will allow for exactly two boys?

7. An eight-cylinder car has eight wires running from the spark plugs to the distributor cap. An unwelcome prankster has removed all the wires from the distributor. In how many possible ways can the wires be reattached?

8. Seven candidates are running for three positions on the local board of supervisors. The candidate with the most votes will be the board president, and the second-place and third-place finishers will have correspondingly lesser positions. How many different outcomes can the election have?

9. A pitcher knows how to throw five different pitches. He needed to throw four pitches before the last batter was called out.

   (a) Assuming he threw each pitch at most once, determine the number of possible arrangements of his pitches.

   (b) Assuming he can use any pitch an unlimited number of times, determine the number of possible arrangements of his pitches.

10. Determine the number of ways a ten-question true-false test can be answered.

11. Determine the number of ways a ten-question multiple-choice test can be answered if there are five possible answers to each question.

12. Determine the total number of five-card hands that can be drawn from a deck of 52 cards.

13. Determine the total number of 13-card bridge hands that can be drawn from a deck of 52 cards.

14. In poker, a straight is five cards in consecutive numerical order. The suits of the cards does not matter.

   (a) Find the number of ways to draw a straight beginning with a 5 and ending with a 9.

   (b) Find the number of ways to draw any straight. (Note: An ace must be used as the highest or lowest card. It can be part of either A, 2, 3, 4, 5 or part of 10, J, Q, K, A but cannot be used in K, A, 2, 3, 4.)

15. In poker, a straight flush is five cards of the same suit in consecutive numerical order.

   (a) Find the number of ways to draw a straight flush beginning with the 5 of hearts and ending with the 9 of hearts.

    (b) Find the number of ways to draw a straight flush beginning with a 5 and ending with a 9.

    (c) Find the number of ways to draw any straight flush. (Note: An ace must be used as the highest or lowest card. It can be part of either A, 2, 3, 4, 5 or part of 10, J, Q, K, A but cannot be used in K, A, 2, 3, 4.)

16. In bridge, a yarborough is a 13-card hand containing only cards numbered 2 through 9. Find the number of ways in which to deal a yarborough.

17. A basketball league is looking to add two more teams to the league. If 18 cities have applied for franchises, in how many ways can the league add 2 more cities?

18. In a dog show, a German shepherd is supposed to pick the correct 2 objects from a set of 20 objects. In how many ways can the dog pick the two objects?

19. Eight people on a committee are going to divide into subcommittees of two. How many different subcommittees can be formed?

20. An auditorium has scheduled three basketball games, two concerts, and four poetry readings. You have a ticket allowing you to attend three of the events. In how many ways can you go to two of the poetry readings and one of the other events?

21. In a seven-card poker hand, find the number of hands containing four aces.

22. Find the total number of license plates that can be printed by the state of California using the format of a digit, followed by three letters, followed by three numbers. Assume all arrangements of letters can be used.

23. Twenty people are at a party. If each person at the party shakes the hand of everyone else at the party, determine the total number of handshakes.

24. Ten couples are at a party. If each person at the party shakes the hand of everyone else except his or her spouse, determine the total number of handshakes at the party.

25. In the game of Keno, 80 numbers are displayed on a board. Twenty of these numbers are chosen to be the winning numbers. Suppose a person has selected ten numbers on his or her playing card. In how many ways can the person select five of the winning numbers? Leave your answer in terms of $C_{n,r}$.

26. In the game of Keno, 80 numbers are displayed on a board. Twenty of these numbers are chosen to be the winning numbers. Suppose a person has selected 12 numbers on his or her playing card. In how many ways can the person select six of the winning numbers? Leave your answer in terms of $C_{n,r}$.

In a card game such as this one, *The Card Players* by Paul Cezanne, we can determine the likelihood of choosing a particular card on the next draw because probability tells us that the next event can be calculated even though the potential number of outcomes is very large. (The Metropolitan Museum of Art)

Odds play an intrinsic role in wagering on the outcome of an athletic event such as that depicted in *Club Night* by George Wesley Bellows. Unlike odds in card playing, in which the numbers of cards in the deck and in each hand determine the probability of subsequent draws, odds for athletic events are set by odds makers and often are based on complex systems for judging the relative quality of the competitors. (National Gallery of Art)

SECTION   7.2

▼
PROBABILITY AND ODDS

The **probability** of an event is the likelihood that the event will occur. For example, the probability that a flipped coin will land heads up is 1/2. The managers of baseball teams use probability to determine the best hitter to bring into the game. Daily weather forecasts involve probability when they announce a 40% chance of rain. Life insurance companies use probability to determine the premiums on insurance policies. In this section, we use the Basic Counting Law, permutations, and combinations to examine probabilities involved in real-world situations.

The probability of an event is found by dividing the number of ways in which an event can occur by the total number of possible outcomes. To put this in symbols, we let $P(E)$ mean the probability of an event E. This gives

$$P(E) = \frac{\text{number of ways the event can occur}}{\text{total number of possible outcomes}} \qquad \text{where } 0 \le P(E) \le 1$$

Example 1:

Find the probability of drawing an ace from a standard deck of 52 cards.

Solution: In this case, the event is drawing an ace. Because there are four aces in the standard deck, there are four ways to draw an ace out of total of 52 possibilities. This gives

$$P(\text{Ace}) = \frac{4}{52} = \frac{1}{13}$$

What Does Probability Mean?

Before doing some examples, we should discuss what probability means. The probability of a baby being a girl is $\frac{1}{2}$, but this does not mean every second baby is a girl. For example, the Brown family of Horshoe Valley in Ontario, Canada, had a streak of baby boys stretching for 102 years. The streak was finally broken in April 1989 when Rebekah was born.

When the word probability is used, it can have either of two meanings. The first meaning is that of *theoretical probability*. Theoretical probability is what is predicted by mathematics. For example, we say that the probability of a coin landing heads is $\frac{1}{2}$ since the coin has two sides and only one of the sides is heads.

If we flip ten coins, we might find that we get 6 heads and 4 tails. To say that the probability of getting a head is $\frac{6}{10}$ is an example of *experimental probability*. This means we arrived at the value through an experiment rather than only through mathematical calculations.

When an event is assigned a certain probability, let's say $\frac{1}{2}$, it means that in a large number of trials, $\frac{1}{2}$ of the trials will result in the given event. The larger the number of trials, the closer the actual probability will be to $\frac{1}{2}$. For example, suppose 10 coins are tossed and 7 of the coins land heads. From this, we would say that the experimental probability of a coin landing heads is

$$\tfrac{7}{10} = 0.7$$

If 1000 coins were tossed with 523 landing heads, the experimental probability would be

$$\tfrac{523}{1000} = 0.523$$

As we increase the number of coin tosses, the experimental probability will become close to the theoretical probability. The idea that the experimental probability is close to the theoretical probability when the experiment deals with a large number of trials is known as the **Law of Large Numbers**.

In essence, probabilities cannot be used to predict individual events. Probabilities can only determine what long-range outcomes will be.

Example 2:

During the 1989 NFC Championship game, Joe Montana had a pass completion rate of 86%. This means that the probability that any given pass will be completed is 0.86. If Montana threw 36 passes during the game, how many of them were complete?

Solution: Since the probability that a pass is complete is 0.86 and 36 passes were thrown, the number of complete passes is

$$0.86 \times 36 = 30.96 \approx 31.$$

Calculating Probabilities

The remainder of this section is devoted to determining the probabilities of various events.

Example 3:

A pair of standard six-sided dice is rolled once. What is the probability that the sum of the dice is 8?

Solution: Since each die can have the same value, the selection is done with replacement. As we found in Section 7.1, permutations and combinations can only be used when the selection is done without replacement. Therefore, we cannot use combinations or permutations in this problem. Instead, we list all the possibilities and the sum of the two dice.

$1 + 1 = 2$	$1 + 2 = 3$	$1 + 3 = 4$	$1 + 4 = 5$	$1 + 5 = 6$	$1 + 6 = 7$
$2 + 1 = 3$	$2 + 2 = 4$	$2 + 3 = 5$	$2 + 4 = 6$	$2 + 5 = 7$	$\mathbf{2 + 6 = 8}$
$3 + 1 = 4$	$3 + 2 = 5$	$3 + 3 = 6$	$3 + 4 = 7$	$\mathbf{3 + 5 = 8}$	$3 + 6 = 9$
$4 + 1 = 5$	$4 + 2 = 6$	$4 + 3 = 7$	$\mathbf{4 + 4 = 8}$	$4 + 5 = 9$	$4 + 6 = 10$
$5 + 1 = 6$	$5 + 2 = 7$	$\mathbf{5 + 3 = 8}$	$5 + 4 = 9$	$5 + 5 = 10$	$5 + 6 = 11$
$6 + 1 = 7$	$\mathbf{6 + 2 = 8}$	$6 + 3 = 9$	$6 + 4 = 10$	$6 + 5 = 11$	$6 + 6 = 12$

There are 36 different ways to roll the dice, and 5 of these ways have a sum of 8. Therefore, P(rolling 2 dice with a sum of 8) $= \frac{5}{36}$. This means that if we were to roll the dice 36 million times, we should expect that approximately 5 million of the rolls will land with a sum of 8. It does not mean that 5 of every 36 rolls will give this total.

Example 4:

Find the probability of correctly connecting six spark plug wires to a distributor cap.

Solution: Since we need to reconnect all the wires in the correct order and each wire can be used only once, we need to use permutations with $n = 6$ and $r = 6$. The number of different arrangements of the wires is $P_{6,6} = 6! = 720$. Since only one of these arrangements is correct, the probability of randomly selecting the correct order is $\frac{1}{720}$.

Example 5:

Find the probability of drawing 4 queens when choosing 5 cards from a deck of 52 cards.

Solution: We need to find the number of ways to draw four queens in a five-card hand and the total number of five-card hands that are possible.
Since we want to choose all four of the queens and one additional card to complete the five cards, the number of ways to draw the hand is

$$C_{4,4} \times C_{48,1} = 1 \times 48 = 48$$

The number of ways to draw 5 cards from a 52-card hand is

$$C_{52,5} = \frac{52!}{5!\,(52 - 5)!}$$

$$= \frac{52 \times 51 \times 50 \times 49 \times 48 \times 47 \times \cdots \times 1}{5 \times 4 \times 3 \times 2 \times 1 \times 47 \times \cdots \times 1}$$

$$= \frac{52 \times 51 \times 50 \times 49 \times 48}{5 \times 4 \times 3 \times 2 \times 1}$$

$$= 52 \times 51 \times 10 \times 49 \times 2 = 2,598,960$$

Thus, the probability of drawing 4 queens in 5 cards from a standard 52-card deck is

$$\frac{48}{2,598,960} = \frac{1}{54,145} = 0.00001847$$

This means that, on the average, four queens will appear in a five-card poker hand once every 54,145 hands.

In the examples that follow, we will not show all the computations. Instead, we will have the answer in the following form:

$$\frac{C_{4,4} \times C_{48,1}}{C_{52,5}} = \frac{1 \times 48}{2,598,960} = \frac{1}{54,145}$$

In this way, the solutions will be presented, but the page will not be filled with calculations.

Example 6:

    (a) Find the probability of drawing 3 queens and 2 kings from a standard deck of 52 cards when 7 cards are dealt.

    (b) Find the probability of drawing 3 cards of one rank and 2 cards of another rank from a standard deck of 52 cards when 7 cards are dealt.

Solution:

    (a) The number of ways to draw the three queens is $C_{4,3}$. Similarly, there are $C_{4,2}$ ways to draw two of the four kings. Since we are drawing a total of 7 cards, we need to draw 2 more cards from the 44 cards remaining in the deck. There are $C_{44,2}$ ways to do this. We can now compute the desired probability.

$$P(3 \text{ queens, 2 kings}) = \frac{C_{4,3} \times C_{4,2} \times C_{44,2}}{C_{52,7}} = \frac{4 \times 6 \times 946}{133,784,560}$$

$$= \frac{22,704}{133,784,560} = 0.00017$$

    (b) Since there are 13 choices for the set of three cards and 12 choices for the set of two cards, the probability of three cards of one rank and two of another is

$$P = \frac{13 \times C_{4,3} \times 12 \times C_{4,2} \times C_{44,2}}{C_{52,7}} = \frac{13 \times 4 \times 12 \times 6 \times 946}{133,784,560}$$

$$= \frac{3,541,824}{133,784,560} = 0.0265$$

In Example 12 of the previous section, we briefly discussed the game Blackjack. We mentioned that some casinos like to use several decks of cards at once. In the next example, we investigate whether using more than one deck changes the probability of drawing a blackjack.

Example 7:

Find the probability of drawing an ace and a ten-point card when drawing two cards from

(a) a standard deck.

(b) two standard decks.

Solution:

(a) Of the four aces, we want to pick one. Of the 16 ten-point cards we also want to pick one card. Thus, the number of winning hands is $C_{4,1} \times C_{16,1}$. The total number of hands possible is $C_{52,2}$. Thus the probability of drawing a blackjack is

$$P(\text{blackjack}) = \frac{C_{4,1} \times C_{16,1}}{C_{52,2}} = \frac{4 \times 16}{1326} = \frac{64}{1326} = 0.04827$$

(b) Similarly, if two decks of cards are used,

$$P(\text{blackjack}) = \frac{C_{8,1} \times C_{32,1}}{C_{104,2}} = \frac{8 \times 32}{5356} = \frac{256}{5356} = 0.04780$$

By using more than one deck, the casino causes the probability of having a blackjack to decrease and also makes it more difficult for the players to keep track of which cards have been played.

Example 8:

In the game of Keno, 80 numbers are displayed on a board. Twenty of these numbers are chosen to be the winning numbers. Suppose a person has selected 7 numbers on his or her playing card. What is the probability that the person selects 5 numbers correctly?

Solution: This problem is similar to the card problems. We are playing a game with 80 possibilities, 20 of which are considered the winning values. Since we want to select 5 correct numbers from these 20, there are $C_{20,5}$ ways to pick the correct numbers. Since we are picking a total of 7 numbers, we need to also account for the 2 numbers we pick incorrectly. Since there are $80 - 20 = 60$ losing values, the 2 incorrect numbers can be chosen in $C_{60,2}$ ways. Finally, there are $C_{80,20}$ ways in which the 20 winning numbers can be picked. This gives the probability of picking 5 numbers correctly from a playing card of 7 as

$$\frac{C_{20,5} \times C_{60,2}}{C_{80,7}} \approx 0.0086385$$

Odds

In many situations, rather than probability, the term **odds** is used. For example, suppose that the odds of Old Stewball winning the Kentucky Derby are 1 to 35. This means that if the race were run 36 times, Old Stewball would be expected to win once. Another way of saying this is that the odds are 35 to 1 against Old Stewball. Odds provide the same information as probability and are used in the same way.

To convert from probability to odds, use the following formula:

The Jockey by Henri Toulouse-Lautrec shows the age-old fascination with horse racing. (National Gallery of Art)

If the probability is p, then the odds, a/b, are given by

$$\frac{a}{b} = \frac{p}{1 - p}$$

Example 9:

Suppose the San Francisco Giants have a 60% chance of winning the National League pennant. What are the odds of the Giants winning? What are the odds of the Giants not winning the pennant?

Solution: Since the probability is 60%, $p = 0.60$. Hence, the odds of the Giants winning the pennant are

$$\text{odds} = \frac{0.60}{1 - 0.60} = \frac{0.60}{0.40} = \frac{6}{4} = \frac{3}{2} \text{ or 3 to 2}$$

The odds of the Giants not winning the pennant are 2 to 3.

To convert from odds to probability, use the following formula:

If the odds are a/b, then the probability p is

$$p = \frac{a}{a + b}$$

Example 10:

The odds makers in Las Vegas have stated that Wimpy is a 7 to 1 underdog in the upcoming title fight with Popeye. What is the probability that Wimpy will win?

Solution: First, we need to understand that an underdog is the person or team that is expected to lose. Therefore, the odds of Wimpy losing are 7 to 1, which means that odds of Wimpy winning are 1 to 7. Using $a = 1$ and $b = 7$, we find that the probability of Wimpy winning the fight is $p = 1/(1 + 7) = 1/8$. Note that it is important to state the odds in winning terms before finding the probability.

In this section, we discussed the basic concept of probability, namely, that the probability that an event E will occur is

$$P(E) = \frac{\text{number of ways the event can occur}}{\text{total number of possible outcomes}}$$

We saw that various ways may be used to determine the number of outcomes. These methods include the Basic Counting Law, listing the possibilities, combinations, and permutations. We also discussed the concept of probability and its relationship to the Law of Large Numbers. We showed that probabilities cannot be used to determine the outcome of individual events, but that they can be used to determine long-term trends. Finally, we discussed the relationships between odds and probability.

SECTION 7.2

PROBLEMS

1. Two six-sided dice, with sides numbered 1 through 6, are rolled.

   (a) What is the probability that the sum of the two dice is 8?
   (b) What is the probability that the sum of the two dice is 6?
   (c) What is the probability that the sum of the two dice is 1?
   (d) What is the probability that exactly one of the two dice shows a 3?
   (e) If the dice are rolled 9000 times, how many times would you expect the dice to have a sum of 8? a sum of 6?

2. In baseball, if a player has a batting average of 0.314, it means that for every 1000 official at bats, the player gets a hit 314 times. Suppose Joe Ballplayer has a lifetime average of 0.279. How many hits should Joe expect in a season if he has 525 official at bats?

3. In the course of a baseball season, the probability that Joe Ballplayer gets on base is 0.345. If Joe came to bat 500 times during the season, approximately how many times did he reach base?

4. What is the meaning of a weather forecast that says there is a 40% probability of rain?

5. What is the meaning of a political poll that says there is a 63% chance that the candidate will win the election?

6. Five cards are dealt from a standard deck of 52 cards.

    (a) What is the probability of being dealt three kings?

    (b) What is the probability of being dealt three of any rank?

7. Five cards are dealt from a standard deck of 52 cards.

    (a) What is the probability of being dealt an ace and four kings?

    (b) What is the probability of being dealt an ace and four more cards of some other rank?

8. Five cards are dealt from two standard decks mixed together.

    (a) What is the probability of being dealt an ace and four kings?

    (b) What is the probability of being dealt an ace and four more cards of some other rank?

9. Five cards are dealt from two standard decks mixed together.

    (a) What is the probability of being dealt three kings?

    (b) What is the probability of being dealt three cards of any rank?

10. In horse racing, an "exacta" occurs when you correctly guess which horses will finish first and second. It is important to pick the correct order. If eight horses are in the race, what is the probability of correctly guessing the exacta?

11. In horse racing, a "trifecta" occurs when you correctly guess the order of the first three horses. If six horses are in the race, what is the probability of correctly guessing the trifecta?

12. A basketball league is looking to add two more teams to the league. If 18 cities have applied for franchises and the cities are selected at random, what is the probability that the league adds the two westernmost cities?

13. In a dog show, a German shepherd is supposed to pick the correct 2 objects from a set of 20 objects. What is the probability that the dog picks the two objects by chance?

14. A box of 20 lightbulbs contains two defective bulbs. What is the probability of picking two bulbs from the box and having both bulbs being defective?

15. An auditorium has scheduled three basketball games, two concerts, and four poetry readings. You have a ticket allowing you to attend three of the events. What is the probability that, by selecting three events at random, you attend two of the poetry readings and one of the other events?

16. Fourteen paintings are to be picked at random and placed along a wall. What is the probability that the paintings will be placed on the wall in alphabetical order, according to their titles? Assume that no two paintings have the same title.

17. License plates are printed by the state of California, using the format of a digit, followed by three letters, followed by three numbers. Assume all arrangements of letters can be used. What is the probability that the first digit of a plate is 5?

18. Ten people are on a bus. There are three stops until the end of the line. Assume that it is equally likely for a person to get off at any of the three stops. What is the probability that all the people get off the bus at the last of the three stops?

19. In the game of Keno, 80 numbers are displayed on a board. Twenty of these numbers are chosen to be the winning numbers. Suppose a person has selected 12 numbers on his or her playing card.

(a) What is the probability of selecting zero correct numbers? (Leave answers in terms of $C_{n,r}$.)

(b) What is the probability of selecting six correct numbers?

(c) What is the probability of selecting nine correct numbers?

20. In the game of Keno, 80 numbers are displayed on a board. Twenty of these numbers are chosen to be the winning numbers. Suppose a person has selected 10 numbers on his or her playing card.

(a) What is the probability of selecting zero correct numbers? (Leave answers in terms of $C_{n,r}$.)

(b) What is the probability of selecting five correct numbers?

21. A certain lottery has 49 numbers, 6 of which are the winning numbers for a particular game. To play the game, each participant chooses six numbers. What is the probability of choosing four correct numbers?

22. A certain lottery has 49 numbers, 6 of which are the winning numbers for a particular game. To play the game, each participant chooses six numbers. What is the probability of choosing five correct numbers?

23. In poker, a full house is a five-card hand with three cards of one rank and two cards of another rank. Suppose you are dealt 5 cards from a standard deck of 52 cards.

(a) What is the probability of drawing a full house with three kings and two queens?

    (b) What is the probability of drawing a full house with three kings and two cards of another rank?

    (c) What is the probability of drawing any full house?

24. In poker, a straight flush is five cards of the same suit in consecutive numerical order. Suppose you are dealt 5 cards from a standard deck of 52 cards.

    (a) Find the probability of drawing a straight flush beginning with the 5 of hearts and ending with the 9 of hearts.

    (b) Find the probability of drawing a straight flush beginning with a 5 and ending with a 9.

    (c) Find the probability of drawing any straight flush. (Note: An ace must be used as the highest or lowest card. It can be part of either A, 2, 3, 4, 5 or 10, J, Q, K, A, but it cannot be used for K, A, 2, 3, 4.)

25. (a) Flip a coin 20 times and record the outcomes. How many times does the coin land heads up? Based on these 20 coin flips, what is the probability of the coin landing heads up?

    (b) Repeat part (a).

    (c) From the 40 coins flips, find the probability of the coin landing heads up.

    (d) Repeat part (a).

    (e) From the 60 coins flips, find the probability of the coin landing heads up.

    (f) Does the Law of Large Numbers appear to be holding?

26. (a) If there is a 60% chance of the New York Jets winning the Super Bowl, what are the odds that they win? What are the odds that they lose?

    (b) If the odds of Gumball winning a race are 2 to 11 and the odds of Stewball winning the race are 1 to 5, which horse has the better chance of winning?

27. (a) The odds that the Los Angeles Lakers will win the NBA championship are 7 to 5. What is the probability that the Lakers will win the championship?

    (b) For a recent fight, the champion was given a 75% chance of retaining his title. What were the odds in favor of the champion retaining his title? What were the odds of the champion losing his title?

*28. This problem repeats the experiment performed by Georges Buffon in 1777. Take a piece of paper with regularly spaced lines in one direction and measure the distance between the lines. Call this distance d. Obtain a pin or a short nail and measure its length. Call this length L. (The length of the pin should be less than the distance between two lines. If not, cut the pin with a pair of pliers.) Toss the pin on the paper 100 times and count how many times the pin rests on top of a line. Calculate the probability p that the pin crossed the line. Finally, perform the calculation $(2 \times L)/(d \times p)$. What value does this seem close to?

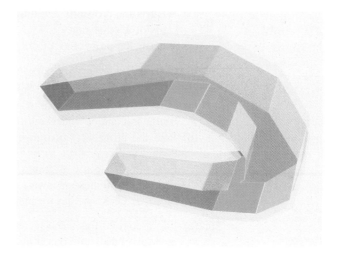

Horseshoe by Ron Davis shows the symbol of good luck valued by many a gambler. (Courtesy of the artist and the John Berrgruen Gallery)

SECTION 7.3

▼

MATHEMATICAL EXPECTATION

Mathematical expectation and **expected value** are the terms used to describe the expected winnings from a contest or a game. Expected value is used throughout the world to determine prizes in contests and premiums on insurance policies. It is also used in the mathematical field called decision theory. In this section, we show how mathematical expectation can be calculated if we know the probabilities of all the possible outcomes of an event.

Suppose a game is played with one six-sided die. If the die is rolled and lands on 1, 2 or 3, the player wins nothing. If the die lands on 4 or 5, the player wins $3. If the die lands on 6, the player wins $12. The following table summarizes this information and computes the probability of each situation.

Event	P(event)	Winnings
1, 2, or 3	$\frac{3}{6}$	$0
4 or 5	$\frac{2}{6}$	$3
6	$\frac{1}{6}$	$12

If you play this game, how much do you think you will win? What is the expected value of this game?

To compute the expected value of the game, add the products of the probability of each event and the amount won if the event occurs.

For this game, the expected value (E.V.) is

$$\text{E.V.} = \frac{3}{6} \times 0 + \frac{2}{6} \times 3 + \frac{1}{6} \times 12 = \$3$$

An expected value of $3 means we would expect to win an average of $3 for each game played. That is, if we played 1000 games, we would expect to win $3000. However, as with probability, this is true only for large numbers of games. If we played three games, the expected winnings are $9, but we could win between $0 and $36.

Suppose the operator of the game decides to charge $1 to play the game. The amount won by the customer would then be reduced by $1. Examining the following table, we can compute the expected winnings for a player, including the cost of the game.

Event	P(event)	Winnings
1, 2, or 3	$\frac{3}{6}$	$-\$1$
4 or 5	$\frac{2}{6}$	$\$2$
6	$\frac{1}{6}$	$\$11$

$$\text{E.V.} = \frac{3}{6} \times (-1) + \frac{2}{6} \times 2 + \frac{1}{6} \times 11 = \$2$$

As might be expected, a charge of $1 to play the game reduces the expected value by $1, from $3 down to $2.

Example 1:

A certain lottery has 49 numbers, 6 of which are the winning numbers for a particular game. The cost of playing the lottery is $1. To play the game, a player must pick six numbers. If a player picks three correct numbers, he or she receives $20. Similarly, picking four correct numbers receives $100, picking five correct numbers receives $10,000, and picking six correct receives $1,000,000. Find the expected value of this game, including the cost of playing.

Solution: First, we need to calculate the probability of correctly guessing the winning numbers. By the methods of the previous sections, this is summarized in the following table along with the winnings at each level. As an example, the probability of selecting three numbers correctly is

$$P(3) = \frac{C_{6,3} \times C_{43,3}}{C_{49,6}} = \frac{\dfrac{6!}{3!(6-3)!} \times \dfrac{43!}{3!(43-3)!}}{\dfrac{49!}{6!(49-6)!}}$$

$$= \frac{20 \times 12,341}{13,983,816} = 0.0176504$$

Similar computations give the following table. Notice that the winnings are reduced by $1 to account for the cost of playing the game.

Event	P(event)	Winnings
0	$\dfrac{C_{6,0} \times C_{43,6}}{C_{49,6}} = 0.4359650$	$-\$1$
1	$\dfrac{C_{6,1} \times C_{43,5}}{C_{49,6}} = 0.4130195$	$-\$1$
2	$\dfrac{C_{6,2} \times C_{43,4}}{C_{49,6}} = 0.1323780$	$-\$1$
3	$\dfrac{C_{6,3} \times C_{43,3}}{C_{49,6}} = 0.0176504$	$\$19$
4	$\dfrac{C_{6,4} \times C_{43,2}}{C_{49,6}} = 0.0009686$	$\$99$
5	$\dfrac{C_{6,5} \times C_{43,1}}{C_{49,6}} = 0.0000185$	$\$9999$
6	$\dfrac{C_{6,6} \times C_{43,0}}{C_{49,6}} = 0.0000001$	$\$999,999$

From this table, we can calculate the expected value:

$$\text{E.V.} = (-1) \times 0.4359650 + (-1) \times 0.4130195 + (-1) \times$$
$$0.1323780 + 19 \times 0.0176504 + 99 \times 0.0009686 +$$
$$9999 \times 0.0000185 + 999,999 \times 0.0000001$$

$$= -\$0.27$$

By doing this calculation we can see that we expect to lose an average of 27 cents every time we play the lottery. This means that the operators of this lottery earn 27 cents every time someone buys a ticket.

Example 2:

A game is called **fair** if the mathematical expectation of the game is zero. Suppose a certain game is fair and costs $3 to play. The probability of winning is 0.6 and the probability of losing is 0.4. How much should you receive for the game to be fair?

Solution: Since the game is fair, we can set up an equation for the expected value of the game with E.V. $= 0$. We will use W to represent the prize for winning. Since it costs $3 to play the game, the amount actually won if we win the game is $W - 3$. The amount won if we lose the game is -3.

$$\text{E.V.} = \left(\begin{array}{c}\text{amount won}\\ \text{if we win the game}\end{array}\right) \times P(\text{winning})$$

$$+ \left(\begin{array}{c}\text{amount won}\\ \text{if we lose the game}\end{array}\right) \times P(\text{losing})$$

$$0 = (W - 3) \times 0.6 + (-3) \times 0.4$$

$$0 = 0.6W - 1.8 - 1.2$$

$$0 = 0.6W - 3$$

$$-0.6W = -3$$

$$W = \frac{-3}{-0.6} = 5$$

For the game to be fair, a player should receive $5 if he wins. Note that this means actual winnings of only $2 since it costs $3 to play the game.

Example 3:

Suppose a certain game is fair and costs $3 if we lose and has actual winnings of $10 if we win. The only possible outcomes of the game are winning and losing. What is the probability of winning?

Solution: Let p be the probability of winning. Since there are only two choices, winning and losing, the probability of losing must be $1 - p$. For example, if the probability of winning is 0.3, the probability of losing must be 0.7. Therefore, since the game is fair, we can set up an equation for the expected value of the game with E.V. $= 0$.

$$\text{E.V.} = (\text{amount won}) \times P(\text{winning}) + (\text{amount lost}) \times P(\text{losing})$$

$$0 = 10p + (-3)(1 - p)$$

$$0 = 10p - 3 + 3p$$

$$0 = 13p - 3$$

$$p = \frac{3}{13}$$

Therefore, the probability of winning the game is 3/13.

Example 4:

Insurance companies determine the premiums for a policy by examining the risk involved. The risk is calculated by looking at statistics involving the situations covered by the policy. This is why auto insurance for a person with a history of speeding violations is much higher than for a 40-year-old career woman with two children and a perfect driving record.

The Lagomorph Insurance Company has a customer, Mr. Roger Abbit, with a $250,000 auto insurance policy. The company believes Mr. Abbit has a 1% chance of collecting on his policy in 1989. If the insurance company tries to maintain an expected value of $200 on each policy, what should Mr. Abbit's premium be?

Solution: Let a = amount of the premium. Since the company thinks Roger has a 1% chance of collecting on the policy, there is a 99% chance that he will not collect.

$$\text{E.V.} = \begin{pmatrix} \text{net amount paid} \\ \text{to company if} \\ \text{Roger collects} \end{pmatrix} \times P\begin{pmatrix} \text{Roger} \\ \text{collects} \end{pmatrix}$$

$$+ \begin{pmatrix} \text{amount paid to} \\ \text{company if Roger} \\ \text{does not collect} \end{pmatrix} \times P\begin{pmatrix} \text{Roger does} \\ \text{not collect} \end{pmatrix}$$

$$200 = (a - 250{,}000) \times 0.01 + a \times 0.99$$

$$200 = 0.01a - 2500 + 0.99a$$

$$200 = a - 2500$$

$$a = 2700$$

This means that the Lagomorph Insurance Company should charge $2700 for this policy.

Decision Theory

The next topic we will discuss is using mathematical expectation to help make decisions. This topic has applications in many areas of business and science. The process of weighing the risks versus the benefits of two or more alternatives is called **decision theory.** Essentially, decision theory computes the expected value for each of the possible outcomes. A decision is made by examining the results and choosing the highest (or lowest) expected value.

Example 5:

An engineering firm, Sasselli Satellites, is expanding its facilities and needs some electrical work done. The firm has received three bids on the work. The first contractor, Vital Parts, says that they will charge $10,000. The second company, Yablok Electric, will charge $11,000 if they finish the job within one week or $9000 if they cannot finish within one week. The third company, Zak Communications, has the low bid of $8500, but it wants an extra $4500 if they can complete the job in less than one week. Sasselli researches the history of all three contractors and finds that they all do very good work. Sasselli also finds out that Yablok Electric completes its work as scheduled 85% of the time and Zak Communications finishes ahead of schedule 20% of the time. Which contractor should Sasselli Satellites choose to do their electrical work if the primary goal is to keep costs low?

Solution: We need to find the expected costs for each of the three contractors. Since all three contractors have a reputation for high-quality workmanship and since cost is the primary consideration, Sasselli Satellites should choose the contractor with the lowest expected cost.

For Vital Parts, the cost will always be $10,000. For Yablok Electric, the cost will be $11,000 with probability 0.85 and $9000 with probability 0.15 ($1 - 0.85 = 0.15$). Therefore, the expected costs for Yablok Electric are

$$11,000 \times 0.85 + 9000 \times 0.15 = \$10,700$$

For Zak Communications, the cost will be $8500 with probability 0.80 and $13,000 ($8500 + $4500 = $13,000) with probability 0.20. Therefore the expected costs for Zak Communications are

$$8500 \times 0.80 + 13,000 \times 0.20 = \$9400$$

From this information, Sasselli Satellites should decide to use Zak Communications.

Example 6:

A bank account is guaranteed to earn a fixed rate of 9% on a $10,000 deposit over the next year. A speculative investment offers the possibility of 15% earnings on the $10,000 if the investment succeeds and a loss of 5% of the $10,000 if the investment fails. Determine the probability of success necessary for the speculative investment to be the better choice.

Solution: In order to choose the better way to invest the money, we need to find the expected gain from each investment over the next year. Since the bank account offers a 9% gain with no possibility of loss, the bank account has an expected value of

$$10,000 \times 0.09 = \$900$$

To find the expected gain from the speculative investment, we need to know the probability of a success. Since this is unknown, we assign it a variable, p. The expected gain from the speculative account is then

$$(10,000 \times 0.15) \times p + [(-10,000) \times 0.05] \times (1 - p)$$

Since we want the speculative account to be the better investment, its expected value must be greater than the expected value of the bank account. From here, it is a matter of solving the inequality for the value of p

$$(10{,}000 \times 0.15) \times p + [(-10{,}000) \times 0.05] \times (1 - p) > 900$$

$$1500p - 500(1 - p) > 900$$

$$1500p - 500 + 500p > 900$$

$$2000p > 1400$$

$$p > 1400 \div 2000$$

$$p > 0.70$$

Thus, for the speculative venture to be the more lucrative investment, the probability of success must be greater than 70%. ◼

SECTION 7.3

PROBLEMS

1. In a certain game, the probability of winning is 0.3 and the probability of losing is 0.7. If a player wins, the player will collect $50. If the player loses, the player will lose $5. What is the expected value of this game? If the game is played 100 times, what are the expected winnings (or losses) of the player?

2. In a game of dice, the probability of rolling a 12 is 1/36. The probability of rolling a 9, 10, or 11 is 9/36. The probability of rolling any other number is 26/36. If the player rolls a 12, the player wins $5. If the player rolls a 9, 10, or 11, the player wins $1. Otherwise, the player loses $1. What is the expected value of this game? If the game is played 100 times what are the expected winnings (or losses) of the player?

3. In a game of dice, the probability of rolling a 12 is 1/36. The probability of rolling a 9, 10, or 11 is 9/36. The probability of rolling any other number is 26/36. If the player rolls a 12, the player wins $8. If the player rolls a 9, 10, or 11, the player wins $2. How much should the player lose when the player rolls any other number if the game is fair?

4. In a certain game, the probability of winning is 0.2 and the probability of losing is 0.8. If the player loses, the player will lose $5. How much does the player collect when the player wins if the game is fair?

5. In the game of Roulette, players bet that a ball will land on a certain number. A player can choose any number from 1 through 36, 0 or 00. It costs $1 to play the game. If the player correctly guesses the number, the $1 is returned and the player receives an additional $35. What is the expected value of this game? Suppose a casino has 100 players, each of whom plays 10 times each hour for 24 hours. Each player bets $1. What is the casino's profit?

6. In the game of Keno, 80 numbers are displayed on a board. Twenty of these numbers are chosen to be the winning numbers. Suppose a person has selected

5 numbers on his (or her) playing card. The probabilities and winnings for each event are given in the table.

Event	Probability	Winnings
0 winning numbers	0.227184	$0
1 winning numbers	0.405686	$0
2 winning numbers	0.270457	$0
3 winning numbers	0.083935	$1
4 winning numbers	0.012092	$10
5 winning numbers	0.000645	$1000

(a) What is the expected value for the game?

(b) How much money will the player have won or lost after 1000 games if each game costs $1.00?

7. Many charities and other organizations use lotteries or other similar marketing devices to acquire funds. (Publisher's Clearinghouse or Reader's Digest may come to mind.) By law in many states, it is required to post the odds of winning the various prizes on the back of the tickets or in some other conspicuous spot.

(a) Fancy that Poultry Magazine is running a contest with the following odds and prizes.

Odds	Prize
1 to 49	$10 (in back issues)
1 to 9999	$50 (in poultry feed)
1 to 99,999	$2000 (in rare ducks)

If tickets are free, find the expected value of your "winning ticket."

(b) Find some real contest being conducted through the mail, by a large company or by a local store. Find the expected value for this contest.

(c) Are either of the contests in parts (a) or (b) worth the 25¢ required for postage?

(d) At what postage rate would the game in part (a) be considered fair?

8. Dennis is in charge of designing a game for the school fund-raiser. Participants will be paying $2 for each game. There will be three levels of prizes. The lowest level has a value of $0.50, the second level has a value of $1, and the third level has an undetermined value. The probability of winning the lowest-level prize is 0.35, the probability of winning the second-level prize is 0.15, and the probability of winning the grand prize is 0.01. The probability of not winning any prize is 0.49. If the school likes to have an expected value of $1 per ticket donated to the school, what should Dennis choose as the value of the grand prize?

9. The batting average of a baseball player gives the probability that the player will get a hit in the next at bat. The table gives the batting averages for a team and the number of at bats the team has in a particular game. Determine the expected number of hits for the team during this game.

Player	Batting Average	At Bats
Appling	0.314	5
Bennett	0.274	5
Casey	0.320	4
Ruth	0.292	4
Greenberg	0.263	4
Harrelson	0.241	4
Kraft	0.212	4
Bradshaw	0.105	4
Hopkins	0.106	4

10. The table gives a partial listing of mortality rates for guinea pigs. It gives the probability of a guinea pig living to a certain age. Assuming that all guinea pigs die by age five, determine the expected age of guinea pigs.

Age	Probability
1	0.14
2	0.07
3	0.26
4	0.29
5	0.24

11. A television game show contestant has current prizes worth $12,500. If the contestant participates in the next round of competition, she will have $50,000 if she wins and $0 if she loses. The contestant uses expected values to decide that she should participate in the next round. What should the probability of her winning be so that she should play the next round?

12. An engineer has provided a customer with the choice of two different procedures for extending the lifetime of a certain structure. The first procedure has a success rate of 93% and will extend the life of the building by 8 years. The second procedure is still experimental and has not been perfected. It will extend the life of the structure by 15 years if the procedure works. However, there is only a 47% success rate. Assume that the customer can afford to use only one procedure and that if a procedure fails, the building will last 2 more years. Which procedure should be used to maximize the expected life of the building?

13. In planting a playing field, a park manager must decide between planting seed or sod. If seed is used, there is a 33% chance that the grass lawn will grow with one seeding and a 67% chance that it will need two seedings. If the lawn is seeded once, it will cost $60. If the lawn needs two seedings, the cost will be $400. Planting sod will cost $300 and has a 100% success rate. Which method is more cost-effective?

14. The circles in the diagram have radii of 2, 8, 16, and 24 inches, respectively.

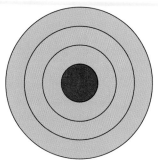

In the game of skeeball, a player rolls a ball up a ramp and wins $10 if the ball lands in the center circle, wins $2 if the ball lands in the second band, wins nothing if it lands in the third band, and loses $1 if it lands in the outer band. If the ball misses the target, the ball is rolled again. The probability that the ball lands in a certain region is the same as the area of that region divided by 576π. The areas of the bands are given in the table

Region	Area
center	4π sq. in.
2nd band	60π sq. in.
3rd band	192π sq. in.
outside band	320π sq. in.

(a) Find the expected value of the game.

(b) Assuming everything else is unchanged, what should the prize be for the inner circle so that the game is fair?

15. The squares in the diagram have sides of 4, 8, 16, and 32 inches, respectively.

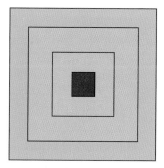

In the game of skeeball, a ball is rolled up a ramp and wins $10 if it lands in the center square, wins $5 if it lands in the second band, wins $1.50 if it lands in the third band, and loses $1 if it lands in the outer band. If the ball misses the target, the ball is rolled again. The probability that the ball lands in a certain region is the same as the area of that region divided by 1024. The areas of the bands are given in the table.

Region	Area
center	16 sq. in.
2nd band	48 sq. in.
3rd band	192 sq. in.
outside band	768 sq. in

(a) Find the expected value of the game.

(b) Assuming that everything else is unchanged, what should the prize be for the inner square so that the game is fair?

CHAPTER   7   **SUMMARY**

KEY TERMS, CONCEPTS, AND FORMULAS

The important terms in this chapter are:

Basic Counting Law: States that if there are n choices for one item and m choices for a second item, there are $n \times m$ ways to pick both items.   p. 357

Combinations: A set of unordered objects chosen from a larger set.   p. 349

Decision theory: The use of mathematical expectation to determine choices.   p. 380

Expected value: The average outcome of an event; this could be the expected amount of money won when playing a game or the anticipated cost of a project based on the associated risks involved in the project.   p. 376

Factorials: The mathematical expression given by $n! = n \times (n - 1) \times (n - 2) \times \cdots \times 2 \times 1$.   p. 344

Fair game: A situation in which the expected value is zero.   p. 378

Law of Large Numbers: States that probabilities predict the chances of an event occurring over an extended number of trials and not for individual events.   p. 367

Mathematical expectation: See **Expected value.**

Odds: Another way of expressing probability where if the probability of an event is p, the odds that the event will occur are given by $p \div (1 - p)$.   p. 370

Permutations: A set of ordered objects chosen from a larger set.   p. 346

Probability: The chances that an event will occur.   p. 365

With replacement: When an object can be used more than once.   p. 356

Without replacement: When an object cannot be used more than once.   p. 356

After completing this chapter, you should be able to:

1. Explain the difference between combinations and permutations.   p. 349
2. Explain the difference between using "with replacement" and using "without replacement."   p. 356
3. Apply the formulas for combinations,

$$C_{n,r} = \frac{n!}{r!\,(n-r)!}$$ p. 348

and permutations,

$$P_{n,r} = \frac{n!}{(n-r)!}$$ p. 350

4. Apply the concepts of probability, odds, and expected value.   p. 365
5. Convert from odds to probability and from probability to odds.   p. 370

SUMMARY
PROBLEMS

1. Find the value of the following:
   (a) $C_{7,4}$
   (b) $P_{7,4}$
   (c) $C_{73,4}$
   (d) $P_{73,4}$

2. (a) Find the number of ways in which 3 aces and 2 kings can be drawn in a 6-card hand from a standard 52-card deck.
   (b) Find the number of ways in which 3 aces and a pair of any rank can be drawn in a 6-card hand from a standard 52-card deck.
   (c) Find the number of ways in which 3 cards of one rank and 2 cards of another rank can be drawn in a 6-card hand from a standard 52-card deck.

3. (a) Find the probability of 3 aces and 4 kings being drawn in a 7-card hand from a standard 52-card deck.
   (b) Find the number of ways in which 3 aces and 4 cards of any rank can be drawn in a 7-card hand from a standard 52-card deck.
   (c) Find the number of ways in which 3 cards of one rank and 4 cards of another rank can be drawn in a 7-card hand from a standard 52-card deck.

4. What is the probability of correctly guessing the top 3 finishers in a greyhound race of 10 dogs?

5. Dodecahedral dice have 12 sides instead of the standard 6 sides. The sides are numbered 1 through 12. What is the probability of rolling two dodecahedral dice and having the sum of the face-up sides equal 8?

6. A certain game is played with two standard six-sided dice. The player will win an amount equal to the sum of the spots on both dice if the sum is greater than 7. The player will lose an amount equal to the sum if the sum is less than or equal to 7. What is the expected value of this game?

7. In the picture are three equilateral triangles. The largest has sides of 2 ft, the next has sides of 1 ft, and the smallest has sides of 0.5 ft.

A ball will be rolled up a ramp toward the target and will win 5 points for hitting the center region, 2 points for hitting the middle region, and 1 point for hitting the outer region. If the ball completely misses the target, the ball will be thrown again. If the probability of hitting a certain region of the target is equal to the area of the region divided by $\sqrt{3}$, and we are given the following information about the areas of the three regions:

The area of the innermost triangle is $\sqrt{3}/16$.

The area of the middle band is $3\sqrt{3}/16$.

The area of the outer band is $3\sqrt{3}/4$.

(a) Find the expected value of the game.
(b) Find the total number of points a player will expect to accumulate in ten tosses that land in the target.

8. What is wrong with the following argument: Since the probability of a flipped coin landing heads up is 0.5, flipping a fair coin ten times will result in five heads and five tails.

*9. The following is a famous problem known as the birthday problem.

(a) In how many ways can 20 days of the year be selected if the same day may be used more than once? Leave your answer in terms of a formula.
(b) In how many ways can 20 days be selected if the same day may be used only once? Leave your answer in terms of a formula.
(c) Calculate the value of the result of part (b) divided by the result of part (a).
(d) Explain why the answer to part (c) is the probability that no 2 people from a set of 20 are born on the same day of the year.
(e) Explain why the probability that at least 2 people from a set of 20 are born on the same day is given by 1 minus the result from part (c).

STATISTICS

The feeling of being merely a statistic in an urban jungle can be sensed in the painting *Urban Freeways* by Wayne Thiebaud. (Courtesy of the artist)

A SHORT HISTORY OF STATISTICS

The word *statistik* was first used in 1749 by Gottfried Achenwall. It comes from the Latin word *statisticus*, meaning "of the state." This is appropriate because, until the 1850s, statistics almost always referred to information about a country or other political body. This information could refer to political, social, or economic conditions and was usually given in the form of tables of numerical data.

When the Great Plague hit England in 1665, mortality rates soared. John Graunt of England (1620–1674), known as the father of vital statistics, published *Natural and Political Observations Made upon the Bills of Mortality*. By studying the English death records, Graunt found patterns in the number of deaths by suicide, disease, and accidents in English cities. He also found that the number of male births exceeded the number of female births. Graunt's work, along with that of William Petty, established the life expectancy tables used by the life insurance companies to determine the premiums that the companies should charge their pol-icyholders. By the mid-1700s, all Western nations were compiling information from periodic censuses, recording such information as age of death, cause of death, and the male-female ratio of births. The availability and use of this information allowed life insurance rates to be determined by scientific methods.

In 1763, the Englishman Thomas Bayes' (1702–1761) posthumous publication *Essay Towards Solving a Problem in the Doctrine of Chances* became one of the first works to argue from a small sample of information to what could be expected from the population as a whole. This was the forerunner of the activities of George Gallup and the Gallup poll. This process involves asking a small percentage of a population their opinions or status on a question and then using this small sample to predict the position of the population as a whole.

In 1806, Adrien-Marie Legendre of France (1752–1833) introduced the method known as ''least squares'' in the supplement to his *New Methods for Determination of a Comet's Orbit*. This method determines the equation of a line that passes through a cluster of points with the least error. The derivation of the method requires calculus, but it is easy to use. It is applied in many areas of study, from economic forecasting to sociology as well as in nearly all the sciences. The method of least squares was also discovered by the great German mathematician, Carl Friedrich Gauss (1777–1855) in 1794, but was not published by Gauss until he released his work in *Theoria motus* in 1809. In this book, Gauss also discussed the bell-shaped curve called the Gaussian, or normal, distribution. This is the distribution used with many standardized testing systems.

Adolphe Quetelet (1796–1874) of Belgium constructed the first statistical break-down of a national census in 1829. He examined the census information to deter-mine possible connections between age of death and various other variables such as season of the year, occupation, age, and economic status.

In 1889, the Englishman Francis Galton (1822–1911) published *National In-heritance*. This was the compilation of 15 years of work on statistical relationships in the area of genetics. One interesting fact determined by Galton was that of regression. Regression is a process that occurs when a biological characteristic reverts to a simpler or more general form. An example of this can be seen with the heights of successive generations in a family. The children of two exceptionally tall people will probably be taller than the average person, but the children usually will not exceed the heights of the parents. In the same way, the children of two exceptionally short people will be taller than the parents, again becoming closer to the height of the average person rather than the heights of the parents.

As was true with probability, statistics developed rapidly in the twentieth cen-tury. In the 1920s Ronald Fisher (1890–1962) studied the problems involved in sampling. Sampling is the procedure followed when selecting a few individuals to determine information about the population as a whole. Fisher's studies showed that the results of a poll are more reliable if the sample is chosen at random.

In 1929 and 1930, A. K. Erlang and J. F. Steffensen studied the phenomenon of the extinction of family names. Certain family names that once were common were slowly but inevitably dying out. When the problem was solved, it was de-termined that it was a form of Darwin's theory of survival of the fittest. Families that were wealthy and in good health were able to raise large numbers of children and to provide these children with the means to succeed in later life. Families in desperate conditions were often in poor health, with many children dying before they reached maturity. Because of this, the less advantaged families had fewer family members to carry on the family name.

New discoveries continue up to the present day. Gertrude Mary Cox wrote the first work of note on statistical design and analysis of complicated experiments in *Experimental Designs*, published in 1950. Many new statistical distributions have been put into use during the 20th century. Others, like Fisher, found that the Gaussian distribution (the standard bell-shaped curve) did not correctly model many real-life situations. Since that time new distributions using time as a variable were needed and developed. Today, magazines and newspapers have statistical presentations every day about a myriad of facts. Stock averages, the latest cancer research, and the status of the national debt are some ever-present examples.

The availability of computers allows anyone to accumulate and arrange numerical data in many ways. It is up to the common person to be able to interpret the data and its presentation to determine the validity of the position the data is being used to support.

CHECK YOUR READING

1. What did statistics refer to until the 1850s?
2. What is sampling?
3. When John Graunt was publishing his mortality statistics, Caleb Cheeshateaumuck became the first American Indian to receive a Bachelor of Arts degree at Harvard College. What year was this?
4. The Indian war near what would later be called Detroit, Michigan, occurred in 1763. What work of Thomas Bayes was published during this year? What was important about this book?
5. What historical figure was the forerunner to George Gallup?
6. Cite some areas where statistics is used in present-day society.
7. During the 1920s, the Soviet states formed the Union of Soviet Socialist Republics and the Cuban chess player José Raoul Capablanca won the world chess championship. What was the statistician Ronald Fisher doing during this period?
8. While Vincent Van Gogh was painting *Landscape with a Cypress Tree* and North Dakota, South Dakota, Montana, and Washington were becoming states, Francis Galton published a statistical work related to genetics. In what year did this occur?
9. The British chemist James Smithson bequeathed funds to found the Smithsonian Museum in Washington, D.C., and Adolphe Quetelet constructed a statistical breakdown of the Belgian national census. In what year did this occur?
10. In 1929–1930, Pablo Picasso was painting *Woman in an Armchair*, and Alketta

Jacobs became the first woman physician in Holland. What were A. Erlang and J. Steffensen studying during this period?

11. Carl Gauss published a work on bell-shaped curves and Charles Darwin and Abraham Lincoln were born during what year?

12. The year 1806 marked the official end of the Roman Empire. What was Frenchman Adrien-Marie Legendre doing during this year?

13. Match each of the following names with the correct event, idea, or occurrence.

(a) Achenwall   Father of vital statistics
(b) Bayes   First to argue from a small sample of information
(c) Cox   First to use the word *statistik*
(d) Fisher   First statistical breakdown of a national census
(e) Galton   Method of least squares
(f) Gauss   Normal distribution (bell-shaped curves)
(g) Graunt   Sampling procedures
(h) Legendre   Statistical relationships in area of genetics
(i) Quetelet   Pioneer in statistical design

RESEARCH QUESTIONS

In order to answer the following questions, you will need to refer to material not contained in the text. Possible sources of information are listed in the Bibliography at the end of this book.

1. Many of the mathematicians and statisticians mentioned in this short history of statistics are also known for other mathematical endeavors or had other interests besides mathematics. Do some research on two of the mathematicians mentioned in this section. Tell something about their lives, their achievements, and their interests.

2. Find other examples of regression. The examples can come from studies of human beings, animals, or other living organisms.

3. What is a ''normal'' curve? What does it look like? What are some applications of this curve?

4. Find some examples of statistics in a recent magazine or newspaper. Describe the situation and how statistics are being used.

5. Look in the reference section of the library and find the names of five different books that have statistical information. Give a two- or three-sentence summary of the contents of each book.

6. What is the Dow Jones average? What does it represent? What is its history?

7. What was the Great Plague? Find some information about the cause of the plague, the number of deaths caused by the plague, and what countries were affected by the plague.

8. What is demography? What are its uses? Cite some examples.

9. What is the meaning of the expression "lie with statistics?" Give some examples of this and explain how each of the examples is a "lie."

SECTION   8.0

▼

REVIEW OF SUMMATION NOTATION

The character Σ is the Greek letter uppercase sigma and is called a **summation** symbol. Like the factorial symbol used in the previous chapter, it has a special use in mathematics and is intended to make expressions more compact. Σ is used to indicate addition of a sequence of terms. For example,

$$\sum_{i=1}^{6} i = 1 + 2 + 3 + 4 + 5 + 6$$

The equation is read "the sum of i where i goes from 1 to 6." This means that we want to add all the integer values from 1 through 6. The terms above and below the summation sign are called the **indices** and indicate the values that begin and end the sum. The expression that follows Σ indicates the operation that is to be performed. For example:

$$\sum_{i=1}^{6} i^2 = 1^2 + 2^2 + 3^2 + 4^2 + 5^2 + 6^2$$

Since the expression to the right of Σ indicates that the values of i must be squared, each of the values 1 through 6 must be squared before they are added.

Example 1:

Compare the values of $\sum_{i=1}^{4} i^2$ and $\left(\sum_{i=1}^{4} i \right)^2$.

Solution: The value of $\sum_{i=1}^{4} i^2$ is

$$\sum_{i=1}^{4} i^2 = 1^2 + 2^2 + 3^2 + 4^2$$

$$= 1 + 4 + 9 + 16$$

$$= 30$$

The value of $\left(\sum_{i=1}^{4} i \right)^2$ is

$$\left(\sum_{i=1}^{4} i \right)^2 = (1 + 2 + 3 + 4)^2$$

$$= 10^2$$

$$= 100$$

Notice that the values are not the same! It is important to pay attention to whether the square is included in the summation or whether the result of the summation is squared.

If the expression following Σ is enclosed in parentheses, the values of the entire expression must be summed. We can see this in the following problems.

Example 2:

Find the value of $\sum\limits_{i=3}^{7} (2i + 1)$.

Solution: Noticing that the values of i start at $i = 3$, we have

$$\sum\limits_{i=3}^{7} (2i + 1) = (2 \cdot 3 + 1) + (2 \cdot 4 + 1) + (2 \cdot 5 + 1)$$
$$+ (2 \cdot 6 + 1) + (2 \cdot 7 + 1)$$
$$= 7 + 9 + 11 + 13 + 15 = 55$$

Example 3:

Find the value of $\sum\limits_{i=1}^{4} (3i + 2)^2$.

Solution: Letting i take on the values from 1 through 4 gives

$$\sum\limits_{i=1}^{4} (3i + 2)^2 = 5^2 + 8^2 + 11^2 + 14^2 = 406$$

One use of summations is to indicate that we want to add a long list of numbers. To do this, we introduce the notation x_i. Read x *sub i*, x_i means the ith measurement of the variable x. For example, if the x_i are the heights of trees, the statement "$x_5 = 62$ ft" means that the height of the fifth tree is 62 ft. The subscript 5 refers only to which tree is being measured, not to the height of a tree.

Example 4:

A group of bird-watchers counted the number of Cooper's hawks that passed the Fort Baker Lookout on five consecutive days. On the first day, the count was 47, the second day the count was 32, the third day 26, the fourth day 28, and the fifth day 25. Use summation notation and x_i to represent the number of hawks that passed the Fort Baker Lookout.

Solution: Let x_i be the number of Cooper's hawks that passed on the ith day. This gives

$$x_1 = 47, \quad x_2 = 32, \quad x_3 = 26, \quad x_4 = 28, \quad \text{and} \quad x_5 = 25$$

The total number of birds that passed the observations point is

$$\sum_{i=1}^{5} x_i = 47 + 32 + 26 + 28 + 25 = 158$$

Operations with Summations

To conclude this section, we will review three rules of summations. First, suppose we have

$$\sum_{i=1}^{5} 3 = 3 + 3 + 3 + 3 + 3 = 5 \times 3$$

Notice that this result is merely the value of the upper index multiplied by the constant inside the summation sign. In general, we can write this as the formula

$$\sum_{i=1}^{n} c = n \times c \qquad \text{where } c \text{ is any constant}$$

Now, look at the problem

$$\sum_{i=1}^{5} 3i = 3(1) + 3(2) + 3(3) + 3(4) + 3(5) = 3 \times (1 + 2 + 3 + 4 + 5) = 3 \sum_{i=1}^{5} i$$

This implies that if a variable inside the summation sign is multiplied by a constant, the constant can come out of the summation sign. In general, this gives the formula

$$\sum_{i=1}^{n} cx_i = c \sum_{i=1}^{n} x_i \qquad \text{where } c \text{ is any constant}$$

For the third rule let's examine the problem

$$\sum_{i=1}^{3} (x_i + y_i) = (x_1 + y_1) + (x_2 + y_2) + (x_3 + y_3)$$

$$= (x_1 + x_2 + x_3) + (y_1 + y_2 + y_3)$$

$$= \sum_{i=1}^{3} x_i + \sum_{i=1}^{3} y_i$$

This implies that if several terms are added together inside of a summation sign, the summation sign can be used on each term separately. In general, this gives the formula

$$\sum_{i=1}^{n} (x_i + y_i) = \sum_{i=1}^{n} x_i + \sum_{i=1}^{n} y_i$$

Example 5:

Use the formulas given to simplify the expression $\sum_{i=1}^{n} (2x_i + 5)$

Solution:

$$\sum_{i=1}^{n} (2\,x_i + 5) = \sum_{i=1}^{n} 2x_i + \sum_{i=1}^{n} 5 \qquad \text{(by using the third rule)}$$

$$= 2 \sum_{i=1}^{n} x_i + \sum_{i=1}^{n} 5 \qquad \text{(by using the second rule)}$$

$$= 2 \sum_{i=1}^{n} x_i + 5(n) \qquad \text{(by using the first rule)}$$

SECTION 8.0

PROBLEMS

Find the values of the following summations.

1. $\sum_{i=1}^{5} (2i - 3)$

2. $\sum_{i=3}^{8} (i^2 - 3)$

3. $\sum_{i=1}^{5} (2i^2 + 3)$

4. $\sum_{i=3}^{8} (i^2 - 2i + 1)$

5. $\sum_{i=1}^{5} i^3$

6. $\left(\sum_{i=1}^{5} i \right)^3$

Use the rules of summations to simplify each of the following.

7. $\displaystyle\sum_{i=1}^{n} 5x_i$

8. $\displaystyle\sum_{i=1}^{n} (5x_i + 3y_i)$

9. $\displaystyle\sum_{i=1}^{n} (5x_i + 3)$

10. $\displaystyle\sum_{i=1}^{n} (x_i + 2)^2$

Write the following expressions using Σ notation.

11. $1 + 2 + 3 + 4 + 5$

12. $3 + 4 + 5 + 6 + 7 + 8 + 9 + 10$

13. $2 + 4 + 6 + 8 + 10$

14. $3 + 6 + 9 + 12 + 15 + 18$

15. The term "average" is generally taken to mean the sum of a sequence of terms divided by the number of terms.

(a) Find the average of 7, 9, 8, and 12.

(b) If there are n terms, x_1 to x_n, use Σ notation to write a formula for the average.

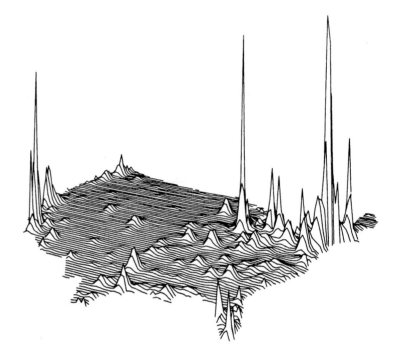

The population-density map (here of the United States) is a unique method of arranging information. (Produced by the Aspex Program at the Harvard Laboratory for Computer Graphics and Spatial Analysis)

SECTION 8.1

▼

ARRANGING INFORMATION

Statistics are numerical data assembled in such a way as to present significant information about a subject. One of the major uses of statistics in daily life is the presentation of information. Standardized tests are used to determine the placement of a student in a class. Executives accumulate and organize data for a presentation. Government officials present findings regarding pollution, demographics, and economics. Magazines and newspapers contain articles with charts and data in almost every issue. No educated person can avoid coming into contact with statistical information. In this section, we discuss a few of the methods by which this information can be presented.

The Data

When a study or a poll is made, much of the information is in numerical form. Merely listed, the results of a survey can be overwhelming. Suppose 100 people respond to a survey with ten questions, each with numerical answers. There will be 10 numbers from each survey, giving a total of 1000 numbers. Most people will not be able to make any pertinent observations when the data are in this form. The following will show how we can help overcome such a difficulty.

Displayed here, listed alphabetically, are the test scores of 70 students who have taken a math placement test. The test has a possible low score of 0 and a possible high score of 25.

12	23	25	5	9	5	24
14	14	15	21	2	18	13
22	16	17	15	19	23	14
11	8	7	16	11	10	19
24	16	11	22	20	14	17
11	13	18	9	6	15	4
6	23	20	13	9	7	15
16	14	21	10	20	3	16
11	22	7	10	11	18	14
15	12	19	25	23	2	21

As we look at that data, there does not appear to be any pattern nor can we make any conclusions about the test scores. In order to examine this data more carefully, one technique is to put the data into categories.

When data are divided into groups, the different categories are called **classes**. The number and size of the classes we choose are determined by the goals of the investigation. Often, studies have predetermined classes. For example, many college courses use the standard groupings 90–100 for an A, 80–89 for a B, 70–79 for a C, 60–69 for a D, and 0–59 for an F. Economic studies concerned with household income have classes such as "below the poverty level (less than $9000 income per year)," "lower middle income ($9000 to $16,000)," and others.

A second criterion for choosing the classes is common sense. It would not be very wise to pick only one class because all the data will fall into that class. In the same way, creating 30 classes for our data would mean that some of the classes would be empty and most of the classes would contain only a few scores. Finally, if we want the number of items in a class to be meaningful, the size of each class should be the same.

For our test data, we do not have any predetermined classes. Since the data vary from 0 through 25, it is convenient to pick five classes. This number was chosen because it allows us to create nearly equal size classes without much difficulty. The classes are 0 through 5, 6 through 10, 11 through 15, 16 through 20, and 21 through 25.

Now that we have chosen the classes, the next step is to determine the number of data values in each class. To do this, we have created the following chart, called a **frequency distribution**. The column labeled **Tally** is used to count the number of scores that fall into a class. The column labeled **Frequency** contains the number of tallies for that class. The entries in the column labeled **Relative Frequency** are found by dividing the frequency for each class by the total number of items, in this case 70. The final column is called **Percentage Frequency**. Its entries are found by multiplying the relative frequency by 100, and they describe what percentage of the data fall into each category.

Frequency Distribution

Class	Tally	Frequency	Relative Frequency	Percentage Frequency
0–5	卌 |	6	0.09	9%
6–10	卌 卌 ||	12	0.17	17%
11–15	卌 卌 |||| 卌 ||	22	0.31	31%
16–20	卌 卌 |||| |	16	0.23	23%
21–25	卌 |||| 卌	14	0.20	20%

With the information presented in this way, we can see that of the 70 test scores, 22 were in the class from 11 through 15. This group comprised 31% of those who took the test.

Having the data organized in this fashion is a great improvement, but it is still a bit intimidating. Many people do not like to look at tables of numbers. Because of this, information can often be presented with greater impact if it is in graphical form. For our discussion, we will examine three of the many types of graphical representations. The first of these is called a **bar graph**. A bar graph uses one axis to represent the different classes while the other axis is used to indicate the frequency for each class.

Bar graphs may be oriented horizontally or vertically and may use either the frequencies or the relative frequencies as the lengths of the bars. The choice of display is left to the person creating the graphs. With a bar graph, it is easy to see which class contains the largest number of test scores. The numbers at the ends of the bar permit the reader to determine the actual number of scores in each class.

Three different bar graphs of our data are shown.

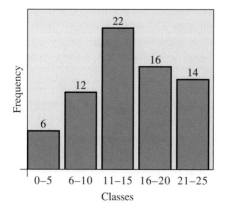

Vertical bar graph with frequencies

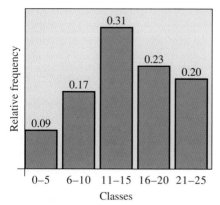

Vertical bar graph with relative frequencies

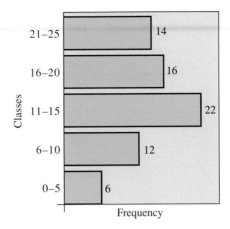

Horizontal bar graph with frequencies

A second way that information from a frequency distribution can be presented is through the use of a **pie chart**. A pie chart is a circular diagram divided into sectors (wedge-shaped pieces). The sectors represent the percentage frequencies. The percentage frequency determines the width of the angle, with the whole circle being 100%. Thus, a percentage frequency of 25% would be represented by one-fourth of a circle.

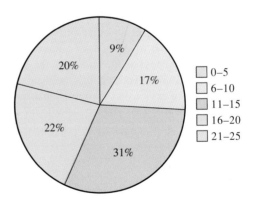

Today's computers accomplish the drawing of pie charts and bar graphs by using chart-drawing software. Often these abilities are incorporated into larger computer software packages, such as spreadsheet programs.

The third type of graphical representation for our data requires us to reexamine the frequency distribution and create another table. This table is called the **cumulative frequency distribution**.

Cumulative Frequency Distribution

Class	Cumulative Frequency	Relative Cumulative Frequency	Percentage Cumulative Frequency
≤ 5	6	0.09	9%
≤ 10	18	0.26	26%
≤ 15	40	0.57	57%
≤ 20	56	0.80	80%
≤ 25	70	1.00	100%

The **cumulative frequency** is the total of all scores up to a certain level. Since there are 6 scores in the 0–5 class and 12 scores in the 6–10 class, the ≤ 10 class has a cumulative frequency of 18. The cumulative frequency for each class is computed by adding the frequencies for all of the original classes below the given level. Similar methods are used to find the relative cumulative frequency and the percentage cumulative frequency.

An important thing to notice is that the cumulative frequency for the last class must be the same as the total number of values in the survey. Similarly, the relative cumulative frequency and the percentage cumulative frequency must add to 1 and 100%, respectively.

The cumulative frequencies can be put on a graph similar to the bar graphs, or they can be put on a graph called a **cumulative frequency polygon**. This is also known as an **ogive** (pronounced *oh'jive*.) The ogive uses the values of the cumulative frequency (or cumulative relative frequency or cumulative percentage frequency) as the values on the vertical axis and the less-than limits as the horizontal values. These points are then connected by a series of straight lines. It is important to notice that an ogive must never decrease.

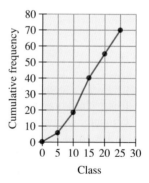

Easy run **Difficult run**

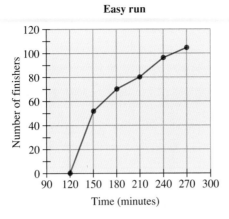

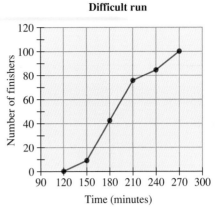

Ogives can be used to compare data that use time as the variable for the classes. For example, two marathons, run in two different cities, have the finishing times presented in the two ogives shown. In each graph, the vertical axis gives the number of runners who finished in a given length of time or less. The graph on the left is steep at the beginning and becomes less steep toward the end. This shows that there were more runners finishing in less than 3 hours in the first race than in the second race. Since the total number of runners in each race is similar, we can conclude that the race represented by the data on the left was an easier race than the race represented by the graph on the right. (This assumes that the abilities of the runners in each race were similar.)

SECTION 8.1

PROBLEMS

1. For the data 2, 4, 6, 1, 7, 9, 5, 3, 7, 6:
   (a) Arrange the data into a frequency distribution with three classes.
   (b) Draw a bar graph and a pie chart for this data.
   (c) Complete a cumulative frequency distribution for the data.
   (d) Draw a cumulative frequency polygon.

2. For the data 2, 4, 3, 7, 2, 8, 6, 3, 7, 5:
   (a) Arrange the data into a frequency distribution with four classes.
   (b) Draw a bar graph and a pie chart for this data.
   (c) Complete a cumulative frequency distribution for the data.
   (d) Draw a cumulative frequency ploygon.

3. The bar graph shown gives the number of seeds of a particular type of cactus that germinated under greenhouse conditions within a specified number of weeks after planting. At the end of six weeks, the experiment was discontinued.

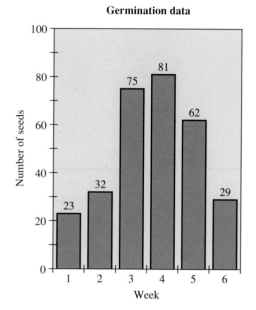

(a) Determine the total number of germinated seeds.

(b) What percentage of the germinating seeds sprouted during the third week?

(c) Make use of the information on the bar chart and create an ogive of the germination data.

4. The pie chart gives the first-year expenditures for the restoration of a run-down farm. The percentages give the percent of the budget used in the respective categories. If the total restoration budget for the first year was $12,500, how much money was spent on landscaping?

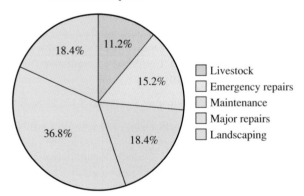

5. The budget data for the Hopkins Poultry Company of Valley View are given in the pie chart taken from the company's annual report. As a major stockholder in the company, you regularly read the report. What is your reaction to the pie chart?

Budget data for Hopkins Poultry Co.

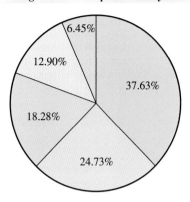

6. The two bar graphs give the sales increases and percent sales increases for four departments of the Acme Widget and Gizmo Company. The departments make widgets, gizmos, dibblers, and sagos.

Increase in sales from June to July (by department) for Acme Widget and Gizmo Company

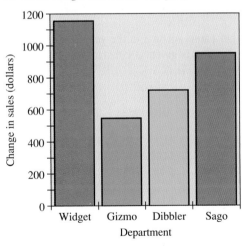

Percent increase in sales from June to July (by department) for Acme Widget and Gizmo Company

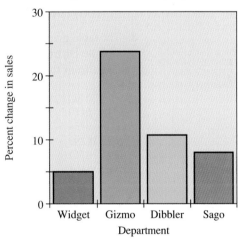

(a) Which department(s) would use the change in sales as an indicator of their growth as a department?

(b) Which department(s) would use the percentage change in sales as an indicator of their growth as a department?

*(c) Explain, using numbers, how the gizmo department can have the lowest increase in sales and yet have the greatest percentage increase in sales.

7. The table gives the per capita expenditures (in dollars) for state and local police protection and correction employment for each state and the District of Columbia. (Data taken from the *Statistical Abstract of the U.S.*)

AL	102.9	AK	532.9	AZ	194.8	AR	76.1	CA	202.6	CO	152.0
CT	135.8	DE	175.9	DC	548.8	FL	160.9	GA	123.9	HI	165.6
ID	102.1	IL	152.7	IN	92.1	IA	108.6	KS	108.9	KY	92.2
LA	144.7	ME	87.5	MD	175.6	MA	139.9	MI	170.8	MN	128.1
MS	74.8	MO	113.6	MT	117.1	NE	111.3	NV	276.4	NH	104.7
NJ	180.5	NM	184.4	NY	216.3	NC	109.0	ND	101.8	OH	121.7
OK	110.8	OR	147.9	PA	124.7	RI	143.2	SC	94.0	SD	103.8
TN	102.1	TX	112.8	UT	133.1	VT	109.9	VA	138.9	WA	169.3
WV	67.2	WI	153.0	WY	202.5						

(a) Arrange the data into a frequency distribution with 11 classes with the first class being 50.1–100.0.
(b) Draw a bar graph for the data.
(c) What is the most typical amount spent per capita for police and correction employment?
(d) Suppose a certain group of citizens in Georgia (GA) want to increase spending on police protection and correction employment. If you were a member of the citizens group, would you use the tabular information in your arguments? Explain your answer.
(e) Give possible explanations why Alaska (AK) and the District of Columbia (DC) have such high expenditures.

8. The table gives the estimated per capita income in the year 2000 for each state and the District of Columbia. Income is given in constant 1972 dollars. (Data taken from the *Statistical Abstract of the U.S.*)

AL	6170	AK	9958	AZ	6891	AR	5982	CA	8035	CO	7829
CT	9134	DE	7709	DC	9467	FL	7120	GA	6719	HI	7461
ID	6290	IL	7763	IN	7042	IA	7132	KS	7750	KY	6285
LA	6719	ME	6187	MD	8112	MA	8207	MI	7419	MN	7509
MS	5601	MO	6984	MT	6506	NE	7244	NV	7652	NH	7413
NJ	8662	NM	6217	NY	7854	NC	6373	ND	7288	OH	7267
OK	7121	OR	7046	PA	7256	RI	7305	SC	6054	SD	6435
TN	6305	TX	7356	UT	5899	VT	6606	VA	7515	WA	7492
WV	5996	WI	7232	WY	7928						

(a) Arrange the data into a frequency distribution with five classes, the first one being 5001–6000.
(b) Draw a bar graph for the data.
*(c) What does it mean for the information to be in constant 1972 dollars?
(d) Estimate the typical per capita income for a U.S. citizen in the year 2000 in constant 1972 dollars.

9. Find some data dealing with the time it takes to complete a task. This could be time required to complete a race, to complete a questionnaire, to drive from one location to another, and so on. The data should consist of at least 30

values. Construct a frequency distribution with at least six classes and draw the ogive for the data.

10. Why must an ogive never decrease?

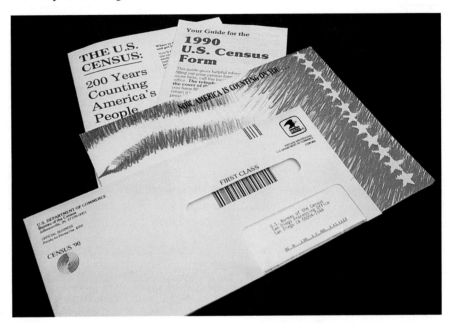

Census forms are an efficient means of collecting the information that is used in the statistical analysis of many facets of American life. (Courtesy of Kurt Viegelmann)

SECTION 8.2

▼

MEASURES OF CENTRAL TENDENCY

Finding an average is a computation that requires only arithmetic skills. It has, however, very important uses in real-world problems. An average allows us to find one value that represents the middle of a set of data. As we shall see, however, the middle of a set of data can be described in different ways. Collectively, these ways of describing the middle value are called **measures of central tendency**. In this section, we introduce four measures of central tendency and describe situations in which one of the four measures is the most appropriate to use.

The Mean

The **mean** or **arithmetic** (pronounced *ar ith met' ic*) **mean** of a set of values is what most people are referring to when they say "**average**." It is found by adding up all the data and then dividing by the number of data values. Statisticians use the symbol μ (read *mu*) for the mean and define it with the formula

▼

$$\text{mean} = \mu = \frac{\sum_{i=1}^{n} x_i}{n} \quad \text{where} \begin{cases} n \text{ is the number of data values} \\ x_i \text{ represent the data values} \end{cases}$$

Example 1:

Find the mean of the numbers 3, 6, 8, 5, 4.

Solution:

$$\mu = \frac{\sum\limits_{i=1}^{5} x_i}{5} = \frac{3 + 6 + 8 + 5 + 4}{5} = \frac{26}{5} = 5.2$$

Example 2:

Find the mean of 1, 1, 1, 1, 3, 3, 5, 5, 6, 6, 6, 6, 6.

Solution: Rather than merely adding all these numbers, it is more convenient to multiply each value by its frequency. This total should then be divided by the total frequency. In other words, rather than doing the computation

$$\mu = \frac{1 + 1 + 1 + 1 + 3 + 3 + 5 + 5 + 6 + 6 + 6 + 6 + 6}{13} = \frac{50}{13} = 3.85$$

it is easier to write

$$\mu = \frac{4(1) + 2(3) + 2(5) + 5(6)}{13} = \frac{50}{13} = 3.85$$

In general, when a set of data has values that appear several times or when the data are grouped into classes, we can use the formula

mean for grouped data $= \mu = \dfrac{\sum\limits_{i=1}^{n} f_i x_i}{\sum\limits_{i=1}^{n} f_i}$ where $\begin{cases} n \text{ is the number of classes} \\ f_i \text{ is the frequency of each class} \\ x_i \text{ represent the data values} \end{cases}$

Example 3:

Find the mean of the following frequency distribution.

Class	Frequency	Class Midpoint x_i
1–5	6	3
6–10	12	8
11–15	22	13
16–20	16	18
21–25	14	23

Solution: In the table, there is a column that we have not previously used. The **class midpoint** is the mean of the boundary values of each class. For example, the boundary values for the first class are 1 and 5. The mean of these two numbers is 3. This gives the midpoint for the class. We use the midpoints since we do not know the actual values of the data in each class. For example, we know that there are six values in the 1–5 class, but we do not know what those values are. As an estimate of these values, we will use the class midpoints. Now, using the formula for the mean of grouped data, we get

$$
\mu = \frac{\sum_{i=1}^{5} f_i x_i}{\sum_{i=1}^{5} f_i}
$$

$$
= \frac{6(3) + 12(8) + 22(13) + 16(18) + 14(23)}{6 + 12 + 22 + 16 + 14}
$$

$$
= \frac{1010}{70}
$$

$$
= 14.43
$$

Another use of the formula for grouped means is to compute a **weighted average**. A weighted average is the mean of a group of numbers in which certain values have more importance, or weight, than do other scores. When computing a weighted average, we **use the weights for each score as frequencies in the mean of grouped data formula**. An example of this type of situation can be seen in the next problem, concerning a student's grade.

Example 4:

A student is trying to calculate his grade in an English class. His total scores are

Midterms	82
Homework	87
Final	92

The course syllabus says that the midterms count for 60% of the grade, homework for 10% of the grade, and the final for 30% of the grade. Compute the student's total score in the class.

Solution: Using the percentages as the weights of the scores in each category, we have

$$
\mu = \frac{0.60(82) + 0.10(87) + 0.30(92)}{0.60 + 0.10 + 0.30} = \frac{85.5}{1.00} = 85.5
$$

The Geometric Mean

Example 5:

An inheritance of $10,000 has been deposited in a bank account earning 9% interest, compounded daily. The amount in the account at the end of each year for five consecutive years is given in the table. We are assuming that, other than adding interest to the account, no deposits or withdrawals are made during the five years.

At the end of 1 year $10,941.62
At the end of 2 years $11,971.91
At the end of 3 years $13,099.20
At the end of 4 years $14,332.65
At the end of 5 years $15,682.24

Find the mean value of the account.

Solution:

$$\mu = \frac{\sum_{i=1}^{5} x_i}{5}$$

$$= \frac{10,941.62 + 11,971.91 + 13,099.20 + 14,332.65 + 15,682.24}{5}$$

$$\mu = \frac{66,027.62}{5}$$

$$\mu = \$13,205.52$$

Since the interest rate was constant, we might have expected the mean to be the value in the account at the end of three years, halfway through the list of five years. However, since the interest earned is proportional to the amount in the account and the account has a higher balance in the later years, more of the total interest will be earned in the later years than was earned in the early years.

To solve the difficulty, we will use the **geometric mean**. The geometric mean is found by using the formula

$$\text{G.M.} = \sqrt[n]{x_1 \times x_2 \times \cdots \times x_n}$$

The geometric mean is most often used for data that are related to exponential models, such as compound interest or radioactive decay.

Example 6:

Find the geometric mean of 2, 8, and 32.

Solution: Since there are three values, we use $n = 3$. Thus,

$$\text{G.M.} = \sqrt[3]{2 \times 8 \times 32} = \sqrt[3]{512} = 8$$

Find the cube root of 512 by using the following buttons on your calculator:

Press	Display
$\boxed{5}\ \boxed{1}\ \boxed{2}\ \boxed{x^y}\ \boxed{3}\ \boxed{1/x}\ \boxed{=}$	8

Example 7:

Find the geometric mean of the values listed in Example 5.

Solution: Since there were five values in Example 5, we need to use $n = 5$. Inserting the data into the formula for the geometric mean gives

$$\text{G.M.} = \sqrt[5]{10{,}941.62 \times 11{,}971.91 \times 13{,}099.20 \times 14{,}332.65 \times 15{,}682.24}$$

$$= \sqrt[5]{3.856776 \times 10^{20}}$$

$$= \$13{,}099.20$$

To achieve this result on a calculator, we need to multiply the five numbers and then press the following keys:

Press	Display
$\ldots\ \boxed{x^y}\ \boxed{5}\ \boxed{1/x}\ \boxed{=}$	13,099.20

Note that this gives the amount in the account at the end of the third year.

The Median

Example 8:

Five houses are listed for sale in a real estate broker's advertisement. The prices are \$269,000, \$256,000, \$249,000 \$235,000, and \$749,000. Find the average price of the houses listed by the agent.

Solution:

$$\mu = \frac{\sum_{i=1}^{5} x_i}{5} = \frac{269{,}000 + 256{,}000 + 249{,}000 + 235{,}000 + 749{,}000}{5}$$

$$= \frac{1{,}758{,}000}{5}$$

$$\mu = \$351{,}600$$

Notice that the average is higher than all but one of the house prices. The reason is that the price of the most expensive house is distorting the meaning of the calculations. The mean price of these five houses is $351,600, but the mean does not accurately reflect the typical or "average" price.

To solve this difficulty, we will use a measure of central tendency called the **median**. The median is found by listing the data in increasing order and choosing the middle value. If there is an even number of items, the median is found by taking the mean of the two middle values. The median is frequently used when there are a few extreme values in the data that will greatly alter the value of the mean.

Example 9:

Find the median price of the housing prices listed in Example 7.

Solution: Listing the data in increasing order gives

$$\$235,000, \$249,000, \$256,000, \$269,000, \$749,000$$

The median price is $256,000 since this is the middle value. This value is much closer to what we would call the "average" price of these five houses. Also notice that increasing the price of the most expensive house will have no effect on the value of the median.

Example 10:

Find the median of the values 0, 3, 4, 9, 16, 90.

Solution: The values are listed in order, so we need only find the middle value. Since there is an even number of values, the median is found by calculating the mean of the center pair of values.

$$\text{median} = \frac{4 + 9}{2} = 6.5$$

The Mode

The **mode** of a set of data is the value that occurs most frequently. It is the only measure of central tendency that can be used with nonnumerical as well as numerical data. For example, if a design consultant wanted to determine the most popular color for exterior house paint, he or she would conduct a survey to find out how many people liked each color. It would not be possible to use methods such as the mean or median.

Example 11:

Determine the mode of the following sets of values.

(a) 1, 2, 2, 3, 4, 6, 6, 6, 8, 9
(b) 1, 2, 2, 3, 4, 6, 6, 7, 8, 9
(c) 1, 2, 2, 3, 4, 4, 6, 6, 8, 9

Solution:

 (a) In the first group of data, the number 6 appears three times, and all the other numbers appear at most twice. Therefore, the mode is 6.

 (b) In the second group, the numbers 2 and 6 both appear twice. No other number appears more than once. In a situation like this, there are two modes, 2 and 6. When a set of data has two modes, it is called **bimodal**.

 (c) In the third set of data, the numbers 2, 4, and 6 all appear twice. When more than two values have the highest frequency, we say that the set of data does not have a mode.

Example 12:

In 1984 there were 61,997,000 families in the United States. Of these families, 30,936,503 had no children, 12,833,379 families had one child, 11,779,430 had two children, 4,463,784 families had three children, and 1,983,904 families had four or more children.

(a) Determine the modal number of children per family.
(b) Determine the mean number of children per family.

Solution:

 (a) Since the class with the highest frequency is the class with no children, the modal number of children is 0.

 (b) Finding an accurate mean of the data will not be possible. Since the final category consists of families with four or more children, we do not know the actual number of children in these families. However, we can use the method of finding the mean for grouped data to give an estimate.

$$\mu = [30{,}936{,}503(0) + 12{,}833{,}379(1) + 11{,}779{,}430(2)$$
$$+ 4{,}463{,}784(3) + 1{,}983{,}904(4)] \div 61{,}997{,}000$$

$$= \frac{57{,}719{,}207}{61{,}997{,}000} = 0.93$$

Since the number of children in the last class may be greater than four per family, we can say that the mean number of children per family is greater than or equal to 0.93.

SECTION 8.2
PROBLEMS

1. For the set of values 2, 4, 7, 2, 1, 8, 9, 10, 9, 6:

   (a) Find the arithmetic mean.
   (b) Find the geometric mean.
   (c) Find the median.
   (d) Find the mode.

2. For the set of values 3, 8, 4, 2, 4, 6, 7, 1, 5, 0:

   (a) Find the arithmetic mean.
   (b) Find the geometric mean.
   (c) Find the median.
   (d) Find the mode.

3. Five players of a basketball team have the following shooting percentages. Also included in the table are the numbers of attempted shots.

Player	Attempts	Percentage
Alexander	523	43%
DiJulio	671	62%
Falbo	420	57%
O'Connor	570	54%
Tebelskis	213	38%

   (a) Compute the weighted mean shooting percentage, using the number of attempts as the weights.
   (b) Compute the mean of the shooting percentages.
   (c) Which of the averages computed gives a better representation of the team shooting percentage? Explain.

4. A student is computing her cumulative grade point average (GPA). During six semesters, she has received 5 C's, 11 B's, and 8 A's. If a grade of C is worth 2 points, a B 3 points, and an A 4 points, compute the student's GPA. (*Hint:* Use the number of grades as the wieghts.)

5. The following table gives the average salary of secondary teachers in each state and the District of Columbia in 1985. Salaries are given in thousands of dollars. (Data taken from the *Statistical Abstract of the U.S.*)

AL	20.2	AK	39.9	AZ	23.7	AR	19.5	CA	27.9	CO	24.8
CT	24.9	DE	23.8	DC	20.6	FL	20.6	GA	21.0	HI	24.6
ID	20.5	IL	27.8	IN	23.5	IA	21.6	KS	21.3	KY	20.1
LA	20.2	ME	19.2	MD	26.3	MA	24.4	MI	28.7	MN	26.8
MS	16.3	MO	21.1	MT	22.8	NE	21.0	NV	23.0	NH	18.5
NJ	25.7	NM	22.8	NY	30.0	NC	20.8	ND	20.3	OH	23.4
OK	19.5	OR	25.8	PA	24.6	RI	28.1	SC	20.6	SD	17.5
TN	20.2	TX	23.4	UT	22.4	VT	19.4	VA	22.5	WA	26.1
WV	19.6	WI	25.2	WY	27.8						

(a) What is the average salary of teachers in Utah?

(b) Find the arithmetic mean of the data.

(c) Find a frequency distribution for the data. Use five classes, starting with $15,100–$20,000.

(d) Find the mean of the frequency distribution.

(e) Find the median salary.

(f) Which of the three results would you use if you were the negotiator for a teachers' union that wants higher salaries? Why?

(g) Which of the results would you use if you were arguing that teachers are well paid? Why?

6. The following table gives the per capita use of water in gallons per day during 1980 for each state and the District of Columbia. (Data taken from the *Statistical Abstract of the U.S.*)

AL	2824	AK	546	AZ	2929	AR	6960	CA	2272	CO	5512
CT	1188	DE	2013	DC	534	FL	2127	GA	1259	HI	2548
ID	19,007	IL	1574	IN	2551	IA	1476	KS	2788	KY	1311
LA	3079	ME	1421	MD	1822	MA	1207	MI	1621	MN	759
MS	1387	MO	1401	MT	13,959	NE	7634	NV	4461	NH	1083
NJ	1356	NM	2989	NY	967	NC	1376	ND	1988	OH	1296
OK	592	OR	2578	PA	1347	RI	527	SC	1983	SD	1000
TN	2176	TX	1466	UT	3125	VT	664	VA	1809	WA	2001
WV	2872	WI	1227	WY	11,368						

(a) How much water would an average family of four living in Utah use per day?

(b) Find the mean per capita water use.

(c) Find the median per capita water use.

(d) Does the high per capita water use in Idaho, Montana, and Wyoming seem to have much effect on the mean?

(e) If you were a member of water conservation group, would you use the median or the mean in your information brochures? Why?

(f) The total number of gallons per day used by Illinois during 1980 was 18 billion gallons. Idaho also used 18 billion gallons per day during 1980. Why is Idaho's per capita usage so much higher?

7. The Malthusian population growth law was discussed in Example 2 of Section 2.3. For the United States, the model is $P = 179,323e^{0.0142t}$, where t is time in years and P is the population.

(a) Find the population given by the model for $t = 0, 20, 40, 60, 80,$ and 100 years.

(b) Find the arithmetic mean of these populations.

(c) Find the geometric mean of these populations.

(d) Does the arithmetic mean or the geometric mean more accurately reflect the central value of these population figures? Explain your answer.

8. Suppose the average height of new recruits to the U.S. Army is desired for a Pentagon study. An alphabetical listing of 20,000 recruits and their heights is available. Explain why using the median would be a difficult task to do by hand.

*9. The following question has nothing to do with statistics. Instead, we want to explore one of the connections between a geometric series, the arithmetic mean, and the geometric mean. As you may recall from algebra, a geometric series is one of the form $a + ar + ar^2 + ar^3 + \cdots$.

   (a) Find the geometric mean of the terms in the geometric series $1 + 10 + 100 + 1000 + 10,000$.
   (b) Find the common logarithm of each of the terms in the geometric series.
   (c) Find the arithmetic mean of the logarithms.
   (d) Find the antilog of this number. (For example, the antilog of 3 is 10^3.)
   (e) State a general relationship between the geometric mean of the terms of a geometric series and the arithmetic mean of the logarithms of those terms.
   (f) Does this relationship work if the data are not the terms of a geometric series? Explain.

SECTION 8.3

▼

MEASURES OF DISPERSION

Suppose the mean, mode, and median for two sets of data are identical. Does this suggest that the data are the same? Consider the two sets of data: 1, 1, 100, 100, 199, 199 and 99, 99, 100, 100, 100, 101, 101. For each set, the mean, mode, and median all equal 100, yet, the data are not the same. Not only are the data not the same, the first set has values that range between 1 and 199, whereas the second set is closely clustered around 100. From this, we can see that we need more tools to help describe a distribution of numbers. Collectively, the tools used to do this are called **measures of dispersion.** A measure of dispersion will provide a tool to determine to what extent the data in a set differ from a central value.

The Range

The **range** of a set of values is the difference between the highest and lowest values in the set.

Example 1:

Find the range of each of the following sets of numbers.

(a) 1, 1, 100, 100, 100, 199, 199
(b) 99, 99, 100, 100, 100, 101, 101

Solution:

(a) The range of the first set of data is $199 - 1 = 198$.
(b) The range of the second set of data is $101 - 99 = 2$.

We can see that the range will provide some help toward solving the problem mentioned in the introductory remarks. However, it will not completely solve the problem. Consider the following two sets of data: 1, 1, 1, 100, 199, 199, 199 and

1, 100, 100, 100, 100, 100, 199. In both sets, the range is 198, but the first set of data has most of its values at the extreme ends, whereas most of the data in the second set have the value of 100. Only two of the numbers are at the extremes. What is needed is a method to determine the average of the distance between each data value and the mean. If this average is high, then the data are spread out. If the average is low, then the data are clustered together.

Standard Deviation

The method we will use to determine how closely the data are clustered around the mean is called the **standard deviation**. The standard deviation is the square root of the average of the squares of the differences between the data values and the mean. Using the Greek letter σ (sigma), we have the formula for standard deviation:

$$\text{standard deviation} = \sigma = \sqrt{\frac{\sum_{i=1}^{n} (x_i - \mu)^2}{n}} \qquad \text{where} \begin{cases} x_i \text{ are the data values} \\ \mu \text{ is the mean of the data} \\ n \text{ is the number of data} \end{cases}$$

Example 2:

Find the standard deviation of the numbers 4, 6, and 11.

Solution: In order to find the standard deviation, we need to first find the mean.

$$\mu = \frac{4 + 6 + 11}{3} = 7$$

Next, we need to subtract the mean from each of the data values and then square the results. Using the formula gives

$$\sigma = \sqrt{\frac{(4 - 7)^2 + (6 - 7)^2 + (11 - 7)^2}{3}}$$

$$= \sqrt{\frac{9 + 1 + 16}{3}}$$

$$= \sqrt{\frac{26}{3}} = 2.94$$

Although this process does not seem too difficult, let's try to find the standard deviation of the numbers 2, 5, 7, 8, 10, 6, and 7. We first find the mean:

$$\mu = \frac{2 + 5 + 7 + 8 + 10 + 6 + 7}{7} = \frac{45}{7} = 6.429$$

Now, finding the standard deviation will involve subtracting 6.429 from each of these values and then squaring the results. Even with the help of a calculator, this will become very awkward. Therefore, before we continue with this problem, we want to use the formulas presented in Section 8.0 to see if we can simplify the equation for the standard deviation. This derivation will involve the use of a great deal of algebra and the three rules of summations that were reviewed in Section 8.0. For your convenience, these rules are given along with the derivation of a simplified equation for standard deviation.

Derivation of the Computing Formula for Standard Deviation

The three rules of summations given in Section 8.0 are

1. $\displaystyle\sum_{i=1}^{n} c = n \times c$ where c is any constant

2. $\displaystyle\sum_{i=1}^{n} cx_i = c \sum_{i=1}^{n} x_i$ where c is any constant

3. $\displaystyle\sum_{i=1}^{n} (x_i + y_i) = \sum_{i=1}^{n} x_i + \sum_{i=1}^{n} y_i$

Starting with our current formula for standard deviation, we have

$$\sigma = \sqrt{\frac{\displaystyle\sum_{i=1}^{n} (x_i - \mu)^2}{n}}$$

By expanding the term inside the square, we get

$$\sigma = \sqrt{\frac{\displaystyle\sum_{i=1}^{n} \left((x_i)^2 - 2x_i\mu + \mu^2 \right)}{n}}$$

Now, using the third rule of summations to distribute the summation sign gives

$$\sigma = \sqrt{\frac{\displaystyle\sum_{i=1}^{n} (x_i)^2 - \sum_{i=1}^{n} 2\mu x_i + \sum_{i=1}^{n} \mu^2}{n}}$$

Since the 2μ in the second term is a constant, by the second rule of summations it can be brought outside the summation sign.

$$\sigma = \sqrt{\frac{\displaystyle\sum_{i=1}^{n} (x_i)^2 - 2\mu \sum_{i=1}^{n} x_i + \sum_{i=1}^{n} \mu^2}{n}}$$

Since the third summation contains only constants, we can use the first rule of summations to get

$$\sigma = \sqrt{\dfrac{\sum\limits_{i=1}^{n} (x_i)^2 - 2\mu \sum\limits_{i=1}^{n} x_i + n\mu^2}{n}}$$

Since $\mu = \dfrac{\sum\limits_{i=1}^{n} x_i}{n}$, $\sum\limits_{i=1}^{n} x_i = n\mu$:

$$\sigma = \sqrt{\dfrac{\sum\limits_{i=1}^{n} (x_i)^2 - 2\mu n\mu + n\mu^2}{n}}$$

Multiplying gives

$$\sigma = \sqrt{\dfrac{\sum\limits_{i=1}^{n} (x_i)^2 - 2n\mu^2 + n\mu^2}{n}}$$

Finally, combining the like terms gives

$$\sigma = \sqrt{\dfrac{\sum\limits_{i=1}^{n} (x_i)^2 - n\mu^2}{n}}$$

This gives the formula we will be using to compute the standard deviation.

Computing Formula for Standard Deviation

$$\sigma = \sqrt{\dfrac{\sum\limits_{i=1}^{n} (x_i)^2 - n\mu^2}{n}} \quad \text{where} \begin{cases} x_i \text{ are the data values} \\ \mu \text{ is the mean of the data} \\ n = \text{the number of data values} \end{cases}$$

In the following example, we use the computing formula to finish the problem begun earlier.

Example 3:

Find the standard deviation of 2, 5, 7, 8, 10, 6, and 7.

Solution: We had determined that the mean was 6.429. However, we did not want to do all the work of subtracting this value from each of the given numbers. The new formula for standard deviation no longer requires this. Instead, we need only square the original data and the mean:

Since

$$\sum_{i=1}^{7} (x_i)^2 = 2^2 + 5^2 + 7^2 + 8^2 + 10^2 + 6^2 + 7^2$$

$$= 4 + 25 + 49 + 64 + 100 + 36 + 49$$

$$= 327$$

We have

$$\sigma = \sqrt{\frac{\sum_{i=1}^{7} (x_i)^2 - n\mu^2}{n}} = \sqrt{\frac{327 - 7(6.429)^2}{7}}$$

$$= \sqrt{\frac{37.676}{7}} = 2.32$$

The computing formula works nicely for individual data, but we have discovered that much of the data found in the real world is in terms of classes. Therefore, as we did for the mean, we need a formula for standard deviation of grouped data. The derivation of this formula is similar to the derivation of the computing formula for standard deviation and is left as a starred(*) problem.

Computing Formula for Standard Deviation of Grouped Data

$$\sigma = \sqrt{\frac{\sum f_i(x_i)^2 - n\mu^2}{n}}$$

Example 4:

Class	Frequency
1–5	6
6–10	12
11–15	22
16–20	16
21–25	14

These data are the test scores used in Example 1 of Section 8.1. Find the mean and standard deviation of these scores.

Solution: Since these are grouped data, we need to use the midpoints of each classes as the x_i. To help with the solutions, we display the calculations in tabular form.

Class	Frequency f_i	x_i	$f_i x_i$	$(x_i)^2$	$f_i(x_i)^2$
1–5	6	3	18	9	54
6–10	12	8	96	64	768
11–15	22	13	286	169	3718
16–20	16	18	288	324	5184
21–25	14	23	322	529	7406
	$\Sigma f_i = 70$	$\Sigma x_i = 65$	$\Sigma f_i x_i = 1010$	$\Sigma(x_i)^2 = 1095$	$\Sigma f_i(x_i)^2 = 17{,}130$

$$\mu = \frac{\Sigma f_i x_i}{n} = \frac{1010}{70} = 14.43$$

$$\sigma = \sqrt{\frac{\Sigma f_i(x_i)^2 - n\mu^2}{n}} = \sqrt{\frac{17{,}130 - 70(14.43)^2}{70}} = \sqrt{36.49} = 6.04$$

What Is All This Good For?

We have now seen how to compute the standard deviation of either grouped or ungrouped data but, so far, we have no real feeling for what standard deviation means or how it can be used. In the remainder of this section, we discuss the meaning of standard deviation in terms of a frequency distribution. In Section 8.4 we discuss how standard deviation can be used.

Example 5:

Consider the following sets of scores from two intermediate algebra classes.

Morning Class	Afternoon Class
78 65 83 91 98 25 67 88 81 77	34 87 81 93 99 24 77 62 98 100
53 76 80 72 75 69 64 62 85 93	57 34 81 72 61 59 68 74 77 94
70 44 85 73 75 63	56 71 70 81 78 83 25 94 31

(a) Find the mean and standard deviation of each class.
(b) Construct the frequency distribution of each class.
(c) Draw a bar chart for each class.
(d) Use the bar chart to draw conclusions about the meaning of standard deviation.

Solution:

(a) To find the mean of each class, use the formula

$$\mu = \frac{\sum\limits_{i=1}^{n} x_i}{n}$$

For the morning class, this gives

$$\mu = \frac{\sum_{i=1}^{26} x_i}{26} = \frac{1892}{26} = 72.77 \approx 73$$

For the afternoon class, the mean is

$$\mu = \frac{\sum_{i=1}^{29} x_i}{29} = \frac{2021}{29} = 69.69 \approx 70$$

To find the standard deviation, we use the computing formula for ungrouped data,

$$\sigma = \sqrt{\frac{\sum_{i=1}^{n} (x_i)^2 - n\mu^2}{n}}$$

For the morning class, this gives

$$\sigma = \sqrt{\frac{\sum_{i=1}^{26} (x_i)^2 - 26(72.77)^2}{26}} = \sqrt{\frac{143,784 - 26(5295.4729)}{26}} = 15.32$$

and the afternoon class has a standard deviation of

$$\sigma = \sqrt{\frac{\sum_{i=1}^{29} (x_i)^2 - 29(69.69)^2}{29}} = \sqrt{\frac{154,939 - 29(4856.6961)}{29}} = 22.05$$

(b) Completing the frequency distributions for each class gives the following:

Morning Class		Afternoon Class	
Class	Frequency	Class	Frequency
0–9	0	0–9	0
10–19	0	10–19	0
20–29	1	20–29	2
30–39	0	30–39	3
40–49	1	40–49	0
50–59	1	50–59	3
60–69	6	60–69	3
70–79	8	70–79	7
80–89	6	80–89	5
90–100	3	90–100	6

(c) The bar charts for both classes are shown here.

Morning class

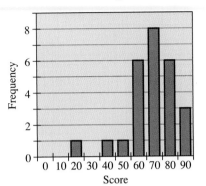

Afternoon class

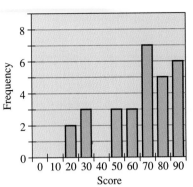

(d) We've now come to the important part of this problem. We have taken two sets of data, found the mean and standard deviation of each set, and drawn the bar graphs for each set of data. Both classes have means close to 70. This is seen in the bar charts by noting that most of the shading is clustered around the bar representing the 70–79 category. The standard deviation of the afternoon class is 22.05 versus 15.32 for the morning class. In the bar graphs, this can be seen by noticing that the afternoon class has more scores 20 units or more away from 70. This observation that the higher standard deviation corresponds to the bar graph showing the greater spread from the mean confirms the discussion at the beginning of this section. At that time, we introduced standard deviation as an indicator of how widely the data values were dispersed from the mean.

SECTION 8.3

PROBLEMS

1. For the set of numbers 3, 6, 10, 14, 17:
   (a) Find the range.
   (b) Find the standard deviation, using the formula $\sigma = \sqrt{\dfrac{\sum\limits_{i=1}^{n}(x_i - \mu)^2}{n}}$.
   (c) Find the standard deviation, using the computing formula.
   (d) Suppose that the original data are changed. The 3 is replaced by 2, and the 17 is replaced by 18. Without doing any calculations, what effect does this have on the standard deviation?

2. For the set of numbers 2, 6, 11, 12, 14:
   (a) Find the range.
   (b) Find the standard deviation, using the formula $\sigma = \sqrt{\dfrac{\sum\limits_{i=1}^{n}(x_i - \mu)^2}{n}}$
   (c) Find the standard deviation, using the computing formula.
   (d) Suppose that the original data are changed. The 2 is replaced by 5, and the 14 is replaced by 12. Without doing any calculations, what effect does this have on the standard deviation?

3. Suppose two frequency distributions are represented by the following bar graphs. Which distribution has a greater standard deviation?

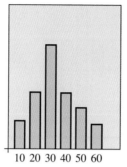

10 20 30 40 50 60

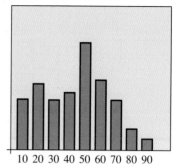

10 20 30 40 50 60 70 80 90

4. The following table gives the estimated per capita income in the year 2000 for each state and the District of Columbia. Income is given in constant 1972 dollars (from Section 8.1, Problem 8).

AL	6170	AK	9958	AZ	6891	AR	5982	CA	8035	CO	7829
CT	9134	DE	7709	DC	9467	FL	7120	GA	6719	HI	7461
ID	6290	IL	7763	IN	7042	IA	7132	KS	7750	KY	6285
LA	6719	ME	6187	MD	8112	MA	8207	MI	7419	MN	7509
MS	5601	MO	6984	MT	6506	NE	7244	NV	7652	NH	7413
NJ	8662	NM	6217	NY	7854	NC	6373	ND	7288	OH	7267
OK	7121	OR	7046	PA	7256	RI	7305	SC	6054	SD	6435
TN	6305	TX	7356	UT	5899	VT	6606	VA	7515	WA	7492
WV	5996	WI	7232	WY	7928						

(a) Arrange the data into a frequency distribution with five classes, the first one being 5001–6000, and then draw the bar graph.

(b) Use the methods discussed in Section 8.2 to find the mean of the grouped data.

(c) Use the computing formula for the standard deviation of grouped data to find σ.

5. The following table gives the per capita expenditures (in dollars) for state and local police protection and correction employment for each state and the District of Columbia (from Section 8.1, Problem 7).

AL	102.9	AK	532.9	AZ	194.8	AR	76.1	CA	202.6	CO	152.0
CT	135.8	DE	175.9	DC	548.8	FL	160.9	GA	123.9	HI	165.6
ID	102.1	IL	152.7	IN	92.1	IA	108.6	KS	108.9	KY	92.2
LA	144.7	ME	87.5	MD	175.6	MA	139.9	MI	170.8	MN	128.1
MS	74.8	MO	113.6	MT	117.1	NE	111.3	NV	276.4	NH	104.7
NJ	180.5	NM	184.4	NY	216.3	NC	109.0	ND	101.8	OH	121.7
OK	110.8	OR	147.9	PA	124.7	RI	143.2	SC	94.0	SD	103.8
TN	102.1	TX	112.8	UT	133.1	VT	109.9	VA	138.9	WA	169.3
WV	67.2	WI	153.0	WY	202.5						

(a) Arrange the data into a frequency distribution with 11 classes, with the first class being 50.1–100.0, and then draw the bar graph.

(b) Use the methods discussed in Section 8.2 to find the mean of the grouped data.

(c) Use the computing formula for the standard deviation of grouped data to find σ.

6. An engineering firm needs to buy a component with a long expected lifetime. The component is available from two different suppliers. The first supplier says that the expected lifetime is 3000 hours with a standard deviation of 100 hours. The second supplier says their component has an expected lifetime of 3000 hours with a standard deviation of 400 hours. If you are the buyer for the engineering firm, which supplier would you choose? Explain your reasoning.

7. If a set of test scores has a standard deviation of zero, what can be said about the scores?

*8. Starting with the formula $\sigma = \sqrt{\dfrac{\sum f_i(x_i - \mu)^2}{n}}$, where $n = \sum f_i$, derive the computing formula for grouped data that is given in the text. Follow the example on page 418.

SECTION 8.4

▼

THE NORMAL DISTRIBUTION

The following curve is the **normal distribution**, also called a **bell curve** or the **Gaussian distribution**. Using this curve, we will connect the concepts of probability and statistics.

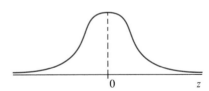

First, let's reexamine the results of the first problem discussed in Section 8.1. The frequency distribution and the bar graph are given again here.

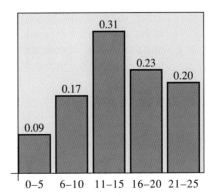

Frequency Distribution

Class	Relative Frequency
0–5	0.09
6–10	0.17
11–15	0.31
16–20	0.23
21–25	0.20

Notice that the height of each rectangle in the bar graph also represents the probability of a data value being in a certain section. For example, the probability that a randomly picked test score will be in the 6–10 class is 0.17. This means that, on the average, 17 out of 100 test scores will be in the class 6–10. This is true since both the probability and the relative frequency for a certain class are calculated by taking the number of items in a group and dividing by the total number of items. Thus, there is a connection between relative frequency, bar graphs, and probability.

Now, suppose we have a set of 100,000 data values that are broken into the classes 0–1.00, 1.01–2.00, . . . , 999.01–1000.00. Since each of the 1000 classes is only one unit wide, the bar graph will consist of many very narrow rectangles. It is easier to represent this as a smooth curve than to draw the 1000 rectangles. This is the purpose of the normal distribution. A set of data is said to be normal if it follows a very definite set of mathematical criteria that is beyond our discussion. Informally, a set of data is said to be normal if 95% of all data values are within two standard deviations of the mean and 50% of the data is on each side of the mean. The normal distribution is used for many mathematical models, ranging from test scores, to the number of defective items coming off a production line, to the analysis of sociological surveys.

Using the normal distribution requires being able to find the area between the x axis and the graph of the normal curve. The equation of the normal curve is $y = (1/\sqrt{2\pi})e^{-x^2/2}$. Even using the powerful tools of calculus, this is a difficult problem. To avoid this difficulty, it is standard practice to use a table of values, called the normal table. The normal table is given in Appendix II. In a normal table, the letter z is used as the independent variable and as the label for the horizontal axis. To use the normal table, look up the desired value of z and read the corresponding probability in the adjacent column.

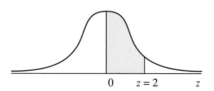

The values in the table give the area between the z axis and the normal curve, bounded on the left by the line $z = 0$ and bounded on the right by the z value being used in the problem. For example, for $z = 2$ the table gives a value of 0.4772. This means that the area of the shaded region in the figure is 0.4772. It also means that the probability that z is between 0 and 2 is 0.4772. In terms of a formula, this is written as

$$P(0 < z < 2) = 0.4772$$

This means that 47.72% of the area under the curve is between $z = 0$ and $z = 2$.

As you can see in the diagram, $z = 0$ is the middle value for the normal distribution. For most real-life problems, the middle or mean is usually a value other than 0. Also, the normal distribution has a standard deviation of 1, which is probably not the case in most situations. Therefore, to make the normal distribution useful, we need to transform information that is given in a problem into z values. To do this we use the formula

$$z = \frac{x - \mu}{\sigma} \qquad \text{where} \begin{cases} x \text{ is a data value} \\ \mu \text{ is the mean of the data} \\ \sigma \text{ is the standard deviation of the data} \end{cases}$$

The z-value gives the number of standard deviations between the mean and a particular score.

Example 1:

The heights of 1000 students are measured and found to have a mean of 70 inches and a standard deviation of 3 inches. Assuming the heights of the students are normally distributed, what is the probability that a man, chosen at random, has a height between 70 and 73 inches?

Solution: The first step is to draw a normal distribution with a mean of 70 and shade in the desired area. Since the mean is 70, that is the value at the center of the distribution. We want to find $P(70 < x < 73)$, where x represents the height of the student. Therefore, the region between 70 and 73 is shaded on the diagram.

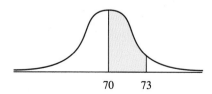

70   73

To find $P(70 < x < 73)$, we need to convert 73 into a z value. Using the formula gives

$$z = \frac{73 - 70}{3} = 1$$

Now, looking up the value $z = 1$ in the normal table, we find 0.3413. This can be interpreted in two ways. We can say that the probability that the student is between 70 inches and 73 inches tall is 0.3413, or we can say that 34.13% of the students are between 70 and 73 inches tall.

Example 2:

Suppose the problem is similar to that in Example 1, except that the standard deviation is 4 inches rather than 3 inches. Find $P(70 < x < 73)$.

Solution: Before doing the calculation, think about the physical meaning of standard deviation. We stated in the previous section that the standard deviation was a measure of how far apart the data were spread. Since the standard deviation in Example 2 is larger than the standard deviation in Example 1, the data are more spread out. Because of this, we should expect $P(70 < x < 73)$ to now be lower.

We can verify this by doing the calculations. First, we need to find the z value. This is

$$z = \frac{73 - 70}{4} = 0.75$$

Looking up $z = 0.75$ in the z table, we get 0.2734. Therefore, $P(70 < x < 73) = 0.2734$, which, as expected, gives a lower value than in Example 1.

Example 3:

In 1979, a study of the educational aspirations of military women under age 21 was undertaken. Results of the study showed that these women hoped to achieve, on the average, 15.301 years of schooling, with a standard deviation of 1.893 years. Assuming this is a normally distributed sample:

(a) What percentage of the women hoped to have more than 15.301 years of school?
(b) What percentage hoped to have between 12 and 15.301 years of school?
(c) What percentage desired to have no more than 12 years of school?
(d) What percentage of the women wanted to have between 16 and 18 years of school?
(e) What percentage of the women wanted to have between 14 and 16 years of school?

Solution:

(a) Since 15.301 is the mean, we expect half of the respondents wanted to have more than 15.301 years of education while half did not want more. Therefore, 50% of the women desired to have more than 15.301 years of school.

   To answer the remaining questions, we will sketch a graph of the normal distribution for each question.

(b) To find the percentage of women who hoped to have between 12 and 15.301 years of school, look at the graph.

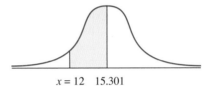

$$x = 12 \quad 15.301$$

As we did in previous examples, we will find the *z* value:

$$z = \frac{12 - 15.301}{1,893} = -1.74$$

This *z* value is negative, but the normal table includes only positive values. However, since the graph of the normal distribution is symmetric with respect to the mean, we can find the area between 12 and 15.301 by using $z = +1.74$. This gives the value $A = 0.4591$. This means that 45.91% of the women surveyed hoped to have between 12 and 15.301 years of school.

(c) In this part of the problem, we are interested in the percentage of women who wanted 12 or fewer years of schooling, so we want to find the area to the left of 12.

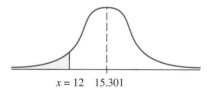

$$x = 12 \quad 15.301$$

Since the normal table only gives areas that are adjacent to the center line of the distribution, we need to do this problem in another way. We use the fact that the area to the left of 15.301 is 0.5000 and the area between 12 and 15.301 is 0.4591. Subtracting these gives $A = 0.5000 - 0.4591 = 0.0409$. Therefore, only 4.09% of the women wanted the equivalent of a high school education or less.

(d) To determine the percentage of women who wanted to have between 16 and 18 years of schooling, we again look at a picture.

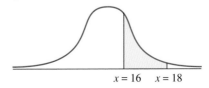

$$x = 16 \quad x = 18$$

As was true in part (c), we cannot get the desired area directly since the area is not adjacent to the middle of the distribution. As we did in part (c), we need to look at two separate areas and subtract the smaller from the larger to get the final answer.

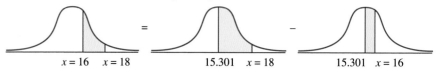

$$x = 16 \quad x = 18 \qquad\qquad 15.301 \quad x = 18 \qquad\qquad 15.301 \quad x = 16$$

With the help of some pictures, we can see that if we want to find the area between 16 and 18, we can do it by finding the area between 15.301 and 18 and then subtracting the area between 15.301 and 16. To do this, we will need two z values. For $x = 18$, we have

$$z = \frac{18 - 15.301}{1.893} = 1.43$$

which gives an area of 0.4236. For $x = 16$, we have

$$z = \frac{16 - 15.301}{1.893} = 0.37$$

giving an area of 0.1443. Therefore, the probability that one of the women surveyed wanted between 16 and 18 years of education is $0.4236 - 0.1443 = 0.2793$. This means that 27.93% of the women hoped to have between 16 and 18 years of schooling.

(e) For the final part of this problem, we want to determine the percentage of women who wanted to have between 14 and 16 years of schooling.

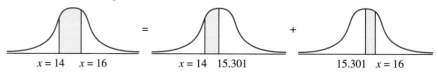

$$x = 14 \quad x = 16 \qquad\qquad x = 14 \quad 15.301 \qquad\qquad 15.301 \quad x = 16$$

As we can see from the pictures, this problem is similar to part (d) except that since the mean is between the values of 14 and 16, we need to add the two areas to find the area of the combined regions. For $x = 14$, we have

$$z = \frac{14 - 15.301}{1.893} = -0.69$$

which gives an area of 0.2549. For $x = 16$, we have

$$z = \frac{16 - 15.301}{1.893} = 0.37$$

giving an area of 0.1443. Therefore, since $0.2549 + 0.1443 = 0.3992$, we can say that 39.92% of the women surveyed aspired to have between 14 and 16 years of education.

To summarize the last example, we used the normal table to determine the probability of an event occurring. Even though the normal table only gives $P(0 < z < c)$, where c is some number, we found that using the formula $z = \dfrac{x - \mu}{\sigma}$ allows us to determine the probability of an event if we know the mean and the standard deviation.

The final topic for this section is to use the normal table to reverse the above process. In this type of problem, we know the percentage or probability but we want to determine the value of z or x that gives this probability. The next two examples will demonstrate what we mean.

Example 4:

Find the values of c that make the following statements true.

(a) $P(0 < z < c) = 0.2580$ (b) $P(c < z < 0) = 0.2580$

(c) $P(0 < z < c) = 0.3000$ (d) $P(z > c) = 0.0563$

Solution: As we have done in previous examples, we will draw a picture for each problem. The picture will help us understand what needs to be done.

(a) The shaded part of the following diagram represents the area or the probability. The problem is to determine the value of c that makes $P(0 < z < c) = 0.2580$. We need to look in the z table for the z value that gives a corresponding area of 0.2580. Doing so gives $z = 0.70$. This means $P(0 < z < 0.70) = 0.2580$.

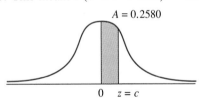

$A = 0.2580$

(b) To find the solution to $P(c < z < 0) = 0.2580$, we know that the value of c must be negative since c is less than 0. Since the value of the area is the same as it was in part (a) and we know that c must be negative, we know that $P(-0.70 < z < 0) = 0.2580$.

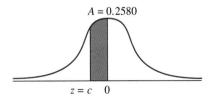

$A = 0.2580$

(c) The problem $P(0 < z < c) = 0.3000$ is very similar to part (a). The difference arises when we try to find the value 0.3000 in the area column of the z table. For $z = 0.84$, $A = 0.2995$, and $z = 0.85$ gives $A = 0.3023$. Since neither of these values is

0.3000, we need to make some compromises. The choices are to find a table that has more digits of accuracy, use a mathematical technique called interpolation, or choose the value of A that is closest to 0.3000. Because this is only a survey course, we choose the easiest method, picking the closest value, which is $A = 0.2995$. Therefore, we will say $P(0 < z < 0.84) \approx 0.3000$.

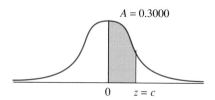

(d) The problem $P(z > c) = 0.0563$ is different from parts (a), (b), and (c), since the specified area is given by $z > c$, which means that the area is at the far right tail (light-colored region). Since the normal table only gives areas that are adjacent to the mean, using the dark-colored area gives $0.5000 - 0.0563 = 0.4437$. The normal table now gives $P(z > 1.59) = 0.0563$.

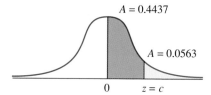

Example 5:

A certain college instructor, Sam N. Legree, has a fixed grading policy. Sam always gives the top 8% of the students A's; the next 15% receive B's, 54% receive C's, 15% receive D's, and 8% receive F's. Assuming that the scores are normally distributed with a mean of 72 and a standard deviation of 12, determine the scores that receive each grade.

Solution: Because there are five different grades, we must divide the normal distribution into five different regions, as shown in the following

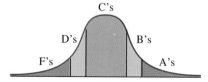

diagram. Since the A's occupy the top 8%, we have the diagram shown. As we did in part (d) of the previous example, look at the area between the mean and some value of x, labeled c. Using $A = 0.5000 - 0.0800 = 0.4200$, we find $z = 1.41$.

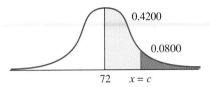

Since we are dealing with a problem where $\mu = 72$ and $\sigma = 12$, use the formula $z = (x - \mu)/\sigma$. This gives

$$1.41 = \frac{x - 72}{12}$$

$$16.9 = x - 72$$

$$88.9 = x$$

This means that all students scoring 88.9 or higher will receive a grade of A.

Since 15% of the students will receive B's, the scores that will receive a grade of B are shown in the following diagram in the light-colored region marked 0.1500. To find the area of the dark region, we use the fact that 50% of the scores must be greater than the mean. Since 8% receive A's and 15% receive B's, we find the dark area to be $0.5000 - 0.0800 - 0.1500 = 0.2700$.

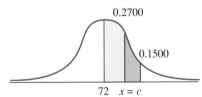

Using $A = 0.2700$, we find $z = 0.74$. Using the formula

$$z = \frac{x - \mu}{\sigma}$$

$$0.74 = \frac{x - 72}{12}$$

$$8.9 = x - 72$$

$$80.9 = x$$

Thus, students with scores between 80.9 and 88.9 will receive B's.

To find the scores for the other three grades, we use the fact that the normal distribution is symmetric about the mean.

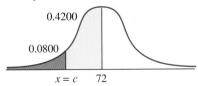

To find the scores receiving a grade of F, look at the lowest 8% of the scores. Since the diagram is the mirror image of the picture used to find the A grades, we know that $z = -1.41$.

$$-1.41 = \frac{x - 72}{12}$$

$$-16.9 = x - 72$$

$$55.1 = x$$

This means that all students scoring 55.1 or lower will receive a grade of F.

The scores earning D's are found in a similar way. From our work on the B's, we have $z = -0.74$. This gives

$$-0.74 = \frac{x - 72}{12}$$

$$-8.9 = x - 72$$

$$63.1 = x$$

This means that all students scoring between 55.1 and 63.1 will receive a grade of D.

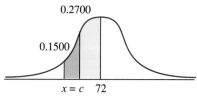

At this point we have only to determine the scores that will earn a grade of C. Since the highest score that will earn a D is 63.1 and the lowest score that will earn a B is 80.9, all scores between 63.1 and 80.9 will receive a grade of C.

SECTION 8.4

PROBLEMS

In Problems 1–8, determine indicated ar

1.

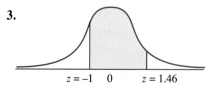

2.

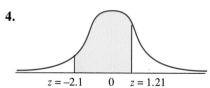

3.

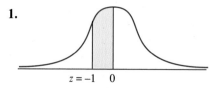

4.

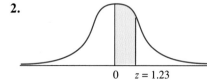

5.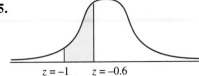
$z = -1$ $z = -0.6$

6.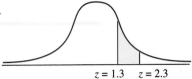
$z = 1.3$ $z = 2.3$

7.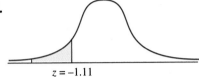
$z = -1.11$

8.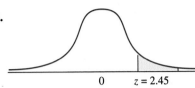
0 $z = 2.45$

In Problems 9–14, determine value of c that will give the indicated area under the normal curve.

9.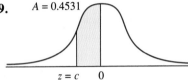
$A = 0.4531$
$z = c$ 0

10.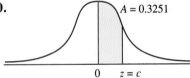
$A = 0.3251$
0 $z = c$

11.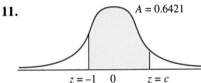
$A = 0.6421$
$z = -1$ 0 $z = c$

12.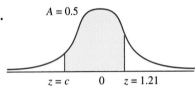
$A = 0.5$
$z = c$ 0 $z = 1.21$

13.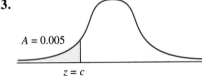
$A = 0.005$
$z = c$

14.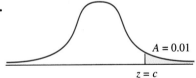
$A = 0.01$
$z = c$

15. A survey of blue-collar workers found that the workers had a mean of 17.34 years of experience, with a standard deviation of 11.14 years. Assume that the experience level is normally distributed.

(a) What percentage of the blue-collar workers in the survey had between 11 and 15 years of experience?

(b) Find the probability that a blue-collar worker in the survey, selected at random, had more than 15 years of experience.

16. A study was made of black families with a female as the head of the household. Among working mothers of age 30 or more, the mean number of hours worked per year was 1582.2, with a standard deviation of 728.5 hours. Assume that the number of hours worked is normally distributed.

(a) What percentage of the women in the study worked between 1000 and 1582.2 hours per year?

(b) What percentage of the women in the study worked less than 1000 hours per year?

(c) Assuming a 40-hour work week, how many full work weeks are represented by 1582.2 hours?

17. A survey of women aged 14–21 determined that the mean travel time to work was 17 minutes with a standard deviation of 13 minutes. Assume that the travel time is normally distributed.

(a) What is the probability that a woman from this survey, chosen at random, traveled more than 20 minutes to reach work?

(b) What percentage of the women traveled between 10 and 20 minutes to get to work?

(c) What percentage of the women traveled between 5 and 10 minutes to get to work?

18. A survey of men aged 14–21 determined that the mean travel time to work was 19.7 minutes with a standard deviation of 20 minutes. Assume that the travel time is normally distributed.

(a) What is the probability that a man from this survey, chosen at random, traveled more than 30 minutes to reach work?

(b) What percentage of the men traveled between 10 and 30 minutes to get to work?

(c) What percentage of men traveled between 5 and 10 minutes to get to work?

19. A study of men aged 35–57 at increased risk of coronary disease found that the average number of cigarettes smoked per day was 21.7 with a standard deviation of 20.5. Assuming the number of cigarettes smoked is normally distributed, determine the number of cigarettes smoked by the 10% of the group who were the heaviest smokers.

20. The University of Ohlone accepts, unconditionally, students who score in the top 10% nationally on the S.A.T. exam. For those students in the next 15% on the S.A.T. exam, the university accepts the students on the basis of their grades in the senior year of high school. Assume the S.A.T. average is 950 with a standard deviation of 280.

(a) Determine the lowest S.A.T. score a student may have and be accepted to the University of Ohlone unconditionally.

(b) Determine the S.A.T. scores that will allow a student to enter Ohlone, dependent on his or her senior-year grades.

21. Pick one of the following topics (or decide on one of your own) for a statistical investigation. Collect 40 or more data values for your topic. Arrange the data in a frequency distribution and draw a bar graph and an ogive for the data. Find the mean and standard deviation for the data. Finally, determine the cutoff for the top 10% of the data.

(a) Season-ending batting averages of baseball players

(b) Bowling scores of your bowling league

(c) Lengths of the most popular songs on the radio according to the *Billboard* charts

(d) Winning times in the 100-m dash at the collegiate level for track meets across the country

(e) Weights of chickens sold in the grocery store

CHAPTER 8	SUMMARY

KEY TERMS, CONCEPTS, AND FORMULAS

The important terms in this chapter are:

Average: The term used by many people when they are referring to the arithmetic mean.   p. 407

Bar graph: A graphical representation of grouped data formed with rectangles.   p. 400

Central tendency: A general term describing the middle value of a set of data; usually refers to mean, mode, or median.   p. 407

Class: A category into which data are distributed; used in frequency distributions.   p. 399

Class midpoints: The mean of the boundary values for a class.   p. 409

Cumulative frequency: The sum of the frequencies of a given class and all lower classes.   p. 402

Dispersion: A general term describing how far data are spread from a central value.   p. 416

Frequency: The number of times a data value or a class value occurs.   p. 399

Mean: The arithmetic mean; the sum of the data values divided by the number of data values.   p. 407

Median: The middle value of a set; found by listing the data in increasing numerical order and picking the middle value; if there are an even number of data values, it is the arithmetic mean of the middle pair.   p. 412

Mode: The data value that occurs most frequently.   p. 412

Normal distribution: A statistical distribution that models many real-world situations; the bell-shaped curve.   p. 425

Ogive: A graphical representation of cumulative frequency.   p. 402

Pie chart: A graphical representation of percentage frequencies using sectors of a circle.   p. 401

Range: The difference between the highest and lowest data values.   p. 416

Statistics: Numerical data assembled in such a way as to present information about a given subject.   p. 398

Standard deviation: A method of measuring dispersion of data from the mean.   p. 417

Weighted average: The mean of a group of numbers in which certain values have greater importance, or weight, than do other values.   p. 409

After completing this chapter, you should be able to:

1. Organize data into tables, charts, and graphs.   p. 398

2. Use and explain the concepts of central tendency and dispersion.   p. 407

3. Know which measure of central tendency is most appropriate for a situation and how to calculate or find that value.   p. 407

4. Find the standard deviation of either grouped or nongrouped data.   p. 417

5. Use the mean and standard deviation of two sets of data to compare the distributions of the two sets.   p. 421

6. Use the normal table.   p. 425

SUMMARY

PROBLEMS

1. Given the numbers 2, 4, 6, 8, 3, 6, 7, 9, 1, 3, find
   (a) The mean
   (b) The geometric mean
   (c) The median
   (d) The mode
   (e) The range
   (f) The standard deviation

2. The following table gives the per capita city government employment levels of the 30 most populous U.S. cities as of 1980. The listing is given with the cities in descending order of population. The employment level is given as full-time equivalent employment per 10,000 population. (Data taken from the *Statistical Abstract of the U.S.*)

New York, NY	451	San Antonio, TX	128	New Orleans, LA	225
Chicago, IL	150	Indianapolis, IN	174	Jacksonville, FL	202
Los Angeles, CA	138	San Francisco, CA	310	Seattle, WA	188
Philadelphia, PA	189	Memphis, TN	342	Denver, CO	244
Houston, TX	111	Washington, DC	651	Nashville, TN	374
Detroit, MI	179	Milwaukee, WI	145	St. Louis, MO	280
Dallas, TX	153	San Jose, CA	60	Kansas City, MO	145
San Diego, CA	81	Cleveland, OH	160	El Paso, TX	104
Phoenix, AZ	114	Columbus, OH	122	Atlanta, GA	187
Baltimore, MD	514	Boston, MA	444	Pittsburgh, PA	135

(a) Arrange the data into a frequency distribution with seven classes, with the first class being 1–100. Draw the bar graph.

(b) Use the methods discussed in Section 8.2 to find the mean of the grouped data.

(c) Use the formula for standard deviation of grouped data to find σ.

3. Draw a pie chart for the classes created in part (a) of Problem 2.

4. In 1984, there were 170 million eligible voters in the United States. They were distributed by age as follows:

Age	Voters
18–20-years olds	11.2 million
21–24	16.7 million
25–34	40.3 million
35–44	30.7 million
45–64	44.3 million
65 and older	26.7 million

(a) Draw an ogive for this data.

(b) If this set of data was presented as a bar graph, why could the graph be considered misleading?

5. Suppose you need to purchase 500 resistors rated at 10 ohms. It is critical that the resistance not vary substantially from the rated value. Two companies have told you they can supply the part for the same low, low price. Both companies claim their resistors are rated at 10 ohms. However, company A says the standard deviation of their resistors is 0.6 ohm, and company B says the standard deviation of their resistors is 1.8 ohms. Which company should you choose as your supplier? Explain your answer.

6. A survey of white-collar workers found that the workers had a mean of 18.14 years of experience, with a standard deviation of 10.08 years. Assume the experience level is normally distributed.

(a) What percentage of the white-collar workers had between 10 and 20 years of experience?

(b) What percentage of the workers had between 5 and 10 years of experience?

(c) Find the probability that a blue-collar worker selected at random had more than 15 years of experience.

(d) Find the probability that a blue-collar worker selected at random had more than 25 years of experience.

7. An algebra class averaged 73 on the first midterm with a standard deviation of 14.2. If the top 10% received A's, the next 20% received B's, the next 40% received C's, the next 20% D's, and the final 10% F's, use the normal distribution to determine which scores receive which grades.

9

CALCULUS

Calculus can be used to analyze the curves, volumes, and areas of structures such as the *Interior of Saint Peter's, Rome* by Giovanni Paolo Pannini. (National Gallery of Art)

A SHORT HISTORY OF CALCULUS

Mathematics is one of the courses considered by many as an essential part of the training of the well-educated person. Like speaking a foreign language, reading a work by Shakespeare, or reciting poetry, understanding some mathematics was (and still is) the sign of a well-versed person. For many, calculus is the culmination of such mathematical training.

Calculus is the study of two mathematical processes called differentiation and integration. Both involve functions and the concept of very small increments of the variables in the functions. Because understanding the full scope of calculus requires a good grasp of algebra, geometry, and trigonometry, many students have difficulty with calculus. However, the basic concepts of calculus are not difficult. Some of the ideas in calculus have been studied for over 2000 years, long before modern algebra was invented. In this chapter, we examine the two basic concepts of calculus and some of their applications.

The first concept of calculus is the determination of areas bounded by curves or lines. The ancient Babylonians and Greeks developed formulas to determine areas of regular geometric figures such as triangles and rectangles, but the areas of circles and ellipses presented a greater challenge. Because the Greeks did not have a clear understanding of π, they could only determine the approximate area of a given circle. Their knowledge of the area of a circle was that the ratio of the areas of two circles was equal to the ratios of the squares of their diameters.

By the fifth century B.C., to find the area of a circle, the concept of an **infinitesimal** was used. An infinitesimal is a very small quantity of some item. For example, the number 0.0000 . . . 0001 is an infinitesimally small number. As another example, imagine a very small square, divide it into four square sections, and you now have a smaller square. By repeating this process enough times, you have an infinitesimally small square.

The use of infinitesimals led Eudoxus of Cnidus (c. 370 B.C.), to discover the *method of exhaustion*. He used this method to calculate the area of circles or other curved figures in the following manner. Start by inscribing a square inside a circle. Drawing four radii, one to each corner of the square, will create four triangles. Bisect each of these triangles with four more radii of the circle. Connect the endpoints of the radii to form an octagon consisting of eight triangles. Continue the process to create 16-, 32-, 64-, . . . sided polygons. As the number of sides increases, so does the number of triangles. As the number of triangles gets very large, the area of each triangle becomes very small. The area of each triangle is infinitesimally small. As can be seen from the inscribed square and octagon, the areas of the successive polygons will soon fill the circle, eventually exhausting the uncovered portion of the circle.

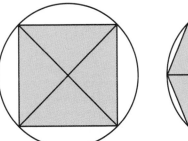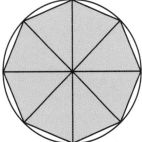

This method is the central idea behind the topic in calculus called **integration**. Integration is a method for finding areas of regions by filling the desired region with shapes of known area. By creating a large enough number of smaller pieces, the area of the unknown region can be found by adding the areas of the smaller pieces. This method can also be used for finding volumes of solids and lengths of curves.

Archimedes of Syracuse (c. 225 B.C.), one of the greatest mathematicians and scientists of ancient history, also used infinitesimals. After using an inductive process to discover formulas for areas of curved regions and volumes of solids, Archimedes used the method of exhaustion to determine and prove formulas for the following geometric figures:

Surface area of spheres and spherical segments

Volumes of spherical segments and the segment of a hyperboloid of revolution

Areas of spirals and parabolic segments

In terms of the circles discussed above, Archimedes would argue as follows. By inscribing a series of polygons inside the circle, the area of the circle must be greater than the area of a polygon with a large number of sides. Similarly, by circumscribing polygons around the circle, the area of the circle must be smaller than the area of a polygon with a large number of sides. As the number of sides of the polygon increase, the difference between the area of the circle and the area of the polygon decreases.

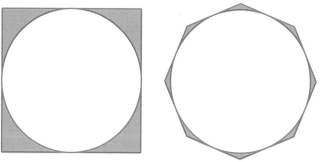

The method of exhaustion was an exceptional achievement for the Greek mathematicians. It allowed them to accurately determine the areas of curves regions. However, there are two difficulties with the method of exhaustion. The first is that the method is cumbersome to use because it requires a large number of calculations. The second difficulty is that a many-sided polygon is not a circle. No matter how many sides the inscribed polygon has, it will never become a circle. Although the method makes sense intuitively and gives accurate solutions, 2000 years passed between its invention and when it became firmly grounded in algebraic terms.

As has been true in many other areas of mathematics, little progress in the development of calculus was made between the era of the Greeks and the Renaissance of the 16th century. For calculus, the 17th century was the beginning of an era of great discoveries.

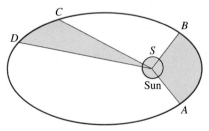

In 1609, Johann Kepler gave his three laws of planetary motion. One of these was that planets sweep out equal areas in equal times as they travel along their orbits. This means that as a planet travels along its elliptical path around the sun, if the areas of the regions *ASB* and *CSD* are equal, then the time required to travel from *A* to *B* is the same as the time required to travel from *C* to *D*. This is important because it required that Kepler determine the areas of elliptical sectors. He found the areas by a method called the *sum of the radii*.

The next major event in the history of integration is the work of Bonaventura Cavalieri, *Geometria Indivisibilibus*, first published in 1635. In this work, Cavalieri, influenced by Kepler, described a term called *indivisibles*. Indivisibles are objects that cannot be broken into smaller pieces. Like infinitesimals, indivisibles divide an object into many small pieces. Cavalieri thought of a line as an infinite collection of points; the points were the indivisibles for the line. The indivisibles for a surface were lines, and the indivisibles for a solid were planes. By combining the indivisibles, Cavalieri determined the length, area, or volume of the original figure. For example, think about a salami that has been thinly sliced. The total volume of the salami is the sum of the slices. The slices of the salami are the indivisibles that, when added together, form the entire salami.

The second central idea in calculus, finding the slope of a tangent line to a curve, a process called **differentiation**. Finding the slope of a line tangent to a curve at a point *P* can be used for an important problem: determining the minimum or maximum point on a curve.

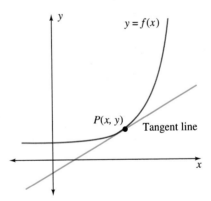

Like integration, differentiation has been studied for more than 2000 years. Though it was not investigated as intensively as integration, differentiation was studied by mathematicians, among whom were Aristotle (384–322 B.C.), Pierre de Fermat (1601–1665), and Isaac Barrow (1630–1677). It was Fermat who recognized the connection between the maximum/minimum problem and differentiation.

In 1663, Isaac Barrow, Sir Isaac Newton's predecessor and mentor at Cambridge University in England, was the first to recognize and prove the startling fact that, like addition and subtraction, the operations of integration and differentiation are inverses of each other. With this work, the stage was set for the appearances of Sir Isaac Newton of England (1642–1727) and Gottfried Leibniz of Germany (1646–1716).

Leibniz and Newton are considered the co-inventors of calculus. Though they communicated with each other during the early part of their work, they soon disagreed over who first discovered certain aspects of calculus. This started a major conflict between the mathematicians of England and continental Europe. Today, it is agreed that Leibniz and Newton each formulated the rules of calculus independently, with each man inventing his own terminology and symbolism.

After reading of the gradual development of calculus over 2000 years, it may seem odd to say that Leibniz and Newton are the co-inventors. They are given credit for inventing calculus because they built on the ideas developed through the ages and constructed a set of rules and formulas that could be applied to many functions. Although Archimedes was able to determine the area bounded by a spiral, Newton and Leibniz determined a method that could be applied to many functions without using the tedious method of exhaustion. Barrow had proved that integration and differentiation were inverses of each other by using a cumbersome geometrical argument. Leibniz showed how this could be done with algebra. The work of Newton and Leibniz allowed calculus to be applied with great success to problems in science and engineering. During the 18th and 19th centuries, many of the great discoveries of science were precipitated by the work of these two men.

Due to the work of Newton and Leibniz, calculus became a very powerful mathematical tool. Algebra and geometry could deal with constant speeds, but calculus could help study the motion of objects with changing speeds. Algebra could determine the maximum value of a quadratic function by using the vertex of a parabola, but calculus could be used to determine the maximum value of many types of functions. Geometry could be used to find the areas and volumes of simple shapes, but calculus could be used to find areas between two functions, such as a logarithmic function and a quadratic function, or to determine the volume of curved solids in space.

Despite the significance and power of calculus, the new method was not complete. Leibniz and Newton concentrated on how the method worked and how it could be applied. Some of the details in the foundations had been neglected. This led to conclusions like $1 - 1 + 1 - 1 + \cdots = 1/2$. (Is it possible to add and subtract integers and get a result that is a fraction? See Research Question 7.) Many questioned whether infinitesimals actually existed and whether the new method performed division by zero, a most undesirable technique. As a statement against these methods, Bishop George Berkeley in 1734 wrote a treatise called *The Analyst or a Discourse Addressed to an Infidel Mathematician Wherein It Is Examined Whether the Object, Principles, and Inferences of the Modern Analysis Are More Distinctly Conceived, or More Evidently Deduced, than Religious Mysteries and Points of Faith. . . .* The ''infidel mathematician'' referred to Newton's friend Edmund Halley.

Although the methods in calculus produced great results throughout the 18th and 19th centuries, the discussion over the logical foundations of the methods was not settled until the end of the 19th century. It was only through the work of Augustin-Louis Cauchy of France (1789–1857) and Karl Weierstrass of Germany (1815–1897) that the great invention was put on a solid foundation.

The study of mathematics did not stop at placing calculus on a solid foundation. The 20th century brought its own mathematicians. Some of them continued the study of pure mathematics, some involved themselves with the application of mathematics to other sciences, others investigated using computers in mathematical research, and still others concentrated on the teaching of mathematics. These men and women of mathematics are a very diverse group with a wide range of intellectual interests and personal characteristics. We must keep in mind that they are people just like you and me. They have, however, found mathematics to be an interesting, challenging, enjoyable, and living subject. We are indebted to all the mathematicians from all the cultures of the world for their contributions to the development of mathematics.

CHECK YOUR READING

1. Why are Newton and Leibniz considered the co-inventors of calculus?
2. What is the method of exhaustion? Explain and give examples.
3. While the Great Wall of China was being built in 275 B.C., who was proving geometry formulas?
4. In 1609, the artist Rubens was painting a self-portrait while the artist El Greco was painting *Brother Paravicino*. During this same year, who was investigating the laws of planetary motion?
5. What are integration and differentiation?
6. What are infinitesimals and indivisibles?
7. Bonaventura Cavalieri worked on indivisibles in the same year that Giulio Alenio published the first biography of Christ written in Chinese. What year was this?
8. In 370 B.C., catapults were used as weapons of war, and there were trumpet playing competitions in Greece. What was Eudoxus of Cnidus doing during this time?
9. In 1734, the first official horse race took place in America and George Sale translated the *Koran* into English. What was Bishop Berkeley publishing during this year?
10. While the Persian Wars (c. 460 B.C.) were being fought, what elements of calculus were the Greeks studying?
11. What were Cauchy and Weierstrass working on during the 1800s?
12. The end of a century saw the Great Plague hit London, the completion of the cathedral in Mexico, and the work of Newton and Leibniz relating to calculus. What century was this?

13. Match each of the following names with the correct idea, event, or description.
    (a) Archimedes   Co-inventor of calculus (*use twice*)
    (b) Barrow   Indivisibles
    (c) Cauchy   Logical foundations of calculus
    (d) Cavalieri   Method of exhaustion
    (e) Eudoxus   Proofs of many formulas using method of exhaustion
    (f) Kepler   Teacher of Newton
    (g) Leibniz   Three laws of planetary motion
    (h) Newton

RESEARCH QUESTIONS

In order to answer the following questions, you will need to refer to material not contained in the text. Possible sources of information are listed in the Bibliography at the end of this book.

1. Describe Zeno's Paradox about Achilles and the tortoise. Explain why it is considered a paradox.
2. Investigate some of the inventions and discoveries of Archimedes.
3. Investigate the development of calculus in Japan during the 17th and 18th centuries.
4. What are some of the other inventions or discoveries that are credited to Sir Isaac Newton?
5. Many of the mathematicians mentioned in this section had other interests besides mathematics. Explain some of these other interests. What anecdotes have been recorded about these mathematicians?
6. Investigate the history of the conflict over the priority of discovery of calculus between Newton and Leibniz.
7. As mentioned in the text, calculus was used throughout the 18th century despite not having a firm mathematical foundation. This problem shows how the same series of numbers can be interpreted as having three different (and contradictory) results.
   (a) Use parentheses to show that the series $S = 1 - 1 + 1 - 1 + \cdots$ can be interpreted as being equal to 0.
   (b) Use parentheses to show that the series $S = 1 - 1 + 1 - 1 + \cdots$ can be interpreted as being equal to 1.
   (c) Part (a) showed $S = 0$ while part (b) showed $S = 1$. Add these two equations and show $S = 1/2$.
8. It was mentioned in the text that Archimedes was able to determine the volume and areas of certain geometrical objects. Investigate the following questions.
   (a) What is a hyperboloid? If the hyperboloid was sliced, what would the slices look like?
   (b) What are spherical segments?
   (c) What are parabolic segments?

9. One of Kepler's laws of planetary motion was described in this section. What are the other two laws of planetary motion according to Kepler?

10. Some people associated with modern mathematics are George Pólya, Constance Reid, Garrett Birkhoff, Shiing-shen Chern, Persi Diaconis, Palageya Polubainava-Kochina, Paul Erdős, Raymond Smullyan, Henry Pollak, Olga Taussky-Todd, Martin Gardner, David Blackwell, Irmgard Flügge-Lotz, H.M.S. Coxeter, Paul Halmos, Morris Kline, Benoit Mandelbrot, Brother Alfred Brousseau, F.S.C., Ernest Wilkins, Donald Knuth, Mina Rees, Srinavasa Ramanujan, Grace Chisholm Young, Emmy Noether, and Anthony Barcellos. Do some research on one of these mathematicians or another 20th-century mathematician. Besides investigating his or her contributions to mathematics, discuss the person's interests, personal life, and so on.

*11. In this section, we have traced the development of differential calculus from the point of view of the tangent line to a curve. Another idea critical to the development of calculus is that the velocity of a particle can be found by examining the derivative of the function giving the position of the particle. Research this aspect of the history of calculus.

*12. Suppose that a circle has radius R.

(a) Find the area of a square inscribed in the circle.

(b) If a triangle has a 45° angle between two sides x and y, trigonometry can be used to show that the area of the triangle is $A = xy\sqrt{2}/4$. Use this formula to find the area of a regular octagon inscribed inside a circle of radius R. The answer should be greater than the area of the inscribed square.

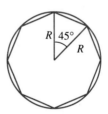

(c) Find the area of a square circumscribed around a circle of radius R.

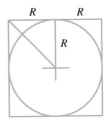

(d) Trigonometry can be used to show that the radius x of an octagon that is circumscribed around a circle of radius R is given by $x = R\sqrt{4 - 2\sqrt{2}}$. Find the area of the octagon circumscribed around a circle of radius R.

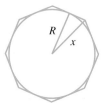

(e) Use the results of parts (b) and (d) to show
$$2\sqrt{2} < \pi < 8(\sqrt{2} - 1).$$

SECTION 9.0

REVIEW

For our overview of calculus, we need an understanding of three concepts from algebra: area, slope, and functions. We assume all students know that the area of a rectangle is length times width. We will briefly review the slope of a line. If you need a more detailed review of slopes, see Section 2.0. Most of this section will be spent on the concept of a function.

Functions

A **function** is a set of ordered pairs (x, y) such that for each value of x there is exactly one value of y. In what are perhaps more familiar terms, for a function $y = f(x)$ (read "f of x"), x is the abscissa and y is the ordinate and y is said to be a function of x.

Example 1:

Determine if the following relationships are functions of the form $y = f(x)$.

(a) $y = 3x + 4$
(b) $2x + 5y = 7$
(c) $x^2 + y^2 = 4$
(d) The situation where x represents the date and y represents the high temperature for the day in Minneapolis, Minnesota.
(e) The situation where x represents the high temperature for the day in Minneapolis, Minnesota, and y represents the date.

Solution:

(a) For $y = 3x + 4$, each value of x will give us only one value of y. For example, if $x = 7$, then $y = 25$. Since each x value has at most one y value, $y = 3x + 4$ is a function.
(b) For $2x + 5y = 7$, for each value of x we get only one y value. For

example, if $x = 3$, we find that $y = 1/5$. Therefore, $2x + 5y = 7$ is a function. *It is considered a function even though the equation is not written in the form $y = \ldots$.*

(c) $x^2 + y^2 = 4$ is not a function. This can be seen by picking a value for x, let's say $x = 0$. Substituting $x = 0$ into the equation gives $y^2 = 4$, which implies that y can be either 2 or -2. Since one value of x gave two values of y, $x^2 + y^2 = 4$ is not a function.

(d) The relationship where x represents the date and y represents the high temperature for the day in Minneapolis, Minnesota, is a function since for any date, there can only be one high temperature.

(e) The relationship where x represents the high temperature for the day in Minneapolis, Minnesota, and y represents the date is not a function. To see this, we need only to pick a value of x, let's say $75°$. Since there have been many days where $75°$ has been the high temperature in Minneapolis, the value $x = 75$ gives us many values of y. Therefore, this situation is not a function.

Since we are primarily concerned with mathematical functions, we want to look at the notation that is used in mathematics, $y = f(x)$. In the previous example, we could write $y = 3x + 4$ as a function by writing

$$f(x) = 3x + 4$$

The only change is in the left side of the equation. Instead of y, the notation for a function is $f(x)$. The notation $f(x)$ does not mean to multiply f and x. It is indicating that if we assign a value to x, this value must be substituted for each occurrence of x in the expression on the right side of the equal sign. We can see this in the following examples.

Example 2:

Find the value of $f(6)$, where $f(x) = 2x^2 - 5x + 8$.

Solution: To find $f(6)$, substitute 6 for each occurrence of x in the equation. This gives us $f(6) = 2(6)^2 - 5(6) + 8$.
$$= 2(36) - 30 + 8$$
$$= 50.$$

Example 3:

Find the value of $f(6)$, where $f(x) = 18$.

Solution: To find $f(6)$, we need to substitute 6 for each occurrence of x in the equation. Since x does not occur in the equation, this gives us $f(6) = 18$. Note that since x does not occur in the equation, it does not matter which value of x we use. In terms of symbols, $f(6) = 18$, but $f(3) = 18$ and $f(321) = 18$. Any value of x will return the same value, 18.

In a function, it does not matter what we substitute for x. In mathematics, we are accustomed to substituting numbers for x. However, there is no reason why we cannot substitute any expression for x, including other variables or more complicated expressions.

Example 4:

For the function $f(x) = 2x^2 - 5x + 8$, find the following:

(a) $f(3)$
(b) $f(q)$
(c) $f(2 + h)$
(d) $f(x + h)$

Solution:

(a) As we did in Example 2, to find $f(3)$ substitute 3 for each occurrence of x. This gives us $f(3) = 2(3)^2 - 5(3) + 8 = 11$.

(b) $f(q)$ means to replace each occurrence of x with q. Changing each occurrence of x to q, we have $f(q) = 2(q)^2 - 5(q) + 8$.

(c) If we want to substitute more complicated expressions for x, we can. $f(2 + h)$ means to replace each occurrence of x with the expression $2 + h$. This gives

$$f(2 + h) = 2(2 + h)^2 - 5(2 + h) + 8$$

$$f(2 + h) = 2(4 + 4h + h^2) - 10 - 5h + 8$$

$$f(2 + h) = 8 + 8h + 2h^2 - 10 - 5h + 8$$

$$f(2 + h) = 6 + 3h + 2h^2$$

(d) Replacing x with $x + h$ gives

$$f(x + h) = 2(x + h)^2 - 5(x + h) + 8$$

$$f(x + h) = 2(x^2 + 2xh + h^2) - 5x - 5h + 8$$

$$f(x + h) = 2x^2 + 4xh + 2h^2 - 5x - 5h + 8$$

The Slope of a Line

The last topic for this review section is the slope of a line. As you may recall, the slope of a line through two points (x_1, y_1) and (x_2, y_2) is given by the expression

$$m = \frac{y_2 - y_1}{x_2 - x_1}$$

We can use this expression to find the slope of a line between two points.

Example 5:

Find the slope of the line through the two points $(2, 6)$ and $(-5, 8)$.

Solution: Using the formula for the slope, we find that the slope of the line between these two points is

$$m = \frac{8 - 6}{-5 - 2} = -\frac{2}{7}$$

This concludes our review material for this chapter. In the rest of the chapter we use these tools to investigate some of the intuitive ideas behind calculus.

SECTION 9.0

REVIEW

Find the value of the following functions at the specified point or expression.

$$f(x) = 8 \qquad\qquad g(x) = 3x - 6 \qquad\qquad k(x) = x^2 + 7x$$

1. (a) $f(4)$ (b) $g(4)$ (c) $k(4)$

2. (a) $f(-3)$ (b) $g(-3)$ (c) $k(-3)$

3. (a) $f(Q)$ (b) $g(Q)$ (c) $k(Q)$

4. (a) $f(M)$ (b) $g(M)$ (c) $k(M)$

5. (a) $f(3 + h)$ (b) $g(3 + h)$ (c) $k(3 + h)$

6. (a) $f(1 + h)$ (b) $g(1 + h)$ (c) $k(1 + h)$

7. (a) $f(x + h)$ (b) $g(x + h)$ (c) $k(x + h)$

8. (a) $f(x - h)$ (b) $g(x - h)$ (c) $k(x - h)$

Determine if the following are functions of the form $y = f(x)$.

9. $y = 3x - 4$

10. $y = 3x + 9$

11. $3x + 3y = 7$

12. $5x - 4y = 9$

13. $y = 2x^2$

14. $y = 3x^2$

15. $x = 3y^2$

16. $x = 2y^2$

17. $x^2 + y^3 = 1$

18. $x^3 + y^2 = 1$

19. The line $y = 6$

20. The line $y = 7$

21. The line $x = 8$

22. The line $x = 7$

23. (a) A situation where x represents the time of the sunset in Detroit and y represents the date.
(b) A situation where x represents the date and y represents the time of the sunset in Detroit.

24. (a) A situation where x represents a manufacturer's suggested retail price and y represents the name of the item being sold.
(b) A situation where x represents the name of the item being sold and y represents the suggested retail price.

Find the slope of the line through the following pairs of points.

25. (a) $(-2, 3)$ and $(-4, 13)$ (b) $(2, 7)$ and $(-4, 5)$

26. (a) $(-3, 2)$ and $(-1, 6)$ (b) $(1, 7)$ and $(-5, 9)$

*27. For the function $y = f(x)$, let $(x, f(x))$ and $((x + h), f(x + h))$ be two points. Find an expression for the slope of a line through these two points.

SECTION 9.1

▼

THE SLOPE OF A CURVE

In algebra, some of the many topics studied are slopes of lines and the maximum or minimum values of parabolas. The graphs of many different functions, such as circles and exponential functions, are also studied. In this section, we discuss how to find the slope of a curve. In Section 9.2, we will look at how we can use the slope of any curve to determine maximum or minimum points.

Let's look at the graph of the equation $y = 3x^2 + 1$ and draw a line that intersects the graph in two points: at point P, where $x = 0$ and at point Q, where $x = h$. **The letter h is used to represent any value except zero.** Now, find the slope of the line through points P and Q.

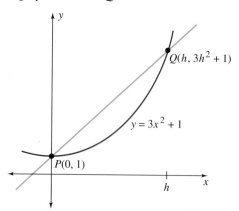

Since the slope of a line is given by $m = (y_2 - y_1)/(x_2 - x_1)$, to find the slope of the line segment PQ we first find the y coordinates of the points P and Q. This can be done by substituting the x values into the equation $y = 3x^2 + 1$. For $x = 0$, we have $y = 1$, and $x = h$ gives $y = 3h^2 + 1$.

Using the points $(0, 1)$ and $(h, 3h^2 + 1)$, we can find the slope of the line through the points P and Q.

$$m = \frac{y_2 - y_1}{x_2 - x_1} = \frac{3h^2 + 1 - 1}{h - 0} = \frac{3h^2}{h} = 3h \qquad \text{(provided } h \neq 0\text{)}$$

We now know that the slope of the line through P and Q is given by $m = 3h$. This means that the slope of the line will depend on the value of h.

Look at the following series of diagrams that show point Q moving along the curve toward P. What happens to the slope of the line PQ? If you determined that

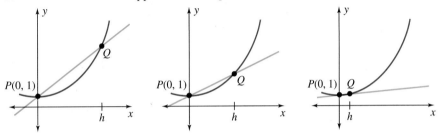

the slope was getting close to zero as point Q moved closer to point P, you were correct. As h takes on smaller values, the distance between the points decreases and the slope of the line segment PQ approaches 0. This can also be seen by looking again at the formula we had for the slope and letting h get close to 0. Since $m = 3h$, if h approaches zero, then the slope of the line PQ approaches zero. In addition, as h gets close to 0, the line will intersect the graph in two points, P and Q, that are very close together. When, in a region very near to point P the line intersects the curve only at the point P, the line is called the **tangent line to the curve** at the point P.*

The following pictures give three examples of tangent lines.

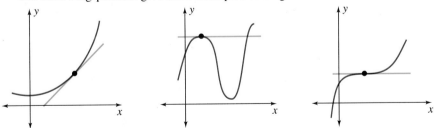

The following pictures give examples of lines that are not tangent to the curve.

---

*This statement is true only for functions whose graphs do not include any sharp points or jumps in the graph. Functions whose graphs contain sharp points or jumps will not be discussed here.

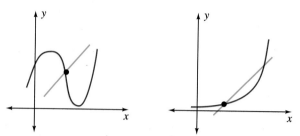

We are discussing the slope of the tangent line because the **slope of the curve at a point P** is defined as the slope of the tangent line at a point P. The slope of the curve is such an important topic that mathematicians have a specific name for it. The slope of a curve, or function, at a point P is called the **derivative** of the function at the point P, and the process for finding a derivative is called **differentiation**.

Example 1:

Find the slope of the tangent line to the curve $y = x^2 + 4x$ at the point $(2, 12)$.

Solution: We start by sketching a graph of the function. As we did before, to find the slope we need to have two points P and Q. Point P is the point $(2, 12)$. We want to pick point Q a certain distance away from point P, so we pick the x coordinate of Q as $2 + h$. To find the y coordinate of Q, substitute $2 + h$ for x in the function $y = x^2 + 4x$. This gives

$$y = (2 + h)^2 + 4(2 + h)$$
$$= 4 + 4h + h^2 + 8 + 4h$$
$$= 12 + 8h + h^2$$

Thus, point Q is given by $(2 + h, 12 + 8h + h^2)$.

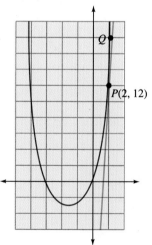

We can now use points P $(2, 12)$ and $Q(2 + h, 12 + 8h + h^2)$ to find the slope of the line containing points P and Q.

$$m = \frac{(12 + 8h + h^2) - 12}{(2 + h) - 2} = \frac{8h + h^2}{h} = 8 + h \qquad \text{(provided } h \neq 0)$$

To find the slope of the tangent line to $y = x^2 + 4x$ at $x = 2$, let the points P and Q get close together. In other words, let h get close to 0. As h takes on a value close to 0, the formula $m = 8 + h$ reduces to $m = 8$. This implies that, at $x = 2$, the slope of the tangent line to the curve is 8.

In the two previous problems, we found the slope of the tangent line at a particular point. For instance, we found at the point $(2, 12)$ that the slope of the tangent line to $y = x^2 + 4x$ is 8. We also stated that the slope of the tangent line at a point is the same as the slope of the curve at that point. However, as we can see from the diagram, the slope of the curve changes, depending on the point being examined. At points A and D, the slope of the tangent line is positive, with the

curve being steeper at point D than at A. At point C, the slope is negative, while the slope of the tangent line is approximately zero at point B. Since **slope** represents the steepness of a line and since the steepness of a curve depends on the point being discussed, the slope of a curve is not a constant. Instead, the slope of a curve is changing and can be found by a formula.

In the previous example, we chose two points to find the slope. One x value, $x = 2$, was given, and the other value was chosen to be $x = 2 + h$. Suppose we are given an arbitrary function, $y = f(x)$, and want to find the slope of the curve at some point $(x, f(x))$. The second point will be chosen as $(x + h, f(x + h))$. Now that the points are chosen, use the points to calculate the slope.

$$m = \frac{y_2 - y_1}{x_2 - x_1} = \frac{f(x + h) - f(x)}{(x + h) - x} = \frac{f(x + h) - f(x)}{h}$$

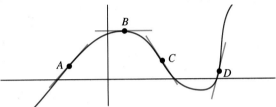

After finding the slope, we move the points close together. This is done by letting h approach 0. The notation used to indicate this is

$$\lim_{h \to 0} \qquad \text{which is read ''limit as } h \text{ gets close to 0''}$$

Though this notation looks peculiar, it simply means that the value of h becomes smaller and smaller until it is very close (but never equal) to zero. This has the effect of keeping the first point stationary while sliding the second point on the curve toward the first.

This discussion leads to the definition of the derivative of a function $f(x)$.

> The derivative of a function $y = f(x)$ at a point x is
>
> $$\frac{dy}{dx} = \lim_{h \to 0} \frac{f(x + h) - f(x)}{h}$$

Example 2:

Find the derivative of the function $y = x^2 + 4x$.

Solution: Notice that this is the same function that was discussed in Example 1. In Example 1, we determined the derivative (slope of the tangent line) when $x = 2$. Now, we want to find the value of the derivative at any point. Therefore, we will repeat the work done in Example 1 using the variable x rather than the number 2.

The first point is $(x, f(x))$. For the second point, the x coordinate is $x + h$ and the y coordinate is $f(x + h)$, where

$$f(x + h) = (x + h)^2 + 4(x + h)$$
$$= x^2 + 2xh + h^2 + 4x + 4h$$

This means that the derivative of $y = x^2 + 4x$ is

$$\frac{dy}{dx} = \lim_{h \to 0} \frac{f(x + h) - f(x)}{h}$$

$$= \lim_{h \to 0} \frac{x^2 + 2xh + h^2 + 4x + 4h - (x^2 + 4x)}{h}$$

$$= \lim_{h \to 0} \frac{2xh + 4h + h^2}{h}$$

$$= \lim_{h \to 0} (2x + 4 + h)$$

$$= 2x + 4$$

Notice that this gives a formula for the slope of the curve. The equation

$$\frac{dy}{dx} = 2x + 4$$

means that the slope of the curve at any value of x can be determined by substituting the value of x into the equation. For instance, in Example 1, we found that at the point (2, 12), the slope of the curve is 8. We can verify this by substituting $x = 2$ into the equation $dy/dx = 2x + 4$. As expected, this gives the slope as $2(2) + 4 = 8$. Similarly, at the point (1, 5), the slope of the curve is $2(1) + 4 = 6$.

Example 3:

Find the x value of the point on the curve $y = x^2 + 4x$ where the slope is 0.

Solution: From Example 2, we know that the slope of the curve at any point is $dy/dx = 2x + 4$. Since we want to find the point where the slope of the curve is 0, set the equation for the slope equal to 0 and solve for x.

$$2x + 4 = 0$$

$$2x = -4$$

$$x = -2$$

This means that, at $x = -2$, the slope of the curve, or the slope of the tangent line to the curve, is zero. To visualize this, sketch the graph of $y = x^2 + 4x$ by plotting a few points. Notice that at $x = -2$, we are at the vertex of the parabola, and the tangent line is horizontal.

x	y
-4	0
-3	-3
-2	-4
-1	-3
0	0
1	5

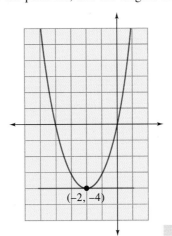

$(-2, -4)$

In this section, we discussed one of the two main topics in calculus, the derivative. A derivative gives the slope of a curve at any point. In particular, we found how we can determine the slope of a curve and how we can determine the point(s) where the derivative is equal to zero. The next section shows how the slope of the curve can help us sketch the graph of a function and how the derivative can be applied to problems involving maximum and minimum points. The next section also gives a method for finding derivatives without resorting to the long algebraic process that was used here.

SECTION 9.1

PROBLEMS

1. The graph represents the function $y = f(x)$. Determine which point(s) satisfy the following conditions.

(a) $\dfrac{dy}{dx} = 0$

(b) $\dfrac{dy}{dx}$ is positive

(c) $\dfrac{dy}{dx}$ is negative

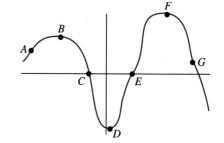

2. The graph represents the function $y = f(x)$. Determine which point(s) satisfy the following conditions.

(a) $\dfrac{dy}{dx} = 0$

(b) $\dfrac{dy}{dx}$ is positive

(c) $\dfrac{dy}{dx}$ is negative

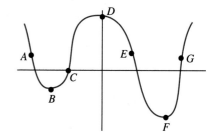

3. In the diagram, the value of the derivative at $x = 1$ is 0.5, and the value of the derivative at $x = 4$ is 2. What can you say about the value of the derivative at $x = 2$?

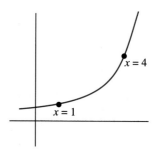

4. For the line $y = 6x + 2$:

   (a) Find the slope of the line, using the methods of algebra.
   (b) Find the derivative.
   (c) What do you think is the derivative of the line $y = mx + b$?

5. For the line $y = 5x - 1$:

   (a) Find the slope of the line, using the methods of algebra.
   (b) Find the derivative.
   (c) What do you think is the derivative of the line $y = mx + b$?

6. Find the derivative of $y = 2x^2 - 6x$ at the point $(1, -4)$.

7. Find the derivative of $y = 3x^2 - x$ at the point $(1, 2)$.

8. Find the derivative of $y = 3x^2 + 2$ at the point $(1, 5)$.

9. Find the derivative of $y = 5x^2$ at any point on the curve.

10. Find the derivative of $y = 2x^2$ at any point on the curve.

11. Determine the x coordinate of the point where the derivative of $y = 2x^2 - 4x$ equals zero.

12. Determine the x coordinate of the point where the derivative of $y = 5x^2 + 20x$ equals zero.

*13. Find the derivative of each of the following:

   (a) $y = x^2$
   (b) $y = x^3$
   (c) $y = x^4$
   (d) Based on the answers to parts (a), (b), and (c), what do you think the derivative of $y = x^{23}$ is?

Restaurant by the Sea by John Register shows a young man in deep contemplation, the kind of contemplation that is commonly engaged in by calculus students. (Courtesy of Magnolia Editions)

SECTION 9.2

▼

USING DERIVATIVES

In the previous section, we found derivatives of linear and quadratic functions. Despite the fact that these curves can be understood without the use of calculus, it was still a difficult chore to find the derivatives. Therefore, before discussing how derivatives can be applied, we want to reexamine how to find a derivative.

Shortcuts for Finding Derivatives

If you worked Problem 13 in the previous section, you may have guessed how certain differentiations can be performed more quickly. Problem 13 asked you to compute the derivatives of three different functions and to guess the derivative of a fourth function. The results were:

Function	Derivative
$f(x) = x^2$	$\dfrac{dy}{dx} = 2x$
$f(x) = x^3$	$\dfrac{dy}{dx} = 3x^2$
$f(x) = x^4$	$\dfrac{dy}{dx} = 4x^3$
$f(x) = x^{23}$	$\dfrac{dy}{dx} = 23x^{22}$

You were expected to grind out the first three results, whereas the fourth result was to be obtained using inductive reasoning (guessing). Notice that each of the first three functions has a derivative with a coefficient that is the same as the exponent in the original function. The derivative has an exponent that is 1 less than the original exponent. If you noticed this pattern, you probably were able to guess correctly the derivative of $f(x) = x^{23}$. If we continue this inductive reasoning a bit further, we arrive at the following formula:

Power Rule for Derivatives

If $f(x) = x^n$, then the derivative of $f(x)$ is $\dfrac{dy}{dx} = nx^{n-1}$.

Although we have not proven it, the power rule is true for any constant exponent. The exponent can be a fraction, a negative number, or even an irrational number.

Example 1:

Use the power rule to find the derivatives of the following functions:

(a) $f(x) = x$
(b) $f(x) = x^{-3}$
(c) $f(x) = x^{1/2}$

Solution:

(a) For $f(x) = x = x^1$,

$$\frac{dy}{dx} = 1x^0 = 1$$

(b) For $f(x) = x^{-3}$,

$$\frac{dy}{dx} = -3x^{-3-1} = -3x^{-4}$$

(c) For $f(x) = x^{1/2}$,

$$\frac{dy}{dx} = \frac{1}{2}x^{1/2-1} = \frac{1}{2}x^{-1/2}$$

Example 2:

Find the derivative of the line $y = 5$.

Solution: The line $y = 5$ does not contain any x's but we can find the derivative by realizing that the line $y = 5$ is a horizontal line and that the slope of a horizontal line is 0. Therefore, since the slope of a function can be found by using the derivative, the derivative of $y = 5$ must equal 0.

Since this is true for every horizontal line, we can generalize this with the following formula:

(1) If $f(x) = k$, where k is any constant, $\dfrac{dy}{dx} = 0$.

Each of the problems in Example 1 consisted of a single term with a coefficient of 1. To determine how to approach a function that contains more than one term or a function whose coefficient is not 1, we will look at the derivatives that were completed in the examples and odd-numbered problems from the previous section.

Original Problem	Functions	Derivatives
Section 1, Example 2	$y = x^2 + 4x$	$\dfrac{dy}{dx} = 2x + 4$
Section 1, Problem 9	$y = 5x^2$	$\dfrac{dy}{dx} = 10x$
Section 1, Problem 11	$y = 2x^2 - 4x$	$\dfrac{dy}{dx} = 4x - 4$

In the first of these, the derivative of x^2 is, as expected, $2x$. The derivative of $4x$ is 4. Since Example 1 of this section showed the derivative of x is 1, it appears that the derivative of $4x$ is merely 4 times the derivative of x. Since Problem 9 showed that the derivative of $5x^2$ is given by $10x$, and the rule stated that the derivative of x^2 is $2x$, it appears that the derivative of $5x^2$ can be calculated as $5 \times 2x = 10x$. This pattern repeats itself in the third example and leads us to the following two rules for derivatives.

(2) If $f(x) = kx^n$, then $\dfrac{dy}{dx} = knx^{n-1}$.

(3) The derivative of $f(x) \pm g(x)$ equals the sum (difference) of the derivatives of $f(x)$ and $g(x)$.

Example 3:

Find the derivatives of the following functions.

(a) $f(x) = 8x^5$
(b) $f(x) = 4x^3 - 6x^2 + 5x + 1$

Solution:

(a) For $f(x) = 8x^5$, we use rule 2 to get $dy/dx = 8 \cdot 5x^4 = 40x^4$.
(b) For $f(x) = 4x^3 - 6x^2 + 5x + 1$, we need to use rule 2 for the derivatives of the first three terms and rule 1 for the derivative

of the fourth term. From rule 2, the derivative of $4x^3$ is $4 \cdot 3x^2 = 12x^2$, the derivative of $6x^2$ is $6 \cdot 2x^1 = 12x$, and the derivative of $5x$ is 5. By rule 1, the derivative of 1 is 0. Therefore, by rule 3, if $f(x) = 4x^3 - 6x^2 + 5x + 1$,

$$\frac{dy}{dx} = 12x^2 - 12x + 5$$

In summary, we have three rules to help us find derivatives. To find the derivatives of polynomial functions, we no longer need to use the algebraic process of the previous section. Instead, we can find derivatives of polynomials by using the three rules repeated here.

(1) If $f(x) = k$, where k is any constant, $\dfrac{dy}{dx} = 0$.

(2) If $f(x) = kx^n$, then $\dfrac{dy}{dx} = knx^{n-1}$.

(3) The derivative of $f(x) \pm g(x)$ equals the sum (difference) of the derivatives of $f(x)$ and $g(x)$.

Applications of the Derivative

The first application of the derivative that we will consider is how the derivative can help graph functions. In algebra, the graphing of parabolas is accomplished with the help of finding the location of the vertex of the parabola. The vertex gives the location of the maximum or minimum point of the parabola. We will now discuss how we can use derivatives to determine the maximum or minimum points of any curve.

As can be seen in the diagram, a curve may have several maximum and minimum points. If we use the common English usage of the word maximum, there can only be one maximum or highest point for a graph. In mathematics, this is called an absolute maximum.

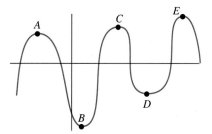

To indicate that we are concerned with all the points that are at the top of a loop of the curve, the term **relative maximum** is used. A relative maximum is a point that is higher than all the points very close by. Similarly, a **relative minimum** is a point that is lower than all the points very close by. The graph shows three relative maximums, located at points A, C, and E. There are also two relative minimums, located at B and D.

If we redraw the diagram, including the tangent lines at the relative maximum and relative minimum points, we will be able to see the role that the derivative plays in determining relative maximum and relative minimum points. Notice that

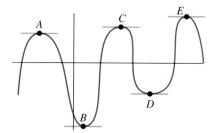

each of the five tangent lines in the drawing is horizontal. Since the slope of a horizontal line is zero, **we can determine the relative maximum or relative minimum points of a curve by setting the derivative equal to zero**.

Example 4:

Find the relative maximum and minimum points of the curve
$y = 6x^3 - 8x + 1$.

Solution: First, sketch the graph for integer values of x. From the graph, we can see that there is a relative maximum point near $x = -1$ and a relative minimum point near $x = 1$. However, we cannot tell from the graph exactly where the relative maximum and relative minimum points are located.

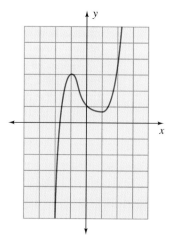

The relative maximum and relative minimum points occur where the slope of the tangent line is equal to zero. Therefore, we can find the locations of the relative maximum and relative minimum points by setting the derivative equal to 0 and comparing the resulting values of x with the information from the graph.

From our rules for derivatives, we know that the derivative of $y = 6x^3 - 8x + 1$ is $dy/dx = 18x^2 - 8$. Now that we have the derivative, we can determine the location of the relative maximum point on the curve by setting the derivative equal to 0.

$$18x^2 - 8 = 0$$

$$18x^2 = 8$$

$$x^2 = 4/9$$

$$x = \pm 2/3$$

Since we have two solutions for x, we should look at the graph to determine which is the solution to the question. We knew from our graph that the relative maximum point was located near $x = -1$. Therefore, we know that the curve reaches its relative maximum at $x = -2/3$.

To determine the y value at the relative maximum point, we substitute the value $x = -2/3$ into the equation $y = 6x^3 - 8x + 1$. This gives

$$y = 6\left(\frac{-2}{3}\right)^3 - 8\left(\frac{-2}{3}\right) + 1 = \frac{41}{9} \approx 4.56$$

In the same way, we find that the relative minimum value of the equation occurs at $x = 2/3$. This gives a y value of

$$y = 6\left(\frac{2}{3}\right)^3 - 8\left(\frac{2}{3}\right) + 1 = \frac{-23}{9} \approx -2.56$$

Now that we have this new information, we can draw the graph again. Notice that we are now able to add new details to the graph since we know the exact locations of the relative maximum and relative minimum points.

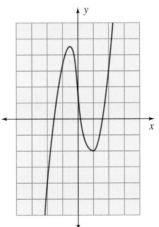

Calculus is a very powerful mathematical tool and has many applications. The standard calculus course requires two or three semesters to learn all the techniques and uses. Because of this, we cannot possibly study the many areas in which calculus plays a role. We do however, present the following examples.

Example 5:

Find the dimensions of the rectangular region with maximum area that can be enclosed by 120 ft of fencing. The fencing should form the perimeter of the region and one interior fence that divides the area into two equal sections. (We know there will be a maximum since there is a given amount of available fencing.)

Solution: We start by drawing the rectangle and writing equations that model the situation. Since this is a rectangle, we know that the perimeter of the figure and the length of the interior fence are given by

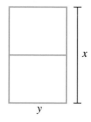

We also know that the total area of a rectangle is

$$A = xy$$

Since we want to find the maximum area, we will express the area as a function of one variable. To do this, solve the first equation for y and substitute the value of y into the second equation.

$$2x + 3y = 120$$

$$3y = 120 - 2x$$

$$y = \frac{120 - 2x}{3} = 40 - \frac{2}{3}x$$

Substituting for this result for y into the equation for area gives

$$A = x\left(40 - \frac{2}{3}x\right) = 40x - \frac{2}{3}x^2$$

We can now find the derivative of $f(x)$ and use it to determine the maximum value of the area.

$$\frac{dA}{dx} = 40 - \frac{2}{3}(2x) = 40 - \frac{4}{3}x$$

Setting the derivative equal to zero and solving for x gives:

$$40 - \frac{4}{3}x = 0$$

$$40 = \frac{4}{3}x$$

$$40\left(\frac{3}{4}\right) = x$$

$$30 = x$$

Since $y = 40 - (2/3)x$, substituting $x = 30$ gives $y = 20$. This means that the maximum area for the region fenced in by the 120 ft of fencing is $30 \times 20 = 600$ sq ft.

Example 6:

A closed rectangular box is to be constructed from 2400 sq cm of cardboard. If the box has a square base of side x and a height y, find the values of x and y that form the box of maximum volume. (We know there will be a maximum since there is a given amount of available cardboard.)

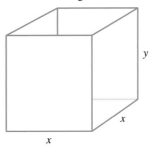

Solution: Since the box has a square base, the area of the top and the bottom of the box are given by x^2. The four sides of the box each have area xy, so the total surface area (S.A.) of the box is

$$\text{S.A.} = 2x^2 + 4xy$$

Since the total amount of cardboard available is 2400 sq cm, we have the equation

$$2400 = 2x^2 + 4xy$$

The question asks us to find the maximum volume of the box. Since we can find the relative maximum by taking the derivative of an equation, we need to find the equation for the volume of the box. Using the formula volume = length $\times$ width $\times$ height, we have

$$V = x^2y$$

Since this expression has two variables, we can use the surface area equation to solve for y in terms of x, and substitute for y in the volume equation.

$$2400 = 2x^2 + 4xy$$

$$2400 - 2x^2 = 4xy$$

$$\frac{2400 - 2x^2}{4x} = y$$

Substituting this value of y into the expression for the volume gives

$$V = x^2 y$$

$$V = x^2 \left(\frac{2400 - 2x^2}{4x} \right)$$

$$V = 600x - \frac{x^3}{2}$$

To find the maximum, compute the derivative, set the derivative equal to 0, and solve for x.

$$\frac{dV}{dx} = 600 - \frac{3x^2}{2}$$

$$0 = 600 - \frac{3x^2}{2}$$

$$\frac{3x^2}{2} = 600$$

$$x^2 = 400$$

$$x = 20 \quad \text{(Since x represents a dimension of the box, it must be positive.)}$$

Substituting $x = 20$ into $y = \dfrac{2400 - 2x^2}{4x}$ gives $y = 20$. Therefore, the box of maximum volume for a given surface area is a cube. In this case, the cube has dimensions $20 \times 20 \times 20$.

In summary, this section has covered two topics. The first topic was a study of some of the shortcuts used to determine the derivative of a polynomial. The second topic was how the derivative can be used to determine the relative maximum or relative minimum value of a function. The problem set that follows will give you some practice in working with both topics.

SECTION 9.2

PROBLEMS

Find the derivatives of the functions in Problems 1–8.

1. $f(x) = 2x + 5$

2. $f(x) = 2x - 7$

3. $y = 4x^5$

4. $y = 3x^8$

5. $y = 4x^5 - 5x^2$

6. $y = 2x^5 - 3x^2$

7. $f(x) = x^5 - 3x^2 + 7x + 5$

8. $f(x) = x^5 - 7x^2 + 3x + 4$

9. (a) Sketch the graph of the line $y = 3x + 7$. Does this graph have any relative maximum or relative minimum points?

    (b) Find the derivative of $y = 3x + 7$. Can the derivative equal 0? If so, find the point(s) where $dy/dx = 0$.

10. (a) Sketch the graph of $y = x^2 + 2x$. Does this graph have any relative maximum or relative minimum points?

    (b) Find the derivative of $y = x^2 + 2x$. Find the point where $dy/dx = 0$.

    (c) Is the point found in part (b) a relative maximum or a relative minimum point?

11. (a) Sketch the graph of $y = -x^2 + 4x$. Does this graph have any relative maximum or relative minimum points?

    (b) Find the derivative of $y = -x^2 + 4x$. Find the point where $dy/dx = 0$.

    (c) Is the point found in part (b) a relative maximum or a relative minimum point?

12. (a) Sketch the graph of $y = -x^2 + 6x$. Does this graph have any relative maximum or relative minimum points?

    (b) Find the derivative of $y = -x^2 + 6x$. Find the point where $dy/dx = 0$.

    (c) Is the point found in part (b) a relative maximum or a relative minimum point?

13. (a) Plot points to sketch the graph of $y = 2x^3 - 6x$.

    (b) Find the derivative of $y = 2x^3 - 6x$.

    (c) Find all the points where $dy/dx = 0$.

    (d) Determine which of these points is a relative maximum and which is a relative minimum.

14. (a) Plot points to sketch the graph of $y = 2x^3 - 6x + 12$.

    (b) Find the derivative of $y = 2x^3 - 6x + 12$.

    (c) Find all the points where $dy/dx = 0$.

    (d) Determine which of these points is a relative maximum and which is a relative minimum.

15. The path traveled by a frog is given by $h = (-1/98)x^2 + (6/7)x$, where x is the horizontal distance traveled and h is the height in inches at any point along the path.

    (a) Determine the x value that gives the maximum height.

    (b) Determine the maximum height.

16. A ball is thrown vertically in the air with an initial speed of 139.33 ft/s from an initial height of 9 ft. The equation describing the height of the ball at any time is $h = -16t^2 + 139.33t + 9$, where t is the time in seconds and h is the height in feet.

(a) Determine the time when the ball reaches its maximum height.

(b) Determine the maximum height.

17. Use calculus to solve the following problem. A chicken farmer wants to build a fenced area for her free-roaming chickens. Because she wants to separate the different breeds, she wants to have three adjacent pens, as shown at the right. If 1200 ft of fencing are available, what is the largest total area that can be fenced off for the chickens?

(*Hint*: Area = xy and total fencing = $4x + 2y$.)

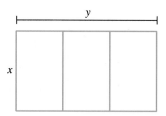

18. Use calculus to solve the following problem. An orchid fancier is building a fiberglass enclosure next to his house, as shown in the diagram. Since the house will be used for one side of the enclosure, only three sides will need to be enclosed by the fiberglass. The roof of the greenhouse is to be built of some other material. If 60 ft of the fiberglass walls are available, what is the maximum rectangular area that can be enclosed?

(*Hint*: Area = xy and total length of walls = $2x + y$.)

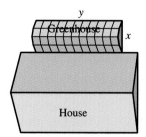

*19. Use calculus to solve the following problem. A contractor wants to build a covered box that is twice as long as it is wide. The height is to be determined by the amount of wood available. If the contractor has 48 sq ft of plywood available, find the dimensions of the box with maximum volume. (*Hint*: Volume $= 2x^2h$ and total plywood $= 2(2x^2) + 2(2xh) + 2(xh)$.)

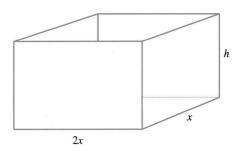

SECTION   9.3

▼

THE AREA UNDER A CURVE

The next topic we consider is **integration**. Integration is a method for finding the area of a region by filling the regions with shapes of known area. Integration has many uses in calculus; however, we will restrict our investigation to finding the area bounded by a curve in a plane. As we saw in the historical section, many methods, such as the Eudoxian method of exhaustion and Cavalieri's indivisibles, have been used to find areas. We will use the method of rectangles, developed by Gilles Persone de Roberval (1602–1675) of France. It is essentially the method used to introduce integration to a modern calculus class.

The problem is to find the area of the region bounded by the lines $y = 2x$, $y = 0$, and $x = 4$. From the formula for the area of a triangle, we know that the area is $(1/2)(4)(8) = 16$. However, we will use a method involving rectangles so that we can arrive at a process for finding any area.

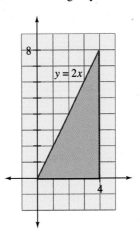

The first step in this method is to divide the region into a number of rectangles. The more rectangles we use, the greater the accuracy of our result. As in the method of exhaustion, we can put the rectangles inside or outside the triangle. In

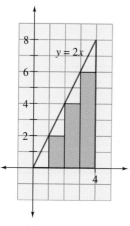

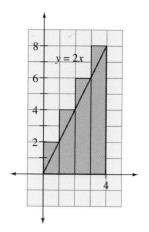

Lower rectangles   Upper rectangles

the first diagram there are four rectangles inside the triangle (one of them has a height of 0), whereas the second diagram has the rectangles extending outside of the triangle. From here, we can anticipate that the area of the lower rectangles will be less than the area of the region, and the area of the upper rectangles will exceed the area of the region.

An improvement on this method is to use rectangles that approximate the region even more closely. Instead of using rectangles that are obviously smaller or larger than the desired area, we can use rectangles that intersect the curve at the midpoint of their top edges, as shown in the diagram. The upper left corner of each rectangle is outside the region and therefore will provide an overestimate of the area. However, each rectangle has some white space above it, underestimating the area of the region. The result should be an approximation that gives a more accurate value of the actual area of the region.

x	y
0.5	1
1.5	3
2.5	5
3.5	7

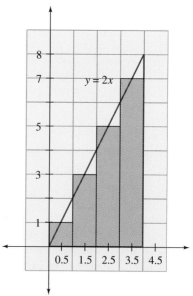

To estimate the area of the region, find the area of the four rectangles. Each rectangle has width 1. We need only find the heights of the rectangles. To do this, we use the fact that the line $y = 2x$ crosses the top of each rectangle at its midpoint. Therefore, the x values are 0.5, 1.5, 2.5, and 3.5. Thus, the heights of the rectangles can be found by substituting these x values into the equation $y = 2x$ as shown in the table. The area of the four rectangles is

$$A = \text{width} \times \text{height of the four rectangles}$$

$$= 1 \times 1 + 1 \times 3 + 1 \times 5 + 1 \times 7 = 16$$

Through the use of four rectangles, intersecting the line $y = 2x$ at the midpoints of their upper edges, we were able to find the correct area. Although we will usually only be able to find the approximate area, the rectangle method appears to work, and can be applied to other regions.

In summary, the rectangle method can be used to find the area bounded by a curve by dividing the desired area into rectangles with the midpoint of the top edge of each rectangle intersecting the curve. The area of the region is estimated by calculating the sum of the areas of the rectangles.

Example 1:

Approximate the area of the region bounded by the x axis, the line $x = 4$, and the curve $y = x^2/4$.

(a) Use the rectangle method with four rectangles.
(b) Use the rectangle method with eight rectangles.

Solution:

(a) Our first step will be to sketch the desired region. As we did before, the region has been divided into four rectangles. The midpoints of the rectangles are 0.5, 1.5, 2.5, and 3.5. Substituting each of these x values into the equation $y = x^2/4$ gives the following y values:

x	y
0.5	0.0625
1.5	0.5625
2.5	1.5625
3.5	3.0625

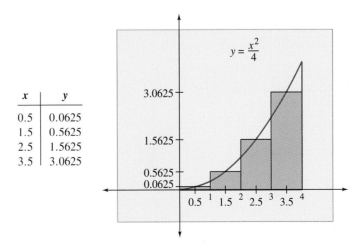

Since the width of each of the rectangles is 1, the sum of the areas of the rectangles is

A = width × height of the four rectangles

$$= 1 \times 0.0625 + 1 \times 0.5625 + 1 \times 1.5625 + 1 \times 3.0625 = 5.25$$

(b) We now want to repeat this process with eight rectangles. Since we want to create eight rectangles in the interval 0 to 4, the width of each rectangle is 1/2, since $(4 - 0)/8 = 1/2$. We can now find the midpoints of each rectangle and its corresponding height, the y value. Since the width of the first rectangle is 1/2 or 0.5, the midpoint of the first rectangle is 0.25. Adding 0.5 gives the midpoint of the second rectangle as 0.75. Repeating this process gives the midpoints of each of the eight rectangles. Using the width of 0.5 and the heights as given by the y values, we have

x	y
0.25	0.0156
0.75	0.1406
1.25	0.3906
1.75	0.7656
2.25	1.2656
2.75	1.8906
3.25	2.6406
3.75	3.5156

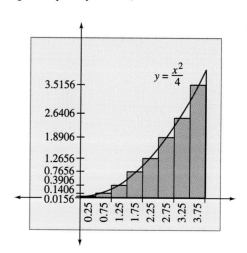

A = width × height of the four rectangles

$$= 0.5 \times 0.0156 + 0.5 \times 0.1406 + 0.5 \times 0.3906$$
$$+ 0.5 \times 0.7656 + 0.5 \times 1.2656 + 0.5 \times 1.8906$$
$$+ 0.5 \times 2.6406 + 0.5 \times 3.5156$$

$$= 5.3124$$

If this problem is repeated with several hundred rectangles, it can be shown that the area is approximately 5.3333. This implies that the actual area is $5\frac{1}{3}$. Thus, using eight rectangles gives a good approximation of the actual area.

Example 2:

A lawn fertilizer company suggests that Weed O Burn be applied at a rate of 2 lb per 1000 sq ft. Because of the potency of the fertilizer, Chauncy, the gardener, wants to accurately determine the area of the irregularly shaped lawn, shown in the figure. His only tool is a 100-ft tape measure. How can Chauncy determine the area? What is the approximate area?

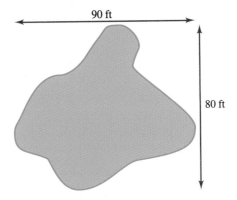

90 ft

80 ft

Solution: To determine the area, Chauncy decides to divide the lawn into 10-ft-wide strips and measure the length of each strip. This will give him a set of rectangles whose combined areas will approximate the area of the lawn. There will be eight rectangles (80 ÷ 10), each being 10 ft wide. The length of each rectangle needs to be measured. The results of Chauncy's measurements for the lengths of the rectangles are given in the figure. Using the formula for the area of a rectangle, we can now find the approximate area of the lawn.

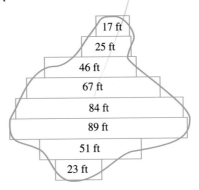

17 ft
25 ft
46 ft
67 ft
84 ft
89 ft
51 ft
23 ft

A = width × length

= 10 × 17 + 10 × 25 + 10 × 46 + 10 × 67 + 10 × 84
+ 10 × 89 + 10 × 51 + 10 × 23

= 4020 sq ft of lawn

This section concludes our short discussion of calculus. In this chapter, we have showed that differentiation gives the slope of a curve and how, with the help of some shortcuts, the derivative can be applied to certain mathematical problems. We also showed that integration gives a method for determining the areas of regions bounded by curves. As is true for differentiation, there are shortcuts for doing integration, but that investigation is beyond the scope of this chapter.

We have presented a very brief overview of calculus. We have not attempted to give a complete explanation of the power and applicability of calculus. However, we hope that you have seen some mathematics that is intriguing enough for you to pursue additional studies in this area.

SECTION 9.3

PROBLEMS

In Problems 1–6, sketch the given area and use the rectangle method with the given number of rectangles to approximate the specified area.

1. The area bounded by the lines $y = -2x + 24$, the x axis, and the y axis, using three rectangles

2. The area bounded by the lines $y = -3x + 24$, the x axis, and the y axis, using four rectangles

3. The area bounded by the lines $y = 2x + 4$, the x axis, the y axis, and the line $x = 8$, using four rectangles

4. The area bounded by the lines $y = 3x + 12$, the x axis, the y axis, and the line $x = 12$, using three rectangles

5. The area bounded by the x axis and the curve $y = 36 - x^2$, using six rectangles

6. The area bounded by the x axis and the curve $y = 12x - x^2$, using six rectangles

7. In the sketch of a small pond, the measurements are 25 ft apart and start 12.5 ft from the ends of the pond. Use the measurements to estimate the area of the pond.

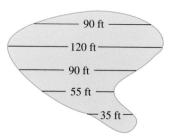

90 ft
120 ft
90 ft
55 ft
35 ft

8. The following figure is drawn to scale. Trace the figure onto your paper. Use a metric ruler and the rectangle method with six horizontal rectangles to find the area of the figure in square centimeters.

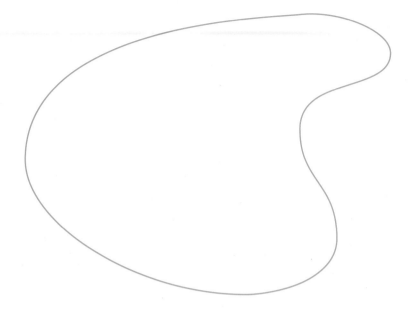

| CHAPTER | 9 | **SUMMARY** |

**KEY TERMS,
CONCEPTS, AND
FORMULAS**

The important terms in this chapter are:

Calculus: An area of mathematics concerning the study of derivatives and integrals.   p. 440

Derivative: The slope of a curve at a point.   p. 454

Differentiation: A process in calculus used to find the slope of a tangent line (derivative).   p. 443

Function: A relation between two variables, often written as $y = f(x)$, such that each x value is associated with at most one y value.   p. 448

Infinitesimal: A very small quantity; a very small change in x or y.   p. 441

Integration: A process in calculus used to find areas of regions in a plane.   p. 447

Relative maximum point: A point on a curve with a y value that is greater than the y values of all points immediately to the left and to the right of the point; found by setting the derivative equal to zero and examining the graph.   p. 463

Relative minimum point: A point on a curve with a y value that is less than the y values of all points immediately to the left and to the right of the point; found by setting the derivative equal to zero and examining the graph.   p. 463

Slope: A measure of the steepness of a line or curve. p. 455

After completing this chapter, you should be able to:

1. Use the formula

$$\frac{dy}{dx} = \lim_{h \to 0} \frac{f(x + h) - f(x)}{h}$$

to find the derivative of a function. p. 456

2. Explain the concepts of tangent lines, slopes of curves, relative maximums and relative minimums, and areas bounded by curves. pp. 452 471

3. Perform the necessary calculations to find slopes of curves, relative maximums and relative minimums, and areas bounded by curves. pp. 460 471

SUMMARY

PROBLEMS

1. Find the value of the following if $f(x) = 2x^2 - 3x + 2$.
   (a) $f(4)$
   (b) $f(m)$
   (c) $f(3 + h)$
   (d) $f(x + h)$

2. Find the value of the following if $f(x) = 3x^2 + 5x - 1$.
   (a) $f(-2)$
   (b) $f(w)$
   (c) $f(5 + h)$
   (d) $f(x + h)$

3. Using the long formula for dy/dx, find the derivative of $y = 3x - 8$.

4. Using the derivative shortcuts find the derivative of $y = x^3 + 6x - 1$.

5. Find the slope of the tangent line to the curve $f(x) = 3x^2 + 5x - 1$ at $x = 3$.

6. Find the slope of the tangent line to the curve $f(x) = 2x^2 - 3x + 2$ at $x = -2$.

7. Use a derivative to find the relative maximum point of $f(x) = -4x^2 - 16x + 2$.

8. Use a derivative to find the relative minimum point of $f(x) = 4x^2 - 24x + 9$.

9. A set of six equal pigpens is to be constructed out of 120 ft of fencing. The arrangement of the pens is given in the diagram. Use calculus to find the maximum total area of the pens. (*Hint:* $A = xy$ and $4x + 3y = 120$.)

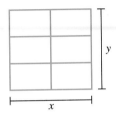

10. A field, adjacent to a barn, is to be divided into four pens, as shown in the following diagram. Because the field is adjacent to the barn, only three outside fences need to be built along with the interior fences. If 3000 ft of fencing are available, use calculus to find the outer dimensions of the field that will give the maximum total area. (*Hint:* $A = xy$ and $3x + 2y = 3000$.)

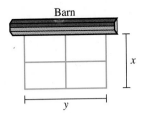

11. Use the rectangle rule with four rectangles to find the area bounded by the curve $y = -2x^2 + 16x$ and the x axis.

12. Use the rectangle rule with three rectangles to find the area bounded by the curve $y = -3x^2 + 18x$ and the x axis.

13. The lawn shown needs to receive 1 lb of fertilizer per 1000 sq ft. Use the given measurements to estimate the fertilizer requirements for the lawn. The measurements across the lawn are 16 ft apart and start 8 ft from the top and end 8 ft from the bottom of the lawn.

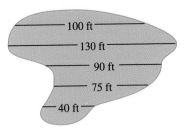

I

CALCULATOR REVIEW

Calculating devices from the abacus to the computer have been used by students to do computation. The computer has given students even more power. It can be a means of entering the world of art, as seen in the student computer-graphics creations *An Interpretation of Picasso's Woman* by Daniel Lim and *Passages* by Sue Chien Chen. (Courtesy of the artists)

A HISTORY OF CALCULATING DEVICES

After humans developed the ability to count and formulate number systems, they began to combine numbers with the operations of addition, subtraction, multiplication, and division. Through the centuries different algorithms were developed to perform these calculations. The use of fingers, charts, tables, rods, algebraic tricks, trigonometric functions, logarithms, and other schemes acted as an aid to computation. Also developed were various pen-and-paper techniques to do the basic operations. The techniques that we use today were developed during the Renaissance period in Europe.

Besides those methods, mechanical devices were also invented to accomplish the task of calculation. The abacus was the first of these calculating devices. With an abacus, calculations are performed by moving beads strung on wires. The abacus was used in ancient Greece and Rome. The Greek historian Herodotus mentioned its use in 400 B.C. The abacus was also found in ancient China with the *suan-pan* being used from about the 12th century in China. For a well-trained user of an abacus, its efficiency and speed of calculation is astounding. In 1947, Kiyoshi Matsuzake of the Japanese Ministry of Communications, using a soroban abacus, beat Private Tom Wood of the U.S. Army of Occupation, using a modern electrically driven mechanical calculator in a contest of speed and accuracy in calculation. Even though Private Wood was an experienced calculator user, the abacus user won four out of five calculation contests.

Computation by mechanical means has also been of concern since ancient times. A geared calculating device built about 80 B.C. was found in the sea near Antikythera Island off northwest Crete. Mechanical calculators that performed calculations with rotating wheels were invented by the German mathematician Wilhelm Schickard (1623), the French mathematician Blaise Pascal (1642), and the German mathematician Gottfried Leibniz (1673). In 1823, English inventor Charles Babbage designed a steam-powered digital calculator; in 1880, U.S. inventor Herman Hollerith constructed a card-driven electromechanical tabulating device; and in 1894, William Burroughs produced the first practical adding machine for business purposes.

In the twentieth century the progress of calculating devices took giant steps. By 1939 Konrad Zuse, Howard Aiken, and John Atanasoff independently constructed automatic electric calculating machines. In 1945 John Mauchly and J. Presper Eckert of the United States introduced ENIAC (Electronic Numerical Integrator and Calculator), the first general-purpose electronic digital computer. This computing marvel weighed 30 tons, contained 18,000 electron tubes, and stood two stories high. However, with the invention of the transistor by Americans William Shockley, Walter Brattain, and John Bardeen in 1948 and the integrated circuit by Jack Kilby of Texas Instruments in 1958, the doors to miniaturization and the microcomputer age were opened. Electric circuits produced on chips of silicon the size of a dime held thousands of circuits. These microchips stimulated the development of electronic calculators and electronic computers. By 1980, scientific calculators and personal computers were available to the consumer at reasonable prices, and super computers that perform hundreds of millions of calculations per second were at work in the scientific community.

A summary of the important dates, inventors, and events connected with the development of calculating devices follows.

c. 400 B.C.	A primitive abacus was first used for computation.
c. 1000	Pope Sylvester II reinstated the counting-board abacus in Europe.
1614	John Napier used logarithms to simplify multiplication and division.
1621	William Oughtred invented the slide rule, as an aid to computation.
1623	William Schickard designed the first mechanical calculating machine, but it was destroyed in a fire before completion. Schickard died of the plague shortly thereafter.

1624	Henry Briggs determined common logarithm tables to 14 decimal places.
1642	Blaise Pascal invented and demonstrated a calculating machine that adds and subtracts.
1674	Gottfried Leibniz constructed a stepped-drum gear calculating machine.
1820	The first commercial calculating machine was made available by Frenchman Thomas de Colmar.
1823	Charles Babbage designed a steam-powered digital calculator.
1843	Ada Augusta Byron, Countess of Lovelace, introduced computer programming techniques of looping and recursion when she wrote a computer program for Charles Babbage's analytic engine.
1880	Herman Hollerith built a card-driven electromechanical tabulating device.
1894	William Burroughs produced the first practical adding machine for business purposes.
1924	Thomas J. Watson formed IBM.
1939	Konrad Zuse, Howard Aiken, and John Atanasoff independently constructed automatic electric calculating machines.
1945	John Mauchly and J. Presper Eckert introduced ENIAC, the first general-purpose electronic digital computer.
1945	A computer team working on a Mark II computer at the Bureau of Ordnance Computation Project at Harvard used the term ''bug'' to refer to a computer glitch when a moth caused computer malfunctions after it actually got inside the Mark II computer.
1948	The transistor was invented, signaling the end of the electron tube.
1952	Grace Brewster Hopper pioneered the writing of computer commands in English.
1958	Jack Kilby of Texas Instruments developed the integrated circuit, which, within 10 years, brought an end to electrically driven mechanical calculators and began the microcomputer age.
1963	The Bell Punch Co. of England produced the first fully transistorized four-function calculator.
1966	United States manufacturers introduced hand-held electronic calculators to the retail market.
1968	U.S. engineer Gilbert Hyatt invented the first microproces-

sor chip. The U.S. Patent Office did not issue a patent until July 17, 1990.

1971	American Edward Roberts began making personal computers, using microchip technology.
1974	Hewlett-Packard Company introduced the first programmable hand-held calculator.
1976	The first supercomputer was designed by Seymour Cray of the United States. The Cray-1 contains 200,000 integrated circuits and does 150,000,000 calculations per second.
1980	Scientific/statistical calculators and personal computers become available at a reasonable price.
1989	The Cray X-MP supercomputer is capable of 300 million calculations per second; the Japanese electronics firm NEC announced its SX-X supercomputer with an expected speed of 20 billion calculations per second.

Humankind's advances in developing calculating devices have been phenomenal. However, the first and most common calculating device is still the human mind. Over the centuries, human minds have performed calculations upon billions of digits. In fact, there have been men and women that have been called ''living calculators'' or calculating prodigies. They have been able to do computations without using ''paper-and-pencil'' algorithms. Their ability to memorize numbers and perform mental calculations is astounding.

Some of the prominent people with these powers, along with some of their feats in computation, are listed here.

Thomas Fuller (b. 1710), a black slave in Virginia, could mentally multiply four- and five-digit numbers and calculate the number of seconds in any period of time.

Johann Dase (b. 1824) of Germany was a professional calculator by the age of 15. He could mentally multiply two 20-digit numbers in 6 minutes and extract the square root of a number with 100 digits in 52 minutes.

Truman Safford (b. 1836) of Vermont mentally raised 365 to the 11th power in no more than a minute.

Gottfried Rückle (b. 1880) of Germany could recite all the factors of each integer less than 1000 by the age of 12.

Alexander Aitken (b. 1895) of New Zealand memorized the first 1000 digits of π, and Hans Eberstark (b. 1929) of Austria recited the first 11,944 digits of π. Eberstark's feat was bettered by Hideaki Tomoyori of Japan and, later, by Creighton Carvello, who memorized the first 20,013 digits of π.

Salo Finkelstein (b. 1896) of Russia could memorize 30 digits of a number after looking at it for only 3 seconds.

Wim Klein (b. 1912) of Holland mentally multiplied two five-digit numbers in 44 seconds.

Shyam Marathe (b. 1931) of India could mentally raise single-digit numbers up to the 20th power.

Shahuntala Dévi (b. 1940) of India extracted the 23rd root of a 501-digit number in 50 seconds.

Many other men and women through out the world have displayed this uncanny ability to work with numbers. Some of those worth mentioning are Jedediah Buxton (b. 1702 in England), Jacques Inaudi (b. 1867 in France), Péricles Diamandi (b. 1868 in Greece), George Bidder (b. 1826 in England), Henri Mondeux (b. 1826 in France), Arthur Griffith (b. 1880 in Indiana), Arumogan (b. 1896 in Ceylon), Maurice Dagbert (b. 1913 in France), Arthur Benjamin (b. 1961 in Cleveland), and Sheng Ke Gon (b. 1969 in China).

CHECK YOUR READING

1. Give evidence that the abacus is really a fast and accurate calculating device.
2. What inventions in electronics made the hand-held calculator and the personal computer realities?
3. In 1614, Sir Walter Raleigh of England wrote *The History of the World*. What was John Napier doing during this year?
4. In 1621, when the potato was introduced in Germany, what calculating device was in use?
5. When the carrier pigeon was used in Greece in 400 B.C., what calculating device was in use?
6. When the Chinese were perfecting gunpowder, around A.D. 1000, what calculating device was in use in Europe?
7. What were Ada, Countess of Lovelace's and Grace Hopper's contributions to computers?
8. What were the feats of India's mental calculators Shyam Marathe and Shahuntala Dévi?
9. When France was annexing Tahiti and the game of Bingo was being invented in Italy in 1880, what was Herman Hollerith building?
10. When the Ford Motor Company was producing its ten millionth automobile in 1924, what was Thomas J. Watson forming?
11. By 1959, Alaska became the 49th state in the United States, Lorraine Hansberry wrote *A Raisin in the Sun* and the ''Cha Cha Cha'' was a popular dance. What happened in electronics just before these events?
12. In 1823, as Mexico was becoming a republic, what was Charles Babbage doing?
13. What are some of the feats connected to memorizing the value for π?
14. Who is credited with pioneering the building of personal computers?
15. Match each of the following names with the correct mathematical discovery or event.

(a) Babbage	Adding machine for business purposes
(b) Burroughs	Automatic electric calculating machine
(c) Carvello	Early American mental calculator
(d) Cray	Electromechanical tabulating machine
(e) Fuller	ENIAC
(f) Hollerith	Integrated circuit
(g) Kilby	Mechanical calculators
(h) Mauchly, Ecker	Memorized 20,013 digits of π
(i) Pascal, Schickard, Leibniz	Steam-powered digital calculator
(j) Shockley, Brattain, Bardeen	Supercomputers
(k) Zuse, Aiken, Atanasoff	Transistor

RESEARCH QUESTIONS

In order to answer the following questions, you will need to refer to material not contained in the text. Possible sources of information are listed in the bibliography at the end of this book.

1. Explain how an abacus works. Give examples showing how it represents numbers and performs the addition of whole numbers.
2. What is Gunter's quadrant? What was it used for?
3. What are Napier's bones? What were they used for?
4. What is a slide rule? Explain how it works?
5. Describe the calculating machine invented by Blaise Pascal and explain how it worked?
6. Do some research on one of the mathematicians or inventors mentioned in this section or any other that contributed to the ability to do computation. Explain his or her contribution to computational devices. What other interests did he or she have? What else is he or she famous for?
7. What are some of the methods used by the mental calculators in performing their computational feats?
8. There have been many calculating machines and devices invented since 1600. Do some research on one of these machines, giving information on the inventors and the machine.
9. Trace the development of the computer in our society. Explain how it has done more than just improve our ability to calculate.
10. Discuss the speed of present-day computers in doing computation.
11. What are the differences between these four types of calculators available on the retail market:
    (a) The four-function calculator
    (b) The scientific/statistical calculator
    (c) The programmable calculator
    (d) The graphing calculator

What Type of Calculator Will You Need?

One of the goals of this book is to provide you with the mathematical skills needed in the real world. Because a large part of the modern world relies heavily on calculators and their ability to handle sophisticated calculations, it is necessary for all students using this book to have a scientific calculator and to be familiar with its use. By a scientific calculator we mean one that includes the following keys:

Trigonometry: sin, cos, and tan

Logarithms: ln x and log x

Exponentials: e^x and x^y

A calculator that contains statistical functions such as MEAN and STANDARD DEVIATION will make the statistics chapter easier, but these functions are not essential. Scientific calculators are usually available for less than $20. They can be found at discount stores, as well as at department stores and electronics shops.

Using Your Calculator

You may be familiar with the basic keys on your calculator, but there may be a few buttons you rarely use. This section will be discussing the keys needed in this course. When we want to indicate that a particular key is being used, the symbol for that key will be enclosed in a box. For example, for $3 \times 4 = 12$, we use the keys

Press	Display
(3)(×)(4)(=)	12

Since we pushed the keys for 3, 4, $\times$, and $=$, these characters are in boxes. The 12 is not in a box since we did not push those keys.

Note

In order to understand this material, it is very important for you to have a calculator available when reading this section. As we do each example, you should try the example on your own calculator. We will demonstrate one method in the text. **However, because of the differences among calculators, this method may not work with your calculator**.

For further help, read your calculator instruction manual or ask your instructor.

The first key we will discuss in the change-of-sign key. It looks like

(±)   or   (+/−)   or   (CHS)

This key is used to create negative numbers in the calculator. On most calculators, to enter a negative value the negative sign must be entered after the number. For example, to enter the value -6, the keys must be pressed in the order

(6)(±)

Example 1:

Use a calculator to find the value of $15 \div (-3)$.

Solution: We know that the answer should be -5. Using a calculator, we get

Press	Display
(1)(5)(÷)(3)(±)(=)	-5

Notice that the parentheses around -3 do not need to be entered into the calculator.

The next key we use is the reciprocal key. It looks like

($\frac{1}{x}$)   or   ($1/x$)

This key provides a shortcut for the division problem $1 \div x$.

Example 2:

Find the decimal value of $1/5$.

Solution: Using the reciprocal key on the calculator gives

$$\boxed{5}\ \boxed{1/x}\ = 0.2$$

Notice that we did not need to push the equals key. The reciprocal key did all the work.

The reciprocal key is especially useful when you add fractions with numerators that are 1's.

Example 3:

Find the decimal value of $1/5 + 1/7 - 1/6$.

Solution: Using the reciprocal key on the calculator gives

Press   **Display**

≈ 0.176190

The third key we discuss is the exponent key. It looks like

$$\boxed{x^y}\quad \text{or}\quad \boxed{y^x}$$

To determine if we are using the key correctly, we will first do a problem to which we know the answer. After that, we will do more complicated examples.

Example 4:

Use a calculator to find the value of 2^3.

Solution: We know that the answer should be 8. Using a calculator, we get

Press   **Display**

$$\boxed{2}\ \boxed{x^y}\ \boxed{3}\ \boxed{=}\qquad\qquad 8$$

Since this is the correct answer, we must be using the calculator correctly.

Example 5:

Use a calculator to find the value of 1.065^{-58}.

Solution: Using a calculator, we get

Press   **Display**

$\boxed{1}\,\boxed{.}\,\boxed{0}\,\boxed{6}\,\boxed{5}\,\boxed{x^y}\,\boxed{5}\,\boxed{8}\,\boxed{\pm}\,\boxed{=}$ ≈ 0.025925

Because the exponent is negative, we needed to use the $\pm$ symbol *after* entering 58. Entering this symbol before 58 may result in an incorrect answer.

From algebra, you may remember that fractional exponents are the same as roots. For example,

$$\sqrt{x} = \sqrt[2]{x} = x^{1/2} \qquad \text{or} \qquad \sqrt[5]{x} = x^{1/5}$$

Although most calculators have a key to calculate square roots, calculators do not have a fifth-root key. As a result, to compute most roots, it is necessary to use fractional exponents.

In the next example, we want to combine the use of the reciprocal and exponent keys to solve problems involving fractional exponents.

Example 6:

Calculate $\sqrt[3]{8} = 8^{1/3}$.

Solution: We know that the answer is 2 since the cube root of 8 is 2. Using the reciprocal key and exponent keys on the calculator gives

Press   **Display**

$\boxed{8}\,\boxed{x^y}\,\boxed{3}\,\boxed{1/x}\,\boxed{=}$ 2

Push the keys again and watch what happens in the display. When the reciprocal key is pushed after hitting 3, the display shows 0.333333333. This is the reciprocal of 3, not the cube root of 8. It is necessary to hit the equals key to complete the calculation.

Example 7:

Calculate $85^{1/25}$.

Solution: Using the reciprocal key and exponent keys on the calculator gives

Press   **Display**

$\boxed{8}\,\boxed{5}\,\boxed{x^y}\,\boxed{2}\,\boxed{5}\,\boxed{1/x}\,\boxed{=}$ ≈ 1.194474

Throughout the book, we will specify the number of places after the decimal point that should be used. To achieve greater accuracy, increase the number of decimal places.

Scientific Notation

The last topic in this review is using scientific notation on a scientific calculator. When we need to enter a number like 4×10^6 on a calculator, we use a button labeled

$$\boxed{\text{EXP}}$$

(On some calculators, this is done by using the MODE button.)

Example 8:

Enter the number 4.23×10^{19} on a calculator.

Solution: Using the EXP button gives

Press

The display of the calculator should now look like the display of the calculator shown above. The gap between the 4.23 and the 19 is what indicates that the calculator is using scientific notation. ▪

Example 9:

Use a calculator to find the value of $(2 \times 10^{19}) \div (8 \times 10^{29})$.

Solution: Using the EXP button gives

Press	Display
② (EXP) ① ⑨ ÷ ⑧ (EXP) ② ⑨ ⑤	2.5 − 11

Notice that the display of your calculator has a − 11 off to the right side of 2.5. Since this is how a calculator displays scientific notation, the answer is 2.5×10^{-11}.

CALCULATOR REVIEW

PROBLEMS

Solve Problems 1–16, using your calculator. If necessary, round off your answers to six places after the decimal place.

1. 1/5

2. 1/4

3. 1/27

4. 1/17

5. $(-6) \div (-8)$

6. $(-12) \div (-4)$

7. $(-6.23) \div (-8.3)$

8. $(-1.56) \div (-2.7)$

9. $3^{2.3}$

10. $3^{-2.3}$

11. $6^{-0.53}$

12. $5^{-4.5}$

13. $81^{1/81}$

14. $17^{-1/17}$

15. $17^{1/17}$

16. $81^{-1/81}$

Solve the following, using the scientific notation key on your calculator.

17. $(2 \times 10^{-9}) \div (5 \times 10^{21})$

18. $(3.2 \times 10^{15}) \times (8 \times 10^{19})$

19. $(5 \times 10^{-9}) - (3 \times 10^{-10})$

20. $(2 \times 10^{-30}) + (8 \times 10^{-29})$

Solve the following, using the reciprocal key on your calculator.

21. 1/6 − 1/5

22. 1/9 + 1/7

23. 1/21 + 1/3 + 1/5

24. 1/8 + 1/13 − 1/5

NORMAL TABLE

This table gives the area under the standard normal curve, between $z = 0$ and the given value of z.

z	Area	z	Area	z	Area	z	Area
0.00	0.0000	0.30	0.1179	0.60	0.2257	0.90	0.3159
0.01	0.0040	0.31	0.1217	0.61	0.2291	0.91	0.3186
0.02	0.0078	0.32	0.1255	0.62	0.2323	0.92	0.3212
0.03	0.0120	0.33	0.1293	0.63	0.2357	0.93	0.3238
0.04	0.0160	0.34	0.1331	0.64	0.2389	0.94	0.3262
0.05	0.0199	0.35	0.1368	0.65	0.2422	0.95	0.3289
0.06	0.0239	0.36	0.1406	0.66	0.2454	0.96	0.3315
0.07	0.0279	0.37	0.1443	0.67	0.2486	0.97	0.3340
0.08	0.0319	0.38	0.1480	0.68	0.2517	0.98	0.3365
0.09	0.0359	0.39	0.1517	0.69	0.2549	0.99	0.3389
0.10	0.0398	0.40	0.1554	0.70	0.2580	1.00	0.3413
0.11	0.0438	0.41	0.1591	0.71	0.2611	1.01	0.3438
0.12	0.0478	0.42	0.1628	0.72	0.2642	1.02	0.3461
0.13	0.0517	0.43	0.1664	0.73	0.2673	1.03	0.3485
0.14	0.0557	0.44	0.1700	0.74	0.2704	1.04	0.3508
0.15	0.0596	0.45	0.1736	0.75	0.2734	1.05	0.3531
0.16	0.0636	0.46	0.1772	0.76	0.2764	1.06	0.3554
0.17	0.0675	0.47	0.1808	0.77	0.2794	1.07	0.3577
0.18	0.0714	0.48	0.1844	0.78	0.2823	1.08	0.3599
0.19	0.0753	0.49	0.1879	0.79	0.2852	1.09	0.3621
0.20	0.0793	0.50	0.1915	0.80	0.2881	1.10	0.3643
0.21	0.0832	0.51	0.1950	0.81	0.2910	1.11	0.3665
0.22	0.0871	0.52	0.1985	0.82	0.2939	1.12	0.3686
0.23	0.0910	0.53	0.2019	0.83	0.2967	1.13	0.3708
0.24	0.0948	0.54	0.2054	0.84	0.2995	1.14	0.3729
0.25	0.0987	0.55	0.2088	0.85	0.3023	1.15	0.3749
0.26	0.1026	0.56	0.2123	0.86	0.3051	1.16	0.3770
0.27	0.1064	0.57	0.2157	0.87	0.3079	1.17	0.3790
0.28	0.1102	0.58	0.2190	0.88	0.3106	1.18	0.3810
0.29	0.1141	0.59	0.2224	0.89	0.3133	1.19	0.3830

z	Area	z	Area	z	Area	z	Area
1.20	0.3849	1.63	0.4484	2.06	0.4803	2.49	0.4936
1.21	0.3869	1.64	0.4495	2.07	0.4808	2.50	0.4938
1.22	0.3888	1.65	0.4505	2.08	0.4812	2.51	0.4940
1.23	0.3907	1.66	0.4515	2.09	0.4817	2.52	0.4941
1.24	0.3925	1.67	0.4525	2.10	0.4821	2.53	0.4943
1.25	0.3944	1.68	0.4535	2.11	0.4826	2.54	0.4945
1.26	0.3962	1.69	0.4545	2.12	0.4830	2.55	0.4946
1.27	0.3980	1.70	0.4554	2.13	0.4834	2.56	0.4948
1.28	0.3997	1.71	0.4564	2.14	0.4838	2.57	0.4949
1.29	0.4015	1.72	0.4573	2.15	0.4842	2.58	0.4951
1.30	0.4032	1.73	0.4582	2.16	0.4846	2.59	0.4952
1.31	0.4049	1.74	0.4591	2.17	0.4850	2.60	0.4953
1.32	0.4066	1.75	0.4599	2.18	0.4854	2.61	0.4955
1.33	0.4082	1.76	0.4608	2.19	0.4857	2.62	0.4956
1.34	0.4099	1.77	0.4616	2.20	0.4861	2.63	0.4957
1.35	0.4115	1.78	0.4625	2.21	0.4864	2.64	0.4959
1.36	0.4131	1.79	0.4633	2.22	0.4868	2.65	0.4960
1.37	0.4147	1.80	0.4641	2.23	0.4871	2.66	0.4961
1.38	0.4162	1.81	0.4649	2.24	0.4875	2.67	0.4962
1.39	0.4177	1.82	0.4656	2.25	0.4878	2.68	0.4963
1.40	0.4192	1.83	0.4664	2.26	0.4881	2.69	0.4964
1.41	0.4207	1.84	0.4671	2.27	0.4884	2.70	0.4965
1.42	0.4222	1.85	0.4678	2.28	0.4887	2.71	0.4966
1.43	0.4236	1.86	0.4686	2.29	0.4890	2.72	0.4967
1.44	0.4251	1.87	0.4693	2.30	0.4893	2.73	0.4968
1.45	0.4265	1.88	0.4699	2.31	0.4896	2.74	0.4969
1.46	0.4279	1.89	0.4706	2.32	0.4898	2.75	0.4970
1.47	0.4292	1.90	0.4713	2.33	0.4901	2.76	0.4971
1.48	0.4306	1.91	0.4719	2.34	0.4904	2.77	0.4972
1.49	0.4319	1.92	0.4726	2.35	0.4906	2.78	0.4973
1.50	0.4332	1.93	0.4732	2.36	0.4909	2.79	0.4974
1.51	0.4345	1.94	0.4738	2.37	0.4911	2.80	0.4974
1.52	0.4357	1.95	0.4744	2.38	0.4913	2.81	0.4975
1.53	0.4370	1.96	0.4750	2.39	0.4916	2.82	0.4976
1.54	0.4382	1.97	0.4756	2.40	0.4918	2.83	0.4977
1.55	0.4394	1.98	0.4761	2.41	0.4920	2.84	0.4977
1.56	0.4406	1.99	0.4767	2.42	0.4922	2.85	0.4978
1.57	0.4418	2.00	0.4772	2.43	0.4925	2.86	0.4979
1.58	0.4429	2.01	0.4778	2.44	0.4927	2.87	0.4979
1.59	0.4441	2.02	0.4783	2.45	0.4929	2.88	0.4980
1.60	0.4452	2.03	0.4788	2.46	0.4931	2.89	0.4981
1.61	0.4463	2.04	0.4793	2.47	0.4932	2.90	0.4981
1.62	0.4474	2.05	0.4798	2.48	0.4934	2.91	0.4982

z	Area	z	Area	z	Area	z	Area
2.92	0.4982	3.20	0.49931	3.47	0.49974	3.74	0.49991
2.93	0.4983	3.21	0.49934	3.48	0.49975	3.75	0.49991
2.94	0.4984	3.22	0.49936	3.49	0.49976	3.76	0.49992
2.95	0.4984	3.23	0.49938	3.50	0.49977	3.77	0.49992
2.96	0.4985	3.24	0.49940	3.51	0.49978	3.78	0.49999
2.97	0.4985	3.25	0.49942	3.52	0.49978	3.79	0.49993
2.98	0.4986	3.26	0.49944	3.53	0.49979	3.80	0.49993
2.99	0.4986	3.27	0.49946	3.54	0.49980	3.81	0.49993
3.00	0.4987	3.28	0.49948	3.55	0.49981	3.82	0.49993
3.01	0.49869	3.29	0.49950	3.56	0.49982	3.83	0.49994
3.02	0.49874	3.30	0.49952	3.57	0.49982	3.84	0.49994
3.03	0.49878	3.31	0.49953	3.58	0.49983	3.85	0.49994
3.04	0.49881	3.32	0.49955	3.59	0.49986	3.86	0.49994
3.05	0.49886	3.33	0.49957	3.60	0.49984	3.87	0.49995
3.06	0.49889	3.34	0.49958	3.61	0.49985	3.88	0.49995
3.07	0.49893	3.35	0.49960	3.62	0.49985	3.89	0.49995
3.08	0.49897	3.36	0.49961	3.63	0.49986	3.90	0.49995
3.09	0.49900	3.37	0.49962	3.64	0.49986	3.91	0.49995
3.10	0.49903	3.38	0.49964	3.65	0.49987	3.92	0.49996
3.11	0.49907	3.39	0.49965	3.66	0.49987	3.93	0.49996
3.12	0.49970	3.40	0.49966	3.67	0.49988	3.94	0.49996
3.13	0.49913	3.41	0.49968	3.68	0.49988	3.95	0.49996
3.14	0.49916	3.42	0.49969	3.69	0.49989	3.96	0.49996
3.15	0.49918	3.43	0.49970	3.70	0.49989	3.97	0.49996
3.16	0.49921	3.44	0.49971	3.71	0.49990	3.98	0.49997
3.17	0.49924	3.45	0.49972	3.72	0.49990	3.99	0.49997
3.18	0.49926	3.46	0.49973	3.73	0.49990	4.00	0.49997
3.19	0.49929						

BIBLIOGRAPHY

Aleksandrov, A. D., *Mathematics—Its Content, Methods, and Meaning,* M.I.T. Press, Cambridge, MA, 1963.

Andrews, W. S., *Magic Squares and Cubes,* Dover Publications, New York, 1960.

Asimov, Isaac, *Asimov's Biographical Encyclopedia of Science and Technology*, Doubleday, New York, 1982.

Asimov, Isaac, *Asimov's New Guide to Science*, Basic Books, New York, 1984.

Ball, W. W. Rouse, *A Short Account of the History of Mathematics*, Dover Publications, New York, 1960.

Barnsley, Michael, *Fractals Everywhere,* Academic Press, New York, 1988.

Beckman, Petr, *A History of Pi*, Martin Press, New York, 1971.

Bell, E. T., *Men of Mathematics*, Simon and Schuster, New York, 1937.

Bell, E. T., *Mathematics Queen and Servant of Science*, Mathematics Association of America, Washington, D.C., 1987.

Boyer, Carl B., *A History of Mathematics*, John Wiley and Sons, New York, 1968.

Boyer, Carl B., *A History of the Calculus,* Dover Publications, New York, 1959.

Burke, James, *Connections*, Little, Brown and Company, Boston, 1978.

Burke, James, *The Day the Universe Changed*, Little, Brown and Company, Boston, 1985.

Cajori, Florian, *The Early Mathematical Sciences in North and South America*, Gorham Press, Boston, 1928.

Cajori, Florian, *A History of Mathematics*, Chelsea Publishing, New York, 1918.

Campbell, Douglas and Higgins, John, eds., *Mathematics: People, Problems, Results,* Wadsworth International, Belmont, CA, 1984.

Dantzig, Tobias, *Number: The Language of Science,* Macmillan Company, New York, 1930.

Durant, Will, *The Age of Faith*, Simon and Schuster, New York, 1950.

Durant, Will, *Our Oriental Heritage*, Simon and Schuster, New York, 1963.

Eves, Howard, *Great Moments in the History of Mathematics*, Mathematics Association of America, Washington, D.C., 1982.

Eves, Howard, *In Mathematical Circles,* vols. 1, 2, Prindle, Weber, & Schmidt, Boston, 1969.

Eves, Howard, *An Introduction to the History of Mathematics*, Saunders College Publishing, Philadelphia, 1990.

Friend, J. Newton, *Numbers: Fun & Facts*, Charles Scribner's Sons, New York, 1954.

Gardner, Martin, *Penrose Tiles to Trapdoor Ciphers*, W. H. Freeman, New York, 1988.

Gillispie, Charles C., *Dictionary of Scientific Biography*, Vols. I–XVI, Charles Scribner's Sons, New York, 1970.

Gleick, James, *Chaos*, Viking Press, New York, 1987.

Grinstein, Louise and Campbell, Paul, eds., *Women of Mathematics*, Greenwood Press, New York, 1987.

Hacking, Ian, *The Emergence of Probability*, Cambridge University Press, Cambridge, Great Britain, 1975.

Heath, Sir Thomas, *Euclid's Elements*, Vol. 1, Dover Publications, New York, 1956.

Heath, Sir Thomas, *A History of Greek Mathematics*, Dover Publications, New York, 1981.

Hildreth, Richard, *The History of Banks*, Augustus M. Kelley Publishers, New York, 1968.

Hogben, Lancelot, *Mathematics in the Making*, Doubleday, New York, 1960.

Holt, Michael, *Mathematics in Art*, Van Nostrand Reinhold, New York, 1971.

Ifah, Georges, *From One to Zero*, Viking Penguin, New York, 1985.

Kline, Morris, *Mathematics in Western Culture*, Oxford University Press, New York, 1953.

Klise, Eugene, *Money and Banking,* 5th ed., Cincinnati South-Western Publishing, Cincinnati, 1972.

Kruskal, William and Tanur, Judith, eds., *International Encylopedia of Statistics*, The Free Press, New York, 1978.

Mandelbrot, Benoit, *The Fractal Geometry of Nature*, W. H. Freeman, New York, 1982.

Marcorini, Edgardo, ed., *The History of Science and Technology, A Narrative Chronology*, Facts on File, New York, 1988.

Menninger, Karl, *Number Words and Number Symbols*, M.I.T. Press, Cambridge, MA, 1958.

Mount, Ellis and List, Barbara, *Milestones in Science and Technology: The Ready Reference Guide to Discoveries, Inventions and Facts*. Oryx Press, Phoenix, 1987.

Newell, Virginia, ed. *Black Mathematicians*, Dorrance and Co., Ardmore, PA, 1980.

Newman, James, *The World of Mathematics*, Simon and Schuster, New York, 1956.

Osen, Lynn, *Women in Mathematics*, M.I.T. Press, Cambridge, MA, 1974.

Parkinson, Claire L., *Breakthrough, A Chronology of Great Achievements in Science and Mathematics*, G. K. Hall, Boston, 1985.

Peitgen, H. O. and Richter, P. H., *The Beauty of Fractals*, Springer-Verlag, New York, 1986.

Peitgen, H. O. and Saupe, D., eds., *The Science of Fractal Images*, Springer-Verlag, New York, 1988.

Peri, Teri, *Math Equals*, Addison-Wesley, Menlo Park, CA, 1978.

Peterson, Ivars, *The Mathematical Tourist*, W. H. Freeman, New York, 1988.

Prenowitz, Walter and Jordan, Meyer, *Basic Concepts of Geometry*, Blaisdell Publishing, Waltham, MA, 1965.

Resnikoff, H. L. and Wells, R. O., *Mathematics in Civilization*, Dover Publications, New York, 1984.

Ritchie, David, *The Computer Pioneers: The Making of the Modern Computer*, Simon and Schuster, New York, 1986.

Seymour, Dale and Britton, Jill, *Introduction to Tessellations*, Dale Seymour Publications, Palo Alto, CA, 1989.

Shaw, W. A., *The History of Currency*, Augustus M. Kelley Publishers, New York, 1967.

Smith, David E., *History of Mathematics*, Dover Publications, New York, 1958.

Smith, David and Mikami, Yoshio, *A History of Japanese Mathematics*, The Open Court Press, Chicago, 1914.

Smith, Steven, *The Great Mental Calculators*, Columbia Press, New York, 1983.

Stewart, Ian, *Does God Play Dice?*, Basil Blackwell, New York, 1989.

Stigler, Stephen M., *The History of Statistics*, Belknap Press, Cambridge, MA, 1986.

Temple, Robert, *The Genius of China*, Simon and Schuster, New York, 1986.

Turnbull, Herbert, *The Great Mathematicians*, New York University Press, New York, 1961.

White, A. D., *A History of the Warfare of Science with Theology in Christendom*, Dover Press, New York, 1960.

Williams, Michael R., *A History of Computing Technology*, Prentice-Hall, Englewood Cliffs, N.J., 1985.

Zaslavsky, Claudia, *Africa Counts*, Chicago Review, Chicago, 1979.

SELECTED ANSWERS

CHAPTER 1

Section 1.1
1. 121,000   3. 1,010,101   5. 1106   7. 734   9. 42,457   11. 7502
13. 37   15. 25,062   17. 11   19. 363   21. 57,068,640

23. a. ⚷ ⑨⑨⑨⑨⑨∩∩∩
    b. ✕HHHH△△△△
    c. MCDXL
    d. —
       千
       四
       百
       四
       十
    e. ′α υ μ
    f. ◄ ◄ ∨ ∨ ∨ ∨ ◀
    g. ····
       ⊕
       ⊕

Section 1.2
1. $1 \times 10^2 + 3 \times 10^1 + 9 \times 10^0$
3. $4 \times 10^2 + 3 \times 10^1 + 7 \times 10^0 + 1 \times 10^{-1} + 5 \times 10^{-2}$
5. $3 \times 10^{-1} + 1 \times 10^{-2} + 4 \times 10^{-3}$
7. $5 \times 10^5 + 4 \times 10^4 + 3 \times 10^3 + 8 \times 10^2 + 6 \times 10^1 + 7 \times 10^0$
9. $5 \times 10^1 + 3 \times 10^0 + 1 \times 10^{-1} + 7 \times 10^{-2} + 1 \times 10^{-3}$
11. $6 \times 10^{-1} + 2 \times 10^{-2} + 1 \times 10^{-3} + 9 \times 10^{-4} + 3 \times 10^{-5}$
13. Tens, hundredths, tens, ten-thousands, tenths, hundredths, thousands, hundredths, ones, ones, hundred-thousandths, thousandths
15. $1/10 + 1/4 = 7/20$ 17. $1/1000 + 1/300 + 1/20 = 163/3000$
19. $12/60 = 1/5$ 21. $10/60 + 10/3600 + 10/216,000 = 3661/21,600$
23. $1/3$ 25. $3/4$ 27. $1/63$ 29. $49/501$ 31. $743\frac{1}{5}$ 33. $101\frac{1}{34}$

35. ◎   ◎
    ||| ∩||

37. ◎   ◎
    ||| |||||

Section 1.3

1. 77   **3.** 5.625   **5.** 2952   **7.** 1132.25   **9.** 40,736   **11.** 136
13. 3101_5 **15.** $14A0_{16}$ **17.** 2431_5, 31000_5 **19.** 556_8, 3720_8
21. $16E_{16}$, $7D0_{16}$ **23.** 313_8, CB_{16} **25.** 7353_8, EEB_{16}
27. a. 52_{16},   **b.** $1\ 010\ 010_2$, 82
29. a. $2B_{16}$,   **b.** $101\ 011_2$, 43
31. a. 39_{16},   **b.** $111\ 001_2$, 57
33. 254_9 is the larger value.   **35.** 3033_4 is the larger value.

Section 1.4

1. a. 1, $\sqrt{49}$, 9   **b.** 0, 1, $\sqrt{49}$, 9   **c.** -11, -4, 0, 1, $\sqrt{49}$, 9
   d. -11, -9.4, $-8\frac{2}{9}$, -4, 0, $\frac{3}{4}$, 1, 6.1212 . . . , $\sqrt{49}$, 9, 10.12
   e. $-\sqrt{50}$, $-\sqrt[3]{7.3}$, $\sqrt{2}$
   f. -11, -9.4, $-8\frac{2}{9}$, $-\sqrt{50}$, -4, $-\sqrt[3]{7.3}$, 0, $\frac{3}{4}$, 1, $\sqrt{2}$, 6.1212 . . . ,
   $\sqrt{49}$, 9, 10.12
   g. $\sqrt{-2}$ **h.** -9.4, $-8\frac{2}{9}$, $\frac{3}{4}$, 6.1212 . . . , 10.12
3. a. T   **b.** F, π **c.** T   **d.** F, 5   **e.** F, -1 **f.** T   **g.** F, 1
   h. F, π **i.** F, $5i$ **j.** F, π **k.** F, $\sqrt{4}$ **l.** T
5. Even numbers have 2 as a factor. Odd numbers do not have 2 as a factor.
7. Square numbers: 1, 4, 9, 16, 25, 36, 49, 64, 81, 100
   Pentagonal numbers: 1, 5, 12, 22, 35, 51, 70, 92, 117, 145
9. All other even numbers have 2 as a proper factor.
11. a. Prime, deficient   **b.** Composite, deficient   **c.** Composite, deficient
   d. Composite, abundant   **e.** Composite, perfect   **f.** Composite, abundant
13. No, yes, no
15.

16	6	8
2	10	18
12	14	4

15	5	7
1	9	17
11	13	3

17. $\frac{22}{7}$ is a rational number (which is approximately $= \pi$), but π is an irrational number.

Chapter 1 Summary

1. a. ꘖ∩∩|||

   b. CXXIII

   c. —
   百
   ≡
   ＋
   ≡

   d. $\rho\kappa\gamma$

   e. ⋁ ⋁   ⋁ ⋁ ⋁

   f. ⋅|⋅
   ...

   g. 123   **h.** $1\ 111\ 011_2$ **i.** 443_5 **j.** 173_8 **k.** $A3_{12}$ **l.** $7B_{16}$

2. a. ↓↓↓↓←←←←→→→   **b.** ↑↑↓↓↓↓←←←→
   c. ↕↔↔↔↑↑↓←   **d.** ↔↑↑↑
3. a. 54, 614, 8945, 3012, 71,750, 10,400   **b.** ä ḃ c, ë ḟ f, ë ḃ ḣ, ä

5. $/\blacktriangledown\times\blacktriangledown,//\times\blacktriangledown\times,//*\times\times**,\blacktriangledown\blacktriangledown\times\times*$

6. 234_7, 1032_7, 21252_7, 2626_7 **7.** $1\ 010\ 011_2$, 83_{10}, 53_{16}

8. For a composite answer, use any multiple of 41.

9. Composite, abundant; prime, deficient; composite, perfect; composite, deficient

10. *Hint:* The sum is 130.   **11.** *Hint:* The sums are (b) 40, (c) 40, and (d) 27.

12. a. $\sqrt{-400}$ **b.** -5, 0, 13, $\sqrt[3]{-27}$ **c.** $-\sqrt{40}$, $\sqrt[4]{19}$, π **d.** 13

    e. All but those listed in c and $\sqrt{-400}$ **f.** All but $\sqrt{-400}$ **g.** 0, 13

Section 2.0

1.

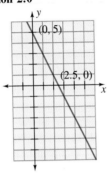

3.

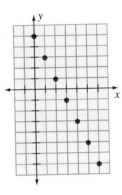

5.

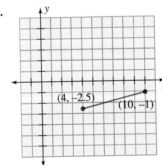

7. $y = 4x - 17$ **9.** $y = (275/4)x + 525$ or $y = 68.75x + 525$

11. Vertex $(-4, -23)$

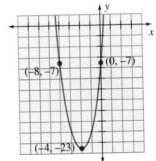

13. Vertex $(-7/8, 49/16)$ or $(-0.875, 3.0625)$

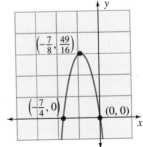

15. Vertex $(-8, -40)$

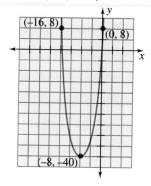

17. 0.80 or -8.80 **19.** 2.15 or -0.15 **21.** 731.162

23. 29.182   **25.** 22.291   **27.** 25,212.463

29.

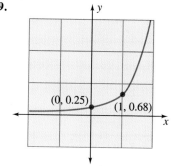

31.

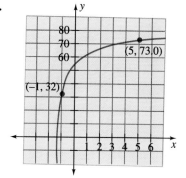

33.

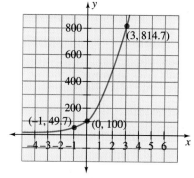

35. An error message is displayed.

Section 2.1

1. a.

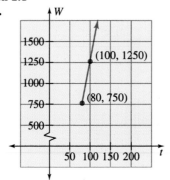

b. $m = 25$; for increase of 1° in temperature, water consumption increases by 25 gal/hour.

c. 1250 gallons

3. a. $V = -1700t + 16{,}500$ **b.** 9.4 years

5. $A = 1.09B$ where A = volume after cooling, B = volume before cooling

7. a. $y = 3t + 27$, where $0 \le t \le 12$ **b.** $0 \le t \le 12$

c.

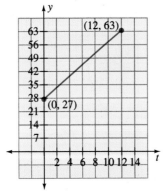

9. a. $S = 180N - 360$ **b.** $N \ge 3$, where N is an integer

11. a. If this were a linear function, each change of 10° in the actual temperature would cause the wind-chill temperature to change by some constant amount. The data shows that this is not true. A temperature change from 40° to 30° causes the wind-chill temperature to fall by 12°, while a temperature drop from 30° to 20° causes a wind-chill drop of 13°.

b. $W = 1.2t - 20$

c. The formula gives an answer 2° warmer than the actual value.

d.

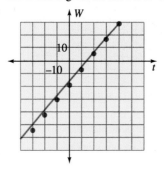

e. Though not exact, the graph does closely approximate the data.

Section 2.2

1. a.

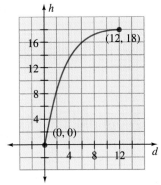

b. Maximum height = 18 ft
3. a. $h = (-1/2)d^2 + 2d + 20$ **b.** 8.63 ft
5. a. $s = -16t^2 + 139.33t + 9$ **b.** 312.33 ft   **c.** 8.8 sec.
7. a. $h = -16t^2 + 640$ **b.** 144 ft   **c.** 6.32 sec.
9. a. $D = 0.0568s^2 + 1.06s$ **b.** At 55 mph, 230 ft; at 65 mph, 309 ft
c. The formula for the stopping distance is accurate to within a few feet.
d. 3249 ft
11. a. $y = -0.000868x^2 + x$ **b.** 288 ft   **c.** 1152 ft   **d.** $576 - 288 = 288$ ft

Section 2.3

1. a. $p = 5^w$ **b.** 244,140,625
3. a

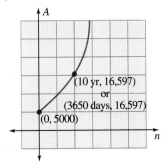

b. $5637.37   **c.** $55,094.10
5. a. 283,300,237   **b.** 287,000,000
c. There were actually more people than was estimated by the formula.
d. The death rate is lower due to medical advances.
7. 6.3 lb/in^2
9. A beginning golfer usually has a high score, which gradually decreases as his/her skills improve. The decrease in the score continues for a period of time but eventually levels off. This decrease in values followed by a leveling off is the behavior exhibited by a decreasing exponential function.

Section 2.4

1. a. 89.2%   **b.** 60.5 inches, or 5' 1/2"
3. a. 27.5 min.   **b.** 65.3 min.

c.

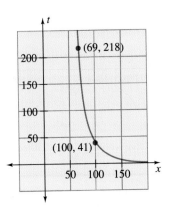

5. While initially a person may lift a small amount of weight, as the person's strength increases, the amount of weight he/she can lift increases. This will continue, but the increases will become small as the person starts lifting heavier weights. This is the type of behavior exhibited by a logarithmic function.

Chapter 2 Summary

1. **a.**

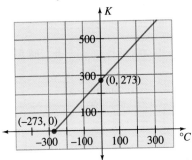

    b. $-273°C$ **c.** 373 K

2. **a.** A constant change in the weight causes a constant change in the calories.
    b. $C = 2.727w + 140$ **c.** 576.32 cal.

3. **a.** The number of logs in each row changes by a constant amount.
    b. $L = -2r + 249$, where r is an integer with $1 \le r \le 124$

    c.

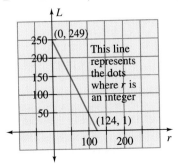

    d. 149   **e.** 124 rows

4. a. $s = 293a - 2535$ **b.** 2739 stamps   **c.** $42.78 \approx 43$ years old

5. a.

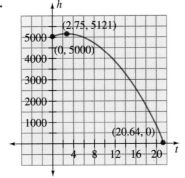

b. 5121 ft   **c.** 20.64 sec.

6. a. $h = -0.001758x^2 + 0.616x$ (in inches)   **b.** 4' 10.5" and 24' 3.5"

7. a. $P = (3/2)t^2 - (1/2)t$

b.

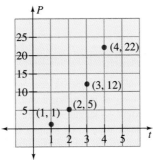

c. 14,950; a pentagon with 100 dots on a side and all the smaller pentagons contained inside

8. a.

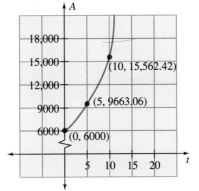

b. $9663.06, $15,562.45, $104,696.41

9. a.

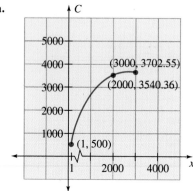

b. $3263.10, $3540.36

c. $3.26, $1.77; as the number of toys produced increases, the cost per toy decreases.

10. a. $A = 3^s$ **b.** $19,683; no   **c.** No, $282,000,000,000 is needed

d. $12,157,665,460,000,000,000; $\approx 303,941,637$ years

CHAPTER 3

Section 3.1

1. It is not a good definition since it does not distinguish a point from all other objects; for example, a moment in time or a unit of length also has no parts.

3. dimension → extent → length → dimension

5. Not all terms can be defined by simpler terms. There must be a starting point for definitions. These are the undefined terms of a deductive system of geometry. Similarly, not all propositions can be proved. There must be some premises to begin a deductive system. These are the postulates of the system.

7. $5 + 6x = 4x - 11 \rightarrow 5 + (-5) + 6x = 4x - 11 + (-5)$ (A3)

$$6x = 4x - 16$$
$$6x - 4x = 4x - 4x - 16 \quad \text{(A3)}$$
$$2x = -16$$
$$x = -8 \quad \text{(A4)}$$

9. According to P3, if two points of a line lie in a plane then the line containing the two points lies in the plane. In the figure, points A and B lie in the plane, but the line containing A and B does not lie in the plane. Thus, the figure is not possible in Euclidean geometry.

11. In the statement of the transitive property, a and c are both equal to b. Thus, they are equal to each other by A2.

13. If two parallel lines are cut by a transversal, each set of corresponding angles is equal.

15. The measure of an exterior angle of a triangle is equal to the sum of the nonadjacent interior angles of the triangle.

17.

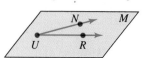

19.

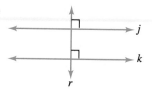

21.

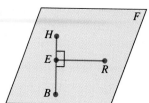

23.

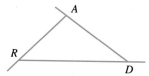

25. *Hypothesis: m* intersects *n*
   Conclusion: m intersects *n* in only one point *Q*

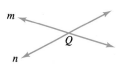

27. *Hypothesis:* ∠1 is an exterior angle of △*ABC*
   Conclusion: ∠1 > ∠*A*, ∠1 > ∠*C*

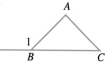

29. *Hypothesis: m* ∥ *n, t* is a transversal; ∠1 and ∠2 are alternate interior angles
   Conclusion: ∠1 = ∠2

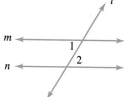

Section 3.2

1. The parallel postulates describe the number of parallel lines to a given line through a point that is not on the line. The Euclidean postulate states that there is only one such parallel. The Riemannian postulate states that there is no parallel, while the Lobachevskian postulate states that there is more than one parallel.

3. Riemannian geometry is based on two postulates that are different from those of Euclidean geometry, while Lobachevskian geometry is based on only one postulate that is different from Euclidean geometry. Since Lobachevskian geometry has more postulates that are the same as Euclidean geometry, we would expect it to have more theorems that are the same as Euclidean geometry.

5. Mathematics does not establish truths about the physical world. It can only give logical descriptions of the physical world based on beginning assumptions (postulates).

7.

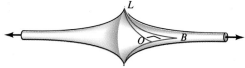

9.

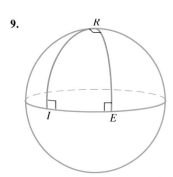

11. $h \parallel k$ and $n \parallel k$, yet h and k intersect at P.
$h \parallel k$ and $n \parallel k$, and h and k are parallel.

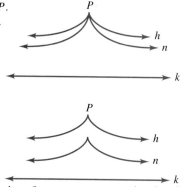

13. By drawing the diagonal of a four-sided plane figure, you get two triangles. Since in Lobachevskian geometry the sum of the angles of a triangle is less than 180°, the sum of the angles of the two triangles would be less than 360°. But a rectangle has four right angles, and the sum of its angles is exactly 360°. Thus, the Lobachevskian four-sided plane figure cannot have four right angles. Therefore, rectangles as defined do not exist in Lobachevskian geometry.

15. The angle at A is obtuse.

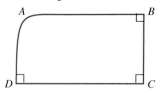

17. *Hint:* The three angles must be equal, and the sum of the angles must be less than 180°.

19. *Hint:* The three angles must be equal, and the sum of the angles must be greater than 180°.

21. *Hint:* If the sum of the angles is greater than 180°, is it possible for two of the three angles to be equal to 90°?

Section 3.3

3. The point is 2.6 cm from one end of the segment.

5. The point is 3.8 cm from one end of the segment.

7. No   **9.** No   **11.** 37.3 ft, 14.2 ft   **13.** 92.0 m, 35.1 m

21. $h = 3.1$ in, $l = 8.1$ in   **23.** $w = 14.6$ cm, $l = 23.7$ cm

25. $w = 5.6$ cm, $h = 3.5$ cm

Section 3.4

1. Sides cross each other   **3.** One of the sides is a curve

5. Convex hexagon   **7.** Concave 13-gon

9. a.

b.

11. a.

b.

13.

Points	Angle
5	72°
6	60°
7	≈51.4°
8	45°
9	40°
10	36°
11	≈32.7°
12	30°
13	≈27.7°
14	≈25.7°
15	24°
16	22.5°
18	20°
20	18°
30	12°
36	10°

15.

17.

19.

21.

23.

Section 3.5

1. A tesselation is a pattern of one or more congruent shapes that cover an area in a plane without overlapping or leaving any gaps
3. A regular nonagon has angles of 140°. Since 360° is not evenly divisible by 140°, a regular nonagon will not tesselate a plane.

In the following answers, note that all diagrams are approximately 40% of actual size and give only four tiles.

5. 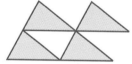   **7.**

9. 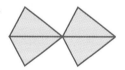   **11.**

13. 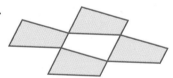   **15.**

17. The sum of the angles for these three polygons does not add to 360°.
19. One possible answer is to use two octagons and a square.
21.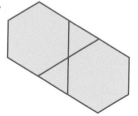

Section 3.6

3.

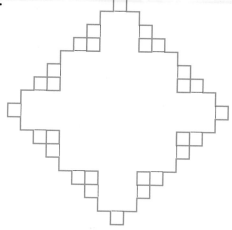

5.

9. 1.36   **11.** 1.21   **13.** 1.29

Chapter 3 Summary

1. See Section 3.1.   **2.** See Section 3.1.

3.

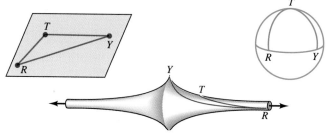

4.

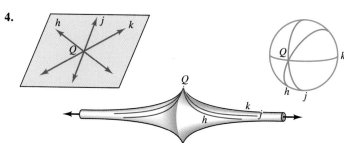

5.

	4 sides	**5 sides**	**6 sides**
Euclidean	360°	540°	720°
Riemannian	>360°	>540°	>720°
Lobachevskian	<360°	<540°	<720°

In Euclidean geometry, the sum of the angles of the polygon can be determined by subtracting 2 from the number of sides and multiplying that result by 180°. The Riemannian sum is always greater than the Euclidean sum, while the Lobachevskian sum is always less than the Euclidean sum.

6. If there were more than one perpendicular to a line from a point that is not on the line, a triangle would be formed that has the sum of its angles greater than 180°. That occurs only in Riemannian geometry. Thus, in Euclidean and Lobachevskian geometry there is only one perpendicular, and in Riemannian geometry there can be more than one perpendicular.

7. See Section 3.2.

8. Answers will vary on this one, depending on the type of geometry chosen.

9. a. Since the line segment is ≈ 1.75 in. long, the segment should be divided ≈ 1.1 in. from one end.
   b. Since the line segment is ≈ 4.4 cm long, the segment should be divided ≈ 2.7 cm from one end.

10. 13.8 inches

11. Either the ratio of the diagonals or the ratio of the sides should be approximately 1.62.

12. a.   **b.**

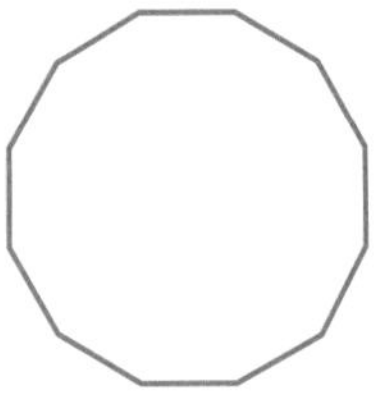

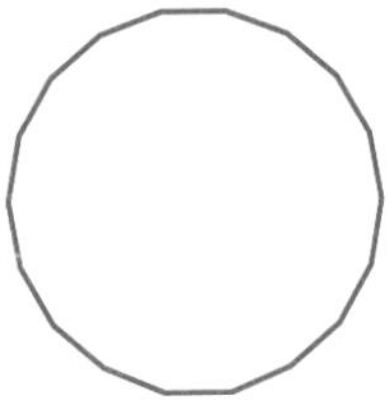

13. a.

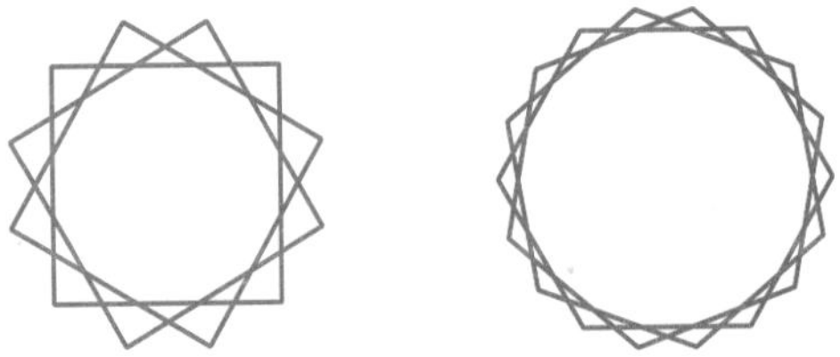

   b.

14. a. 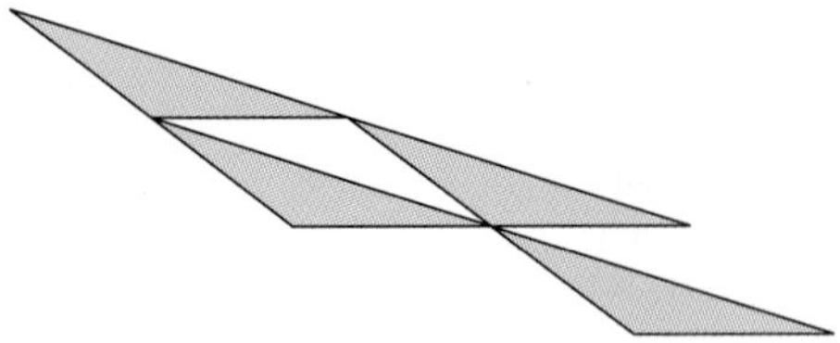   **b.**

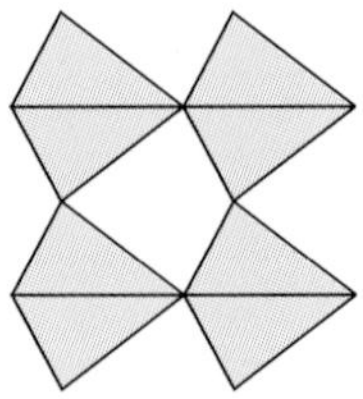

15. a.

b.

c.

d.

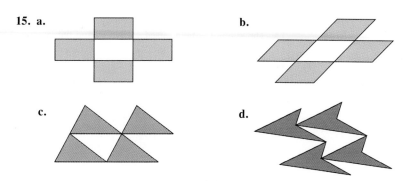

16. *Hint:* Look at 360° divided by the angle for each type of regular polygon.

17.

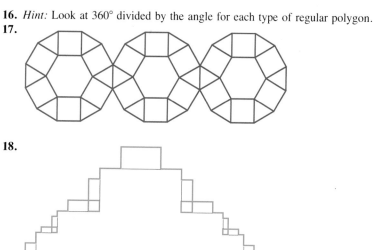

18.

19. 1.29

CHAPTER 4

Section 4.0

1. a. $\{x|x$ is an even whole number $\leq 10\}$ **b.** $\{0, 2, 4, 6, 8, 10\}$

3. a. {apples, bananas, peaches, tomatoes, beans, peas, sprouts}   **b.** {tomatoes}

5. The symbol is being used correctly, and the statement is true.

7. The symbol is being used correctly, but the statement is false. One possible true statement is $\mathscr{F} \not\subset \mathscr{T}$.

9. An incorrect symbol is being used. A true correct statement is $5 \in I$.

11. The symbol is being used correctly, and the statement is true.
13. The symbol is being used correctly, and the statement is true.
15. The symbol is being used incorrectly. One possible correct statement is $\mathcal{F} \subset I$.
17. $\mathcal{U}$

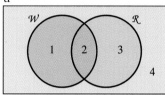

1 = {all women without red hair}
2 = {all women with red hair}
3 = {people who are not women but do have red hair}
4 = {people who are not women and do not have red hair}

19. $\mathcal{U}$

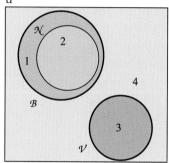

1 = {all books in the library that are not novels}
2 = {all books in the library that are novels}
3 = {all videos in the library}
4 = {all items in the library that are not books and not videos}

Section 4.1

1. Not a statement   **3.** Not a statement   **5.** A statement   **7.** Not a statement
9. My car is not in the shop.   **11.** I like sitting around doing nothing.
13. That is not an example of an exponential equation.
15. Some fish cannot live under water.
17. All numbers are prime numbers.   **19.** No trees are always green.
21. Some of the numbers are positive.
23. *Converse:* If the phone is in use, then you get a busy signal.
Inverse: If you do not get a busy signal, then the phone is not in use.
Contrapositive: If the phone is not in use, then you do not get a busy signal.
25. *Converse:* If the point is 16″ from the center of the circle, then it is on the circle.
Inverse: If the point is not on the circle, then it will not be 16″ from the center of the circle.
Contrapositive: If the point is not 16″ from the center of the circle, it is not on the circle.
27. *Converse:* If I am listening, then G. H. Mutton is speaking.
Inverse: If G. H. Mutton is not speaking, then I am not listening.
Contrapositive: If I am not listening, then G. H. Mutton is not speaking.

29. *Converse:* If the figure is not a hexagon, then it has five sides.
Inverse: If the figure does not have five sides, then it is a hexagon.
Contrapositive: If a figure is a hexagon, then it does not have five sides.

31. The term being defined, ''puppy,'' is named. The words used in the definition should be understood. The statement is biconditional.

33. The term being defined, ''quadratic equation,'' is named. The words used in the definition are already understood. The statement is biconditional.

35. It does not use words in the definition that are already understood.

37. It does not name the term being defined.   **39.** It is not biconditional.

41. It is not biconditional.

For problems 43–53, there are many other correct answers.

43. If x is an integer, then x is a real number.

45. If the product of two real numbers is zero, then at least one of them is zero.

47. Not possible   **49.** If x is a number, then x is a house.

51. If x is a whole number, then x is a prime number.

53. If x is a prime number, then x is a composite number.

Section 4.2

1. In a triangle, the sides opposite equal angles have the same length.

3. The line segment joining the midpoints of two sides of the triangle is one-half the length of the third side.

5. The conclusions of the first four problems were made after observing patterns and are, therefore, examples of inductive reasoning. Deductive reasoning would show that accepted propositions of geometry could logically lead to the same conclusions.

7. For the values of n from 1 to 16, the expression generates prime numbers. But when $n = 17$, the expression gives the answer 289, which is not a prime number.

9. A possible inductive argument:
Research evidence over the last 20 years shows that smoking causes cancer.
My friend died from lung cancer, and he smoked two packs of cigarettes a day.
The U.S. Surgeon General states that one should not smoke.
Therefore, one should not smoke.

A possible deductive argument:
If you smoke, you increase your chances of getting cancer.
If you increase your chances of getting cancer, you increase your chances of an early death.
Therefore, if you smoke, you increase your chances of an early death.
Therefore, if you do not want to die early, you should not smoke.

11. It is not valid. It contains a converse error. This would be valid:
When it is midnight, I am asleep.
It is midnight.
Therefore, I am asleep.

13. It is not valid. It contains an inverse error. This would be valid:
If one is a farmer in Polt County, then one grows corn.
Farmer Ron does not grow corn.
Therefore, Farmer Ron is not a farmer in Polt County.

15. It is a valid syllogism.

17. If a whole number greater than 2 is even, then it is divisible by 2.
If a whole number is divisible by 2, then it is not a prime number.
Therefore, if a whole number greater than 2 is even, it is not a prime number.

19. Anyone that treats you with kindness is a nice person.
My teacher, Mrs. Santos, was very kind to me when I was sick.
Therefore, Mrs. Santos is a nice person.

21. If you are serious about school, you will have less time to watch TV.

23. One of many possible answers:
A: x is a whole number.
B: x is an integer.
C: x is a rational number.
D: x is an irrational number.
E: x equals $\sqrt{2}$.

25. Some numbers are rational.

27. If the car is full of gasoline, we can see Vernal Falls.   **29.** $P \rightarrow \sim S$

Section 4.3

1. 68

3. $A \cap B$ is the empty set.

5. 175

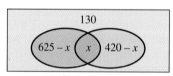

7. a. 120   **b.** 40   **c.** 80   **d.** 130

9. Everyone is a fanatic, an idealist, and a reformer.

11. Only one woman is wealthy.

Section 4.4

1. M = it is midnight, A = asleep

$$M \rightarrow A$$
$$A$$
$$\therefore M$$

3. F = farmer in Polt County, C = grows corn

$$F \rightarrow C$$
$$\sim C$$
$$\therefore \sim F$$

5. S = scalene, W = two equal sides, H = three equal sides

$$\sim S \rightarrow (W \vee H)$$
$$\sim H$$
$$\therefore W$$

7. D = healthy dog, F = four legs, R = run quickly, P = pig, T = two eyes, E = poor eyesight

$$(D \rightarrow (F \wedge R)) \wedge (P \rightarrow (T \wedge E))$$

9. Y = gyred, I = gimbled, T = slithy tove, F = efficient flibbert

$$(Y \vee I) \rightarrow (T \vee F)$$

11.

A	C	$A \rightarrow C$	$\sim C$	$(A \rightarrow C) \vee \sim C$
T	T	T	F	T
T	F	F	T	T
F	T	T	F	T
F	F	T	T	T

The statement is always true.

13.

F	$\sim F$	Q	$\sim F \rightarrow Q$	$\sim Q$	$(\sim F \rightarrow Q) \rightarrow \sim Q$
T	F	T	T	F	F
T	F	F	T	T	T
F	T	T	T	F	F
F	T	F	F	T	T

The statement is true whenever Q is false.

15.

A	B	$\sim B$	$A \wedge \sim B$	$\sim(A \wedge \sim B)$	$\sim A$	$\sim A \vee B$
T	T	F	F	**T**	F	**T**
T	F	T	T	**F**	F	**F**
F	T	F	F	**T**	T	**T**
F	F	T	F	**T**	T	**T**

Since both statements have the same truth values, the statements are equivalent.

17.

P	Q	$P \rightarrow Q$	$(P \rightarrow Q) \wedge P$	$((P \rightarrow Q) \wedge P) \rightarrow Q$
T	T	T	T	T
T	F	F	F	T
F	T	T	F	T
F	F	T	F	T

Since the last column is always true, the argument is valid.

19.

A	$\sim A$	C	$A \rightarrow C$	$\sim A \wedge (A \rightarrow C)$	$(\sim A \wedge (A \rightarrow C)) \rightarrow A$
T	F	T	T	F	T
T	F	F	F	F	T
F	T	T	T	T	F
F	T	F	T	T	F

Since the last column is not always true, the argument is not valid.

21. Let C = chickens, T = talk, M = my chickens. The argument is

$$C \rightarrow \sim T$$
$$M \rightarrow T$$
$$\therefore C \rightarrow \sim M$$

C	M	T	$\sim T$	$C \rightarrow \sim T$	$M \rightarrow T$	$(C \rightarrow -T) \wedge (M \rightarrow T)$	$\sim M$	$C \rightarrow \sim M$	$((C \rightarrow \sim T) \wedge (M \rightarrow T)) \rightarrow (C \rightarrow \sim M)$
T	T	T	F	F	T	F	F	F	T
T	T	F	T	T	F	F	F	F	T
T	F	T	F	F	T	F	T	T	T
T	F	F	T	T	T	T	T	T	T
F	T	T	F	T	T	T	F	T	T
F	T	F	T	T	F	F	F	T	T
F	F	T	F	T	T	T	T	T	T
F	F	F	T	T	T	T	T	T	T

Since the last column is always true, the argument is valid.

23. Let W = fish have wings, E = eagles swim, F = eagles eat fish. The argument is

$$W \to E$$
$$E \to F$$
$$F$$
$$\therefore W$$

W	E	F	$W \to E$	$E \to F$	$(W \to E) \wedge (E \to F)$	$((W \to E) \wedge (E \to F)) \wedge F$	$((W \to E) \wedge (E \to F)) \wedge F) \to W$
T	T	T	T	T	T	T	T
T	T	F	T	F	F	F	T
T	F	T	F	T	F	F	T
T	F	F	F	T	F	F	T
F	T	T	T	T	T	T	F
F	T	F	T	F	F	F	T
F	F	T	T	T	T	F	T
F	F	F	T	T	T	F	T

Since the last column is not always true, the argument is not valid.

Section 4.5

1. In both direct and indirect proofs, we assume the hypothesis to be true. In the direct proof, we show that there is a direct, logical path from the hypothesis to the conclusion of the statement. In an indirect proof, we arrive at a contradiction by assuming the negation of the conclusion. We then conclude that, if the negation of the conclusion is false, the original conclusion must be true.

3.

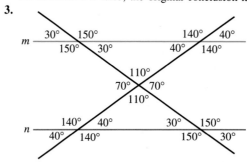

5. *Hypothesis:* Lines l and m are parallel; line n intersects both l and m

Conclusion: $\angle 1 = \angle 2$

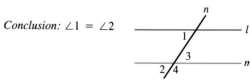

Proof:

1) l and m are parallel lines   1) hypothesis
2) $\angle 3 + \angle 4 = 180°$ 2) straight angle (line n)
3) $\angle 2 + \angle 4 = 180°$ 3) straight angle (line m)
4) $\angle 3 + \angle 4 = \angle 2 + \angle 4$ 4) A2
5) $\therefore \angle 3 = \angle 2$ 5) A3
6) $\angle 3 = \angle 1$ 6) T6
7) $\therefore \angle 1 = \angle 2$ 7) A2

7. *Hypothesis:* △*ABC*

Conclusion: At least one of ∠*A*, ∠*B*, or ∠*C* is ≥60°.

Using an indirect proof:

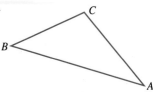

Assumption: All the angles are <60°.

Proof: If all three angles are <60°, then

$$\angle A + \angle B + \angle C < 60° + 60° + 60° = 180°$$

$$\angle A + \angle B + \angle C < 180°$$

This contradicts the theorem that says the sum of the angles of a triangle equals 180° (T7). Therefore, at least one of the angles in the triangle is ≥60°.

9. A direct proof will work well.   **11.** A direct proof will work well.

13. Use an indirect proof.   **15.** Use a direct proof.   **17.** Use a direct proof.

19. Use a direct proof.

Chapter 4 Summary

1. a. *Hypothesis:* If it is after midnight,

Conclusion: I am in bed.

b. If I am in bed, it is after midnight.

c. If it is not after midnight, then I am not in bed.

d. If I am not in bed, then it is not after midnight.

2. Three components of a definition and the additional properties needed for a good definition can be found in Section 4.1 under "Definitions."

a. Not biconditional

Perpendicular lines are lines that intersect at right angles.

b. It uses the same root word in its definition, and, thus, it uses a word in the definition that may not be already understood.

Microscopic: that which can only be seen through a high-powered magnifying device.

c. Not biconditional. Natural numbers are whole numbers that are greater than zero.

3. One of many possible answers: If x is a natural number, then it is a real number.

4. Difference between an inductive and deductive argument: see Section 4.2. There are many possible arguments. Remember that an inductive argument is based on observing results, analyzing experiences, citing authorities, or presenting statistics. A deductive argument follows from accepted facts, assumptions, rules, or laws.

5. a. Using the rule for contrapositives, $Z \rightarrow \sim Y$ is equivalent to $Y \rightarrow \sim Z$. Thus, the argument is

$$X \rightarrow Y$$

$$Y \rightarrow \sim Z$$

$$\sim Z \rightarrow P$$

$$\therefore X \rightarrow P$$

b. Using the rule for contrapositives, "If the geometry is Euclidean, then parallel lines exist" is equivalent to "If there are no parallel lines, then the geometry is non-Euclidean."

Thus, the argument is:

If the geometry is Riemannian, then there are no parallel lines.
If there are no parallel lines, then the geometry is non-Euclidean.
If the geometry is non-Euclidean, then at least one of Euclid's postulates is changed.

∴ If the geometry is Riemannian, then at least one of Euclid's postulates is changed.

6. 170

7. A person is either: a) logical, organized, and a scientist; b) logical, organized, and not a scientist; or c) organized, not logical, and not a scientist.

8. a. Let H = headache, G = grumpy, S = silent, $H \rightarrow (G \lor S)$.
   b. Let G = good weather, B = play baseball, P = have a picnic, $\sim G \rightarrow (\sim B \land \sim P)$.
   c. Let M = study math, G = good job, H = harder to advance, $(\sim M \land G) \rightarrow H$.

9.

A	B	$A \lor B$	$\sim B$	$A \lor \sim B$	$(A \lor B) \land (A \lor \sim B)$
T	T	T	F	T	T
T	F	T	T	T	T
F	T	T	F	F	F
F	F	F	T	T	F

Since the columns for the two statements have the same truth values, the statements are equivalent.

10. Let P = parrot, W = cracks walnuts, A = my animal. The argument is

$$(P \rightarrow W) \land (A \rightarrow \sim W)$$

$$\therefore A \rightarrow \sim P$$

P	W	A	$P \rightarrow W$	$\sim W$	$A \rightarrow \sim W$	$(P \rightarrow W) \land (A \rightarrow \sim W)$	$\sim P$	$A \rightarrow \sim P$	$((P \rightarrow W) \land (A \rightarrow \sim W)) \rightarrow (A \rightarrow \sim P)$
T	T	T	T	F	F	F	F	F	T
T	T	F	T	F	T	T	F	T	T
T	F	T	F	T	T	F	F	F	T
T	F	F	F	T	T	F	F	T	T
F	T	T	T	F	F	F	T	T	T
F	T	F	T	F	T	T	T	T	T
F	F	T	T	T	T	T	T	T	T
F	F	F	T	T	T	T	T	T	T

Since the last column is always true, the argument is valid.

11.

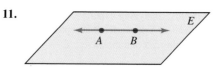

Hypothesis: $\overrightarrow{AB}$ lies in E.
Conclusion: $\overleftrightarrow{AB}$ lies in E.

Proof:

1. $\overrightarrow{AB}$ lies in E	1. Hypothesis
2. $\overrightarrow{AB}$ contains $\overline{AB}$	2. D2
3. $\overline{AB}$ contains points A and B	3. D1
4. A and B lie in E	4. Since A and B are on $\overrightarrow{AB}$
5. ∴ $\overleftrightarrow{AB}$ lies in E	5. P3

12.

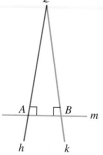

Hypothesis: h and k in same plane; $h \perp m$ and $k \perp m$
Conclusion: $h \parallel k$
Assumption: h not $\parallel k$

Proof: Suppose lines h and k lie in the same plane with $h \perp m$ and $k \perp m$ and h is not parallel to k. Then h and k must intersect at some point Q by the definition of parallel lines. Therefore, in $\triangle ABQ$ formed by the lines intersecting at Q, $Q > 0$, $\angle A = 90°$ and $\angle B = 90°$, since perpendicular lines form right (90°) angles. Since $\angle A + \angle B = 180°$, $\angle A + \angle B + \angle Q > 180°$. This contradicts the triangle-sum theorem, which states that the sum of all three angles of the triangle equals 180°. Therefore, the assumption is false and $h \parallel k$.

13.

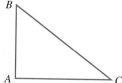

Hypothesis: h, k in same plane; $h \perp m$ at R, $k \perp m$ at Q
Conclusion: h not parallel to k

Proof: Line h and line k are in the same plane with $h \perp m$ at point R and $k \perp m$ at point Q. Consider point R, which is not on line k. By the Riemannian parallel postulate there is no line through R that is parallel to k. Therefore, h is not parallel to k.

14.

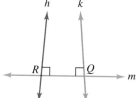

Hypothesis: $\triangle ABC$
Conclusion: Either $\angle A$ is not a right angle or $\angle B$ is not an obtuse angle
Assumption: $\angle A =$ right angle and $\angle B =$ obtuse angle
Proof: Suppose $\triangle ABC$ contained a right angle ($\angle A$) and an obtuse angle ($\angle B$). Then $\angle A + \angle B$ is greater than 180°, since a right angle equals 90° and an obtuse angle is greater than 90°. But this contradicts the Lobachevskian triangle-sum theorem—that the sum of the angles of a triangle is less than 180°. Thus, the assumption is false, and the triangle cannot contain both a right angle and an obtuse angle.

Section 5.0

1. Legs: y, d; hypotenuse: k **3.** Legs: y, k; hypotenuse: d   **5.** 25   **7.** 10.6
9. 67.2   **11.** 15   **13.** 0.8   **15.** No   **17.** Yes   **19.** Yes   **21.** Yes
23. 127.3

Section 5.1
(see page 266 for the round-off rules)

1. $\sin A = 3/5$ $\sin B = 4/5$
     $\cos A = 4/5$ $\cos B = 3/5$
     $\tan A = 3/4$ $\tan B = 4/3$

3. $\sin A = 4/5$ $\sin B = 3/5$
     $\cos A = 3/5$ $\cos B = 4/5$
     $\tan A = 4/3$ $\tan B = 3/4$

5. 0.2181   **7.** 0.1392   **9.** 0.7208   **11.** 4.1022   **13.** 0.9999   **15.** 82.9°
17. 42.1°   **19.** 87.0°   **21.** 68.7°   **23.** $B = 67°, a = 7.0, b = 16.6$
25. $A = 9.7°, B = 80.3°, b = 64.1$ **27.** $X = 56.4°, Y = 33.6, y = 12.9$
29. $Y = 21.5°, x = 5965.8, z = 6412.0$ **31.** 61.9°, 28.1°   **33.** 53.1°, 36.9°
35. 53.1°, 36.9°   **37.** 32.8   **39.** 92.4

Section 5.2
(see page 266 for the round-off rules)

1. 43.3 yd   **3.** $p = 50.0$ ft, $w = 51.4$ ft   **5.** 22.6°, 12.3 ft   **7.** 29.5 ft
9. 114.9 ft   **11.** 7163.4 ft diagonally or 7159.1 ft horizontally   **13.** 4593.0 ft
15. 1483.7 ft

Section 5.3
(see page 266 for the round-off rules)

1. 11.2   **3.** 5.4   **5.** 54.0   **7.** 7.5   **9.** 0.6   **11.** 31.8   **13.** 54.0°
15. 66.0°   **17.** $e = 87.2, y = 87.2, K = 70°$
19. $R = 54.4°, C = 42.7°, A = 82.9°$

Section 5.4
(see page 266 for the round-off rules)

1. 141.4 ft   **3.** 362.3 ft   **5.** 10.5 mi, 89°   **7.** 47.6 mi   **9.** 227.0 yd
11. 0.7, 1.5, 24.2 ft   **13.** 196.8 m   **15.** $d = x \sqrt{2 - 2 \cos A}$

Chapter 5 Summary
(see page 266 for the round-off rules)

1. $A = 28.1°, C = 61.9°$ **2.** $N = 66°, n = 8.8, f = 3.9$
3. $N = 84°, r = 20.3, n = 29.0$ **4.** $B = 68.7°, o = 141.5, r = 57.6$
5. $M = 73.1°, Y = 44.4°, a = 38.0$ **6.** $D = 60.3°, E = 88.2°, B = 31.5°$
7. 41.8°   **8.** 117.8 m   **9.** 4978.8 ft
10. a. 17.0 ft, 176.2 ft   **b.** 48.0 ft, 178.9 ft
11. 213.0 ft   **12.** 13.7 mi, 22.2 mi, 12.1 mi   **13.** 851.8 mi   **14.** 3.7 mi
15. N 11.2° E, N 48.2° W   **16.** 2950.8 yd, 2987.6 yd

CHAPTER 6

Section 6.0
1. 12.513503   **3.** 0.386883   **5.** 1.055751   **7.** 1.181352   **9.** 1.597138
11. 0.661722   **13.** 2.033424   **15.** 1.125815   **17.** 1.948192   **19.** 0.666667
21. 0.933182   **23.** 2.452208

Section 6.1
1. $400.00   **3.** $312.50   **5.** $56.25   **7.** $120.09   **9.** $3720.00
11. $35,466.67   **13.** $3605.00   **15.** $1090.16   **17.** $2500.00   **19.** 2.5 years
21. 25% per year   **23.** $3610.80   **25.** 0.75 year or 9 months
27. 8.11% per year   **29.** $1100.00, $1210.00, $1331.00

Section 6.2
1. $2540.98
3. $6971.04 (If results are not rounded off, $A = \$6970.93$.)
5. $6074.43 for 90 days **7.** $5323.11 **9.** 48 months or 4 years
11. 1.497% monthly or 17.97% annually **13.** The 7.8% account **15.** $9264.84
17. 2107 days or 5.8 years (If results are not rounded off, $n = 2109$ days.)
19. $11,651,302,560 (If results are not rounded off, $A = \$11,627,514,876$.)
21. 1.093713 **23.** 1.267600 **25.** $398.50 **27.** $398.82

Section 6.3
1. $13,954.01 **3.** $409.11 **5.** 123 months or 10 years, 3 months
7. a. $973,151.26 **b.** $57,600 **c.** $915,551.26 **d.** $778,181.07
e. $91,200
9. a. $77,405.71 **b.** $1,166,691.55
11. 152 months or 12 years, 8 months **13.** $307.52

Section 6.4
1. $10,345.11 **3.** $609.11 **5.** 186 months or 15 years, 6 months
7. $1204.88
9. a. $215.41 **b.** $10,339.68 **c.** $2339.68
11. a. $135.38 **b.** 23 months **c.** $748.24

Chapter 6 Summary
1. $12,400 **2.** 7.21%
3. a. $1100.00 **b.** $1103.81 **c.** $1104.71 **d.** $1105.17
4. $5846.10 **5.** 14.32% **6.** $304.28
7. a. $24,160.79 **b.** $8,160.79 **c.** $175,036.37
8. 291 deposits
9. a. $395.14 **b.** $17,225.04
10. 139 months or 11 years, 7 months

CHAPTER 7

Section 7.0
1. 5040 **3.** 6,227,020,800 **5.** 35 **7.** 57,155 **9.** 1 **11.** 1 **13.** 210
15. 342,930 **17.** 5040 **19.** 1 **21.** 35/126 or 0.2778 **23.** 1260
25. a. 1
b. 2 ✕, ☆
c. 1 ✕ ☆
d. 4

27. a. 1
b. 2 ✕, ☆
c. 2 ✕ ☆, ☆ ✕
d. 5

29. 20 ✕ ▢, ✕ ▼, ✕ ❚, ✕ ◆, ▢ ✕, ▢ ▼, ▢ ❚, ▢ ◆,
▼ ✕, ▼ ▢, ▼ ❚, ▼ ◆, ❚ ✕, ❚ ▢, ❚ ▼, ❚ ◆,
◆ ✕, ◆ ▢, ◆ ▼, ◆ ❚

Section 7.1

1. 1728   **3.** $10^{16} = 10,000,000,000,000,000$ **5.** $8 \times 8 \times 10^5 = 6,400,000$

7. 40,320

9. a. 120   **b.** 625

11. 9,765,625   **13.** $C_{52,13} = 635,013,559,600$

15. a. 1   **b.** 4   **c.** 40

17. $C_{18,2} = 153$ **19.** $C_{8,2} = 28$ **21.** $C_{4,4} \times C_{48,3} = 1 \times 17{,}296 = 17{,}296$

23. $C_{20,2} = 190$ **25.** $C_{20,5} \times C_{60,5}$

Section 7.2

1. a. 5/36   **b.** 5/36   **c.** 0   **d.** 5/18   **e.** 1250, 1250

3. 172 or 173

5. If the identical circumstances of the election were to occur many, let's say 1000 times, the candidate would win the election approximately 630 times.

7. a. $(C_{4,1} \times C_{4,4})/C_{52,5} = 0.00000154$

    b. $(C_{4,1} \times 12 \times C_{4,4})/C_{52,5} = 0.0000185$

9. a. $(C_{8,3} \times C_{96,2})/C_{104,5} = 0.0027768$

    b. $(13 \times C_{8,3} \times C_{96,2})/C_{104,5} = 0.036098$

11. $1/P_{6,3} = 1/120$ **13.** $1/C_{20,2} = 1/190$

15. $(C_{4,2} \times C_{5,1})/C_{9,3} = 30/84 = 5/14$ **17.** 1/10

19. a. $(C_{20,0} \times C_{60,12})/C_{80,12}$ **b.** $(C_{20,6} \times C_{60,6})/C_{80,12}$

    c. $(C_{20,9} \times C_{60,3})/C_{80,12}$

21. $(C_{6,4} \times C_{43,2})/C_{49,6} = 0.0009686$

23. a. $(C_{4,3} \times C_{4,2})/C_{52,5} = 0.000009234$

    b. $(C_{4,3} \times 12 \times C_{4,2})/C_{52,5} = 0.000111$

    c. $(13 \times C_{4,3} \times 12 \times C_{4,2})/C_{52,5} = 0.001441$

27. a. 7/12   **b.** 3 to 1, 1 to 3

Section 7.3

1. $11.50, win $1150   **3.** $1

5. $\approx -$0.0526, \approx$1262.40$ (If E.V. is not rounded off, winnings are $1263.)

7. a. $\approx 22.5¢$ **c.** The game would be fair if postage was 22.5¢.   **d.** $\approx 22.5¢$

9. ≈ 9 hits   **11.** $p > 0.25$ **13.** Seed

15. a. $\approx -$0.08$ **b.** $15

Chapter 7 Summary

1. a. 35   **b.** 840   **c.** 1,088,430   **d.** 26,122,320

2. a. $C_{4,3} \times C_{4,2} \times C_{44,1} = 1056$ **b.** $C_{4,3} \times 12C_{4,2} \times C_{44,1} = 12{,}672$

    c. $13 \times C_{4,3} \times 12 \times C_{4,2} \times C_{44,1} = 164{,}736$

3. a. $(C_{4,3} \times C_{4,4})/C_{52,7} = 0.00000003$

    b. $(C_{4,3} \times 12 \times C_{4,4})/C_{52,7} = 0.000000359$

    c. $(13 \times C_{4,3} \times 12 \times C_{4,4})/C_{52,7} = 0.00000466$

4. $1/P_{10,3} = 0.00139$ **5.** 7/144   **6.** ≈ 0.78 **7.** $E = 1.4375$; ≈ 14 points

8. Other results, such as 6 heads and 4 tails, are possible.

9. a. 365^{20} **b.** $P_{365,20}$ **c.** $P_{365,20} \div 365^{20} = 0.589$

    d. There are $P_{365,20}$ ways to pick the 20 different birthdays and 365^{20} total ways to pick the 20 days. Thus, the result in part (c) is the probability of picking 20 different birthdays.

    e. If part (c) is the probability that no 2 of the 20 people have the same birthday, then $1 - (P_{365,20} \div 365^{20}) =$ the probability that at least 2 of the 20 have the same birthday.

Section 8.0

1. 15   **3.** 125   **5.** 225   **7.** $5 \sum\limits_{i=1}^{n} x_i$ **9.** $5 \sum\limits_{i=1}^{n} x_i + 3n$ **11.** $\sum\limits_{i=1}^{5} i$

13. $\sum\limits_{i=1}^{5} 2i$ or $2 \sum\limits_{i=1}^{5} i$

15. a. 9   **b.** $\dfrac{\sum\limits_{i=1}^{n} x_i}{n}$

Section 8.1

1. a.

Class	Frequency
1–3	3
4–6	4
7–9	3

b.

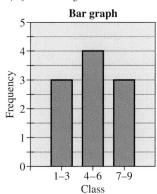

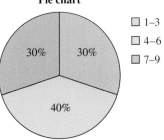

c.

Class	Cum. Frequency
≤3	3
≤6	7
≤9	10

d.

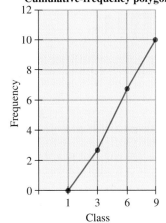

3. a. 302   **b.** 24.8%

c.

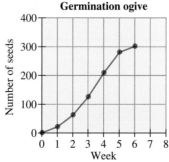

Germination ogive

5. There is no information given about the meaning of any of the categories in the pie chart.

7. a.

Class No.	Class	Frequency
1	50.1–100	7
2	100.1–150	26
3	150.1–200	12
4	200.1–250	3
5	250.1–300	1
6	300.1–350	0
7	350.1–400	0
8	400.1–450	0
9	450.1–500	0
10	500.1–550	2
11	550.1–600	0

b.

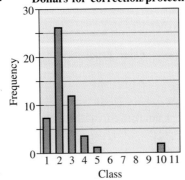

Dollars for correction/protection

c. $100–$150 per capita

d. The per capita costs in Georgia are $123.90. This is in the largest group of the frequency distribution or the bar graph so the citizens' group should not use the frequency distribution or the bar graph. However, the group might decide to use the original data to indicate that there are 27 regions with higher per capita expenditures.

e. Alaska has high costs due to low population spread over large area. D.C. has a large number of foreign and domestic officials requiring protection.

Section 8.2

1. a. 5.8   **b.** 4.61   **c.** 6.5   **d.** Bimodal; 2 and 9

3. a. 53%   **b.** 50.8%

c. Because some players take more shots than other players, the weighted mean gives a better representation of the team's shooting percentage.

5. a. ≈$22,400   **b.** ≈$23,100

c.

Class	Frequency	Class Midpoint
15.1–20.0	8	17.55
20.1–25.0	30	22.55
25.1–30.0	12	27.55
30.1–35.0	0	32.55
35.1–40.0	1	37.55

d. ≈$23,200   **e.** ≈$22,800

f. The median of the data, since it is the lowest measure

g. The mean of the distribution, since it is the highest measure

7. a.

t	P
0	179,323
20	238,219
40	316,457
60	420,392
80	558,463
100	741,881

b. 409,123   **c.** 364,741

d. The population at $t = 50$ would be closer to the geometric mean than to the arithmetic mean. Therefore, while the arithmetic mean gives the "average" of the population figures, the geometric mean gives the population at the time halfway between the beginning and end.

Section 8.3

1. a. 14   **b.** 5.10   **c.** 5.10

3. The second graph has a greater standard deviation since the data is more spread out.

5. a. See section 8.2, Problems 7a and 7b.   **b.** 154.46   **c.** 85.9

7. All scores are the same.

Section 8.4

1. 0.3413   **3.** 0.7692   **5.** 0.1156   **7.** 0.1335   **9.** −1.68   **11.** 0.845

13. −2.575

15. a. 13.25%   **b.** 0.5832

17. a. 0.4090   **b.** 29.64%   **c.** 11.58%

19. 48 cigarettes

Chapter 8 Summary

1. a. 4.9   **b.** 4.09   **c.** 5   **d.** 3 and 6   **e.** 8   **f.** 2.55

2. a.

Class No.	Classes	Class Frequency
1	1–100	2
2	101–200	17
3	201–300	4
4	301–400	3
5	401–500	2
6	501–600	1
7	601–700	1

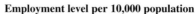

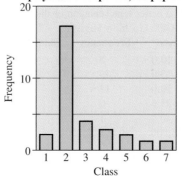

b. 227   **c.** 140.67

3.   **Employment level per 10,000 population**

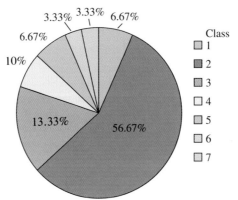

4. a.

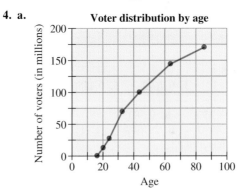

b. Unequal class sizes

5. Company A because of less variation in the product

6. a. 36.24%   **b.** 11.22%   **c.** 0.6217   **d.** 0.2483

7. A's: 91.2–100
B's: 80.4–91.19
C's: 65.6–80.39
D's: 54.8–65.59
F's: 0–54.79

CHAPTER 9

Section 9.0
  1. a. 8   **b.** 6   **c.** 44
  3. a. 8   **b.** $3Q - 6$ **c.** $Q^2 + 7Q$
  5. a. 8   **b.** $3 + 3h$ **c.** $30 + 13h + h^2$
  7. a. 8   **b.** $3x + 3h - 6$ **c.** $x^2 + 2xh + h^2 + 7x + 7h$
  9. Yes   **11.** Yes   **13.** Yes   **15.** No   **17.** Yes   **19.** Yes   **21.** No
  23. a. No   **b.** Yes
  25. a. -5 **b.** $1/3$

Section 9.1
  1. a. B, D, F   **b.** A, E   **c.** C, G
  3. At $x = 2$, the derivative has a value between 0.5 and 2.
  5. a. 5   **b.** 5   **c.** m
  7. 5   **9.** $10x$ **11.** 1
  ***13. a.** $2x$ **b.** $3x^2$ **c.** $4x^3$ **d.** $23x^{22}$

Section 9.2
  1. 2   **3.** $20x^4$ **5.** $20x^4 - 10x$ **7.** $5x^4 - 6x + 7$
  9. a.   No

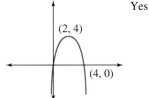

  b. 3; no

  11. a.   Yes

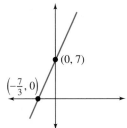

  b. $-2x + 4$; (2,4)   **c.** Maximum
  13. a.

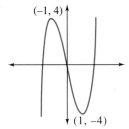

  b. $6x^2 - 6$ **c.** $(-1,4)$; $(1,-4)$ **d.** $(-1,4)$ max; $(1,-4)$ min

15. a. 42 in.   **b.** 18 in.

17. 150 ft by 300 ft; area = 45,000 sq ft   ***19.** 2 ft; 4 ft; $2\frac{2}{3}$ ft, $V = \frac{64}{3}$ cu ft

Section 9.3

1. 144   **3.** 96   **5.** 292   **7.** 9750 sq ft

Chapter 9 Summary

1. a. 22   **b.** $2m^2 - 3m + 2$ **c.** $2h^2 + 9h + 11$

  d. $2x^2 + 4xh + 2h^2 - 3x - 3h + 2$

2. a. 1   **b.** $3w^2 + 5w - 1$ **c.** $3h^2 + 35h + 99$

  d. $3x^2 + 6xh + 3h^2 + 5x + 5h - 1$

3. 3   **4.** $3x^2 + 6$ **5.** 23   **6.** -11 **7.** $(-2, 18)$ **8.** $(3, -27)$

9. 300 sq ft   **10.** 375,000 sq ft   **11.** 176   **12.** 114

13. 6960 sq ft requires $6.96 \approx 7$ lb of fertilizer.

APPENDIX I

1. 0.2   **3.** 0.037037   **5.** 0.75   **7.** 0.750602   **9.** 12.513503

11. 0.386883   **13.** 1.055751   **15.** 1.181352

17. 4×10^{-31} **19.** 4.7×10^{-9} **21.** -0.033333 **23.** 0.580952

INDEX